The Arctic Sky

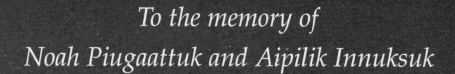

To the memory of
Noah Piugaattuk and Aipilik Innuksuk

Circumpolar moon over Igloolik, NWT, December 1990 (see page 132). Photo: John MacDonald.

The Arctic Sky

INUIT ASTRONOMY, STAR LORE, AND LEGEND

John MacDonald

ROYAL ONTARIO MUSEUM / NUNAVUT RESEARCH INSTITUTE

First published in 1998 by the Royal Ontario Museum, 100 Queen's Park, Toronto, Ontario M5S 2C6
and the Nunavut Research Institute, P. O. Box 1720, Iqaluit, NWT X0A 0H0

Managing Editor/Editor: Glen Ellis
Design/Production: Virginia Morin

Inuktitut translations by Louis Tapardjuk and Leah Otak
Photography by Brian Boyle except where otherwise noted
Chapter-opening block prints by Lucy MacDonald

All artifacts from the Royal Ontario Museum's Bildfell Collection are certified Canadian cultural
property under the terms of the Canadian Cultural Property Export and Import Act.

Canadian Cataloguing-in-Publication Data

MacDonald, John, 1940–
The Arctic sky: Inuit astronomy, star lore, and legend

Co-published by the Nunavut Research Institute.
Includes bibiliographical references and index.
ISBN 0-88854-427-8

1. Astronomy—Arctic regions. 2. Astronomy—Arctic regions—Folklore. 3. Inuit mythology.
4. Inuit—Folklore. I. Royal Ontario Museum. II. Nunavut Research Institute. III. Title.

QB33.A7M32 1998   520'.8997120719   C98-930300-4

The Royal Ontario Museum is an agency of
the Ontario Ministry of Citizenship, Culture and Recreation.

Printed and bound in Canada by Friesen Printers

CONTENTS

★ v ★

SIBERIA

POINT HOPE

WAINRIGHT

POINT BARROW

Arctic Ocean

Bering Strait

NOATAK

Norton
Sound

ANAKTUVUK
PASS

ALASKA

BANKS
ISLAND

SACHS
HARBOUR

Mackenzie Delta

HOLMAN

VICTOR
ISLAND

ARCTIC CIRCLE

COPPERMINE

Coronation
Gulf

Bathurst
Inlet

CANADA

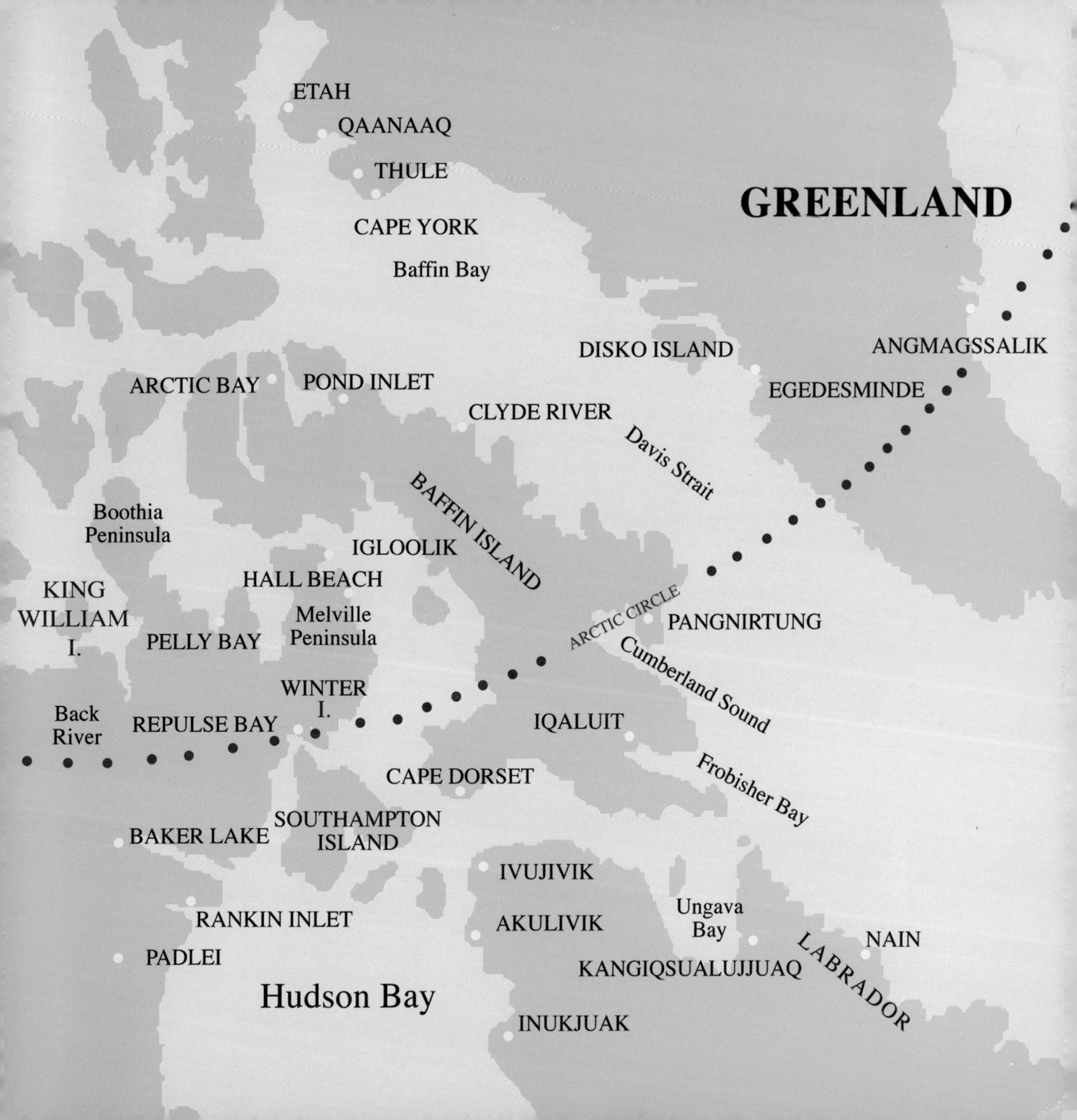

ETAH

QAANAAQ

THULE

CAPE YORK

Baffin Bay

GREENLAND

DISKO ISLAND

ANGMAGSSALIK

EGEDESMINDE

ARCTIC BAY

POND INLET

CLYDE RIVER

Davis Strait

BAFFIN ISLAND

Boothia
Peninsula

IGLOOLIK

HALL BEACH

KING
WILLIAM
I.

PELLY BAY

Melville
Peninsula

ARCTIC CIRCLE

PANGNIRTUNG

Cumberland Sound

WINTER
I.

Back
River

REPULSE BAY

IQALUIT

Frobisher Bay

CAPE DORSET

SOUTHAMPTON
ISLAND

BAKER LAKE

IVUJIVIK

Ungava
Bay

NAIN

RANKIN INLET

AKULIVIK

LABRADOR

PADLEI

KANGIQSUALUJJUAQ

Hudson Bay

INUKJUAK

PREFACE

"Pfft, pfft!"
That is the stars' answer,
and their thanks for being still remembered.
(Ava, *in* Rasmussen 1929)

A practical interest in celestial navigation combined with my residency in the Canadian Eastern Arctic community of Igloolik drew me, perhaps inevitably, into the realm of Inuit star lore. Curious about my use of navigational instruments, older Inuit of the community would sometimes happen by during my observation sessions and gratuitously point out and name a few of *their* stars, gently hinting that my cumbersome gadgetry was hardly necessary for an understanding of the sky. I took the hint.

Thus began a rather straightforward attempt to match Inuit star names with their European counterparts. To my knowledge, this had not been done before, at least not in any methodical or comparative way. Subsequently, I was led into provinces of Inuit life I had seen before only from a distance, among them mythology, spiritual belief, navigation, and the reckoning of time. Perhaps not surprising, since the celestial and atmospheric spheres bear on virtually all aspects of Inuit reality.

What follows, then, is largely an account of these excursions assembled primarily for those who, in an age increasingly dominated by Western perspectives on astronomy, might value a different point of view. Excursions such as these, however, through complex cultural terrain not one's own, are enriched and made memorable through the knowledge, enthusiasm, and patience of one's guides. And so most pressing acknowledgement is to the Inuit elders of Igloolik, named on page x, whose contributions, collectively and individually, through many interviews, are central to this study. Access to the elders' interviews was made possible principally through the painstaking translation work of Louis Tapardjuk and Leah Otak, assisted by George Qulaut and Paul Irngaut. I am also indebted to

Leah Otak for her Inuktitut transcriptions of the Igloolik legends appearing in Chapter 9.

I am grateful to the many people who took a keen interest in the project, variously providing assistance, encouragement, advice, and critical comment. They include Eugene Arima, Louis Tapardjuk, Leah Otak, Aipilik Innuksuk, Emil Imaruittuq, Rosie Iqallijuq, Josiah Inuujak, Nathan Qamaniq, David Sherstone, Robert Petersen, Renee Wissink, Duncan Pryde, Bruce Rigby, Glen Ellis, Virginia Morin, Sandra Shaul, Ken Lister, Tom Clarke, Andrea Gallagher Ellis, George Qulaut, Wim Rasing, Joseph Sonnenfeld, Grant Spearman, Graham Rowley, Gary White, Eva Arreak, Willie Emudluk, Gunther Abrahamson, Michael Fortescue, Keith Greenaway, Mark Kalluak, Michael Shouldice, Norman Hallenday, Ramon Pelinski, Jonathan King, Kenn Harper, Jens Qaavigaq, Jeffrey Hughes, Paul Irngaut, Rhoda Qanatsiaq, Joy and Carl Herman, Jane Mitchell, Marion McColm, Pearl Brown, Ralph and Frederica Knight, Terrence Ryan, Sylvie Côté Chew, Mireille Mathieu, Bryan Robertson, Bernard Saladin-d'Anglure, George Simeon, Paul and Martha Quttiutuqu, Michael Bravo, and Paatsi Qaagutak. That unique blend of support, patience, and understanding, forthcoming only from one's family, was provided unstintingly throughout by Carolyn, Lucy, and William MacDonald.

A number of organizations generously permitted access to their archives and supported the project in other ways. Among these are the Igloolik Inullariit Society; the Avataq Cultural Institute; the Institute for Eskimology, University of Copenhagen; and the Royal Ontario Museum. Permission to undertake the study was granted by the Igloolik Hamlet Council.

(*Above*) Detail from a hunter's record. Engraved ivory.
Port Clarence, Alaska, c. 1900. Royal Ontario Museum.
Gift of Dr. A. C. Panton.

(*Next page*) Noah Piugaattuk of Igloolik, NWT, demonstrates how the Sun's altitude was measured with a mitt to determine the period of *Pualutaniktuɕ*, a time of the year prior to the spring equinox, when the winter was said to be over (see page 114). Photo: John MacDonald.

The observations on Iglulingmiut astronomical traditions—so essential to this
study—were drawn largely from interviews contributed to the Igloolik Oral
History Project by the following Inuit elders:

Eli Amaaq

Hubert Amarualik

Suzanne Niviattian Aqatsiaq

Catherine Aaluluuq Arnatsiaq

Peter Tatigat Arnattiaq

Mark Ijjangiaq

Theo Ikummaq

Emil Imaruittuq

Aipilik Innuksuk

Zipporah Innuksuk

Rosie Iqallijuq

Cain Iqqaqsaq

George Agiaq Kappianaq

Inuki Kunnuk

Pauli Kunuk

Michel Kupaaq

Martha Nasook

Hervé Paniaq

Zachrias Panikpakuttuk

Noah Piugaattuk

Paatsi Qaggutaq

Nathan Qamaniq

Isapee Qanguq

Philip Qipanniq

François Quassa

Joe Tasiuq

Abraham Ulayuruluk

Rachel Uyarasuk

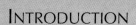

INTRODUCTION

They endow with genius
and life the rigid rock
and the soughing wind, the twinkling stars
and the flashing aurora.

(Emil Bessels, 1884)

★ ★ ★

The celestial and atmospheric spheres were for Inuit, as for all hunting peoples, realms of primary importance and concern. Seasonal and diurnal time were both reckoned and governed by the predictable movements of familiar celestial bodies while the Arctic's unpredictable atmospheric conditions, manifest in the form of favourable or unfavourable weather, were the principal determinants of daily activity and fortune. Beyond this, the Arctic sky held many of the metaphors and symbols shaped by the Inuit intellect to depict, embellish, and explain their distinctive world and its myriad realities.

Compared with the astronomies of those living in more temperate climes, Inuit depictions and personifications of celestial phenomena are rather more elegant than elaborate. The relatively simple projections made by Inuit onto the Arctic sky, at least in terms of the numbers of stars and constellations identified, perhaps reflect their culture's characteristic frugality, tempered by conditions of geography and latitude peculiar to polar regions.

No systematic attempt has been made to describe the star lore or astronomy of the Inuit, or even, in any complete way, to relate Inuit star and constellation names to their European equivalents. For the most part, the existing anthropological and historical records skip lightly over the topic or treat it coincidentally when considering other elements of Inuit culture such as folklore, taboo regimes, and the annual cycle of activities. All this has lulled some recent writers to declare, confidently, that Inuit "have little in the way of star lore" (Ruggles and Saunders 1993:3).

The omission might be ascribed simply to a disinterest in the subject on the part of most students of Inuit culture, a reflection, perhaps, of a similar disinterest in their own astronomical traditions. Nicholas Gubser, for example, unsatisfied about his treatment of Alaskan Nunamiut cosmology, introduces his discussion of their universe with the qualification that his account "reflects the nature of the field situation and the imbalance, as it were, in my own interests" (Gubser 1965:190). The other side of the coin, of course, was the fascination and variety of Inuit culture as a whole, which allowed ethnographers to be drawn into more accessible areas of investigation. John Murdoch's explanation for his failure to study Inuit religion—"such a multitude of other and easier lines of investigation presented themselves" (Murdoch 1892:432)—might equally apply to their astronomy.

The tendency of ethnographers to afford Inuit astronomy only cursory attention has also been compounded by the notion that Inuit star lore, at least at face value, appears rather limited and relatively unimportant, even to the Inuit themselves. This view is borne out by Robert Spencer in his summary of the cosmic view of North Alaskan Eskimos. He concludes that "there was little interest in the more remote celestial bodies. . . . Speculation for its own sake, at least of the kind which went beyond the confines of the immediate world, [was of] little interest"[1] (Spencer 1959:259).

The imaginative cosmology and belief systems of many Inuit groups, including those of North Alaska, hardly support this conclusion. Against Spencer's view there is some irony in noting that, for David Cranz, Inuit speculation about celestial bodies went too far and became a matter for downright suspicion: "But enough of those absurd stories, which indeed none but the weakest heads harbour even in Greenland. Nay it seems to me that the Greenlanders, who have art enough to veil their craftiness with the curtain of stupidity, have often repaid the relations of the Europeans with such romantic tales, to see how far their sense and credulity reaches, or perhaps to make themselves agreeable to them" (Cranz 1767, I:233).

It would be wrong, however, to imply that the subject of Inuit astronomy has been entirely neglected. A number of prominent ethnologists, Franz Boas, Diamond Jenness, and Therkel Mathiassen among them, have tried, with varying degrees of success, to relate Inuit stars and constellations to their European equivalents. Edward Weyer has surveyed and referenced the early literature on the subject and Kaj Birket-Smith in his *Ethnography of the Egedesminde District* helpfully cites all the classical Greenland sources bearing on Inuit astronomy.[2] But many other observers (Emil Bessels, who supplies the epigraph for this introduction, is typical) have been content to make sweeping, often tantalizing, allusions to the richness of Inuit astronomy, at best naming a few stars, identifying some of them and leaving it at that. Others, apparently presented with detailed information, have neglected either to record or to publish it. Jean Malaurie in his *Last Kings of Thule* describes a wonderful scene in which his companion, Olipaluk, explains the seasonal disappearance of the Sun by using stones on a beach to represent the interrelationship of celestial bodies. We are given no real description of this remarkable demonstration other than Malaurie's melodramatic view of the scene: a "chaotic cosmos spread out at our feet . . . on all fours [we] moved about the beach like gods among the stars" (Malaurie 1982:73). The explorer Robert Peary, a trained surveyor and navigator who certainly knew his stars, dismisses the astronomy of the Northwest Greenlanders in a paragraph:

> Their ideas of astronomy are definite, though necessarily limited. They recognize the Great Dipper as a herd of reindeer; the three triangular stars of Cassiopeia are the three stones supporting a celestial stone lamp; the Pleiades are a team of dogs in pursuit of a bear; the three glittering brilliants of the belt of Orion are steps cut by some celestial Eskimo in a steep snowbank to enable him to climb to the top; Gemini are two stones in the entrance to an igloo; Arcturus and Aldebaran are personifications; and the moon and the sun are a maiden and her pursuing lover.[3] [They] estimate time by the movements of the stars, as well as by the position of the sun, and yet, less observant than were the Arab shepherds, they have not noticed that one star is the centre about which all the others move, nor have they set apart the planets, which to them are simply large stars. [Peary 1898, I:494]

The point is that one finds all too often in the writings of anthropologists, missionaries, and explorers, from the earliest times and over the entire Arctic area, vague, unsubstantiated, or incomplete references to stars and other celestial or environmental phenomena of significance to Inuit.

The present study attempts to address this deficiency while seeking to promote a greater interest in Inuit astronomical traditions. From this point of view it is encouraging to see that some of the material gathered in the course of the study is already finding its way into the classrooms of Inuit schools in Canada's Eastern Arctic.

The study's core and principal reference is a series of interviews with several well-informed Inuit elders of Igloolik, NWT, during the winters of 1988 to 1997. With few exceptions the interviews are the product (and by no means the only one) of a major on-going oral-history project organized by the Igloolik Inullariit Elders Society in cooperation with the Igloolik Research Centre. The project has been funded by the former Science Institute of the Northwest Territories, the Nunavut Research Institute, the Government of the Northwest Territories, Indian and Northern Affairs Canada, and the Muttart Foundation of Edmonton, Alberta. Copies of all recordings and transcripts deriving from the project are deposited in the archives of the Prince of Wales Heritage Centre, in Yellowknife, NWT.

Topics covered include naming and identification of stars and constellations; the use of stars in navigation, time-telling, and weather prediction; and some assorted celestial and atmospheric occurrences such as shooting-stars, the aurora borealis, rainbows, and parhelia. In addition, information was gathered on the legends, songs, narratives, beliefs, and terminologies associated with the various phenomena discussed. Material quoted from the Igloolik elders' interviews is identified by the name of the elder, the year of the interview, and an interview number prefixed by the letters "IE". Additional material contributed by Inuit from other parts of the Northwest Territories, Northern Quebec, and Labrador has added significantly to the study's scope.

For comparative purposes, the material deriving from Canadian Inuit sources has been supplemented by selected references drawn from relevant published works and archival documents. The journals of Captain William Edward Parry and his fellow officers of the Royal Navy, who spent the winter of 1822–1823 in Igloolik, are cited frequently. They provide a wealth of information on the astronomy and atmospheric conditions of the area, as well as on the lives and customs of the Inuit met in the Northern Foxe Basin. A number of standard, long-established ethnographic works such as those by Edward William Nelson, Knud Rasmussen, William Thalbitzer, and Diamond Jenness, to name a few, have had their stubble gleaned for cosmic references, some yielding more than others. Also helpful was the star terminology recorded by Therkel Mathiassen in *Material Culture of the Iglulik Eskimos* (Mathiassen 1928:233), although some of the designations recorded by him tend more towards those used by the Inuit of Repulse Bay (Aivilingmiut) and Pelly Bay (Arviligjuarmiut) than of Igloolik proper.

★ ★

*"Some elders recalled
having had the stars
pointed out to them as
children when sitting
beside their fathers on
the sled, making their
slow way over the
frozen ocean towards
some distant camp."*

See page 7.

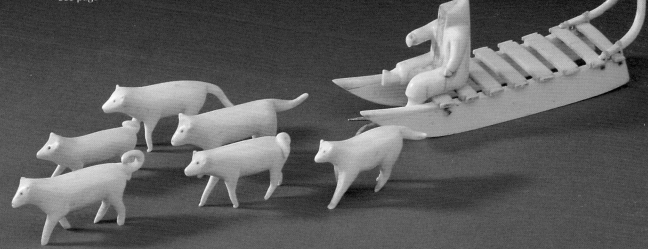

Sculpture of a Dog-Team and Sled. Ivory. Pangnirtung area,
Baffin Island, NWT, 1933–1942. Royal Ontario Museum.
Dr. Jon A. and Mrs. Muriel Bildfell Collection.
Purchased through the generosity of Mr. Donald Ross.

Works of lesser standing, including those devoid of any ethnographic pedigree, were also reviewed and occasionally found to offer up fragments of information not discovered elsewhere. It was also necessary to consult various technical and specialized texts in the fields of astronomy, polar navigation, atmospheric physics, and climatology. A complete listing of all source materials is supplied in the reference list.

From the content of the interviews with the Igloolik elders it is clear that their knowledge of celestial and, to a lesser extent, atmospheric phenomena, is much reduced from what it was a few generations ago. Nor is the remaining knowledge of astronomy equally distributed. Some elders, particularly those who in their younger years had been leaders or were closely associated with leaders, seemed to be better informed. This might suggest that certain aspects of astronomical knowledge were specialized and might have been used to support leaders' decisions concerning matters such as camp moves, hunting excursions, and lengthy trading journeys. Specialization of this sort may have been at work among the Chugach Eskimos of Prince William Sound, Alaska, where "the days of the month were estimated by the stars, but this required special knowledge which did not belong to everybody" (Birket-Smith 1953:115).

Inuit traditional knowledge is characteristically personal, its acquisition and application, in varying degrees, specific to communities, families, and individuals.[4] This point was brought home time and time again in many of the interviews conducted during the course of this study. When imparting information, elders frequently made it plain that they were speaking for themselves, that their opinions were not necessarily correct in any absolute sense, and that other elders might, and in all probability did, have different views. Conversely, the attempt to cross-check information between elders—to reach consensus on certain points—was rarely satisfactory and often counterproductive in that it was seen to question the validity of individual expression and knowledge.

Many of the elders interviewed insisted that the information they possessed about astronomy was meagre compared to that of their parents or grandparents. And, indeed, to many, the names of particular stars had been forgotten, their exact location in the sky uncertain, and the legends and narratives associated with them often remembered as fragments of a more complete story heard long ago. On the other hand, it is also clear that the present generation of elders is virtually the last repository of a more or less detailed knowledge of this subject.

The rapid dilution, even imminent loss, of Inuit star lore is not surprising. Besides the many other factors now inhibiting the transmission of Inuit traditional knowledge to younger generations, the conditions conducive to learning about the celestial sphere simply do not exist to the extent they once did. Frequent, lengthy, and slow-paced dog-team journeys, with camping stops along the way, provided an ideal situation for the thorough transmission of such knowledge. Some elders recalled having had the stars pointed out to them as children when sitting beside their fathers on the sled, making their slow way over the frozen ocean towards some distant camp; others remembered their mothers explaining the wonders of sky while they waited for the men to complete the building of the nightly igloo. By contrast, the swift, foraging snowmobile trips made by Inuit hunters of the present are the very antithesis of dog-team travel and leave little time, opportunity, or inclination for stargazing. Moreover, such trips are almost invariably made by the hunters themselves, other family members joining them only in the spring when perpetual sunlight completely masks the stars.

Significantly, some of the elders interviewed also made the point that in the wintertime they do not notice the stars any more, at least not in any detail, because of the obscuring glare of the community's street lights reflected upwards from the snow. "Light pollution," the anathema of city-dwelling amateur astronomers everywhere, now pervades most Canadian Arctic communities. Nevertheless, by combining the various strands of information gathered through the elders' interviews (a number of these conducted outside in the dead of winter, at some distance from the community's street lights), it proved possible to reconstruct the celestial sphere and its luminous contents more or less as traditionally projected by the Iglulingmiut.

A few words on terminology and related matters. "Iglulingmiut" means the "people of Igloolik" and here properly refers to Inuit living in Igloolik.[5] It does not carry the broader, encompassing definition advanced by Rasmussen and Mathiassen, which includes the Aivilingmiut of Repulse Bay and the Tununirmiut of North Baffin Island, for the good reason that interesting differences exist between these areas, at least on the subject of star lore. It should also be pointed out that some of the elders who contributed information to the study did not spend their formative years in the Igloolik area. In these cases their knowledge of celestial phenomena may relate more to other regions than to Igloolik proper. Such occurrences have been noted where appropriate.

In conformity with current practice I have tended to use the term "Inuit" (Inuk, singular) when referring to contemporary Canadian Eskimos, particularly those living in the Central and Eastern Arctic, while retaining the term "Eskimo" where it occurs in an established ethnographical or historical context. "Eskimo" can also refer to Inuktitut, the language of the Inuit. Words and passages in Inuktitut, particularly those taken from the Igloolik interviews, are rendered in the standard Inuktitut orthography developed under the auspices of the Inuit Cultural Institute (I.C.I.) in 1976.

The spellings of Inuktitut star names and related astronomical terms gathered from various published sources are, for the most part, retained as originally rendered. These spellings vary widely depending on the linguistic competence, ear, and mother tongue of the recorder. Usually, however, it was possible to derive meaning from these spellings based on the contextual evidence provided, and to make reasonable assumptions about the identity and geographical distribution of the star or constellation in question.

(Left) Sculpture of a Loon. Ivory. Thule. Somerset Island, NWT, AD 1200–1700, Royal Ontario Museum. Gift of L. A. Learmonth. (Right) Sculpture of a Loon. Ivory. Neo-Eskimo. Western Arctic, date unknown. Royal Ontario Museum. Gift of John Moore.

CHAPTER 1
The Arctic Sky

When the natives heard that we had been far in the direction of the sun, they asked us whether we had not been in the land to which the sun travelled.

(Gustav Holm, 1911)

★ ★ ★

GEOGRAPHICAL POSITION AND THE CELESTIAL SPHERE

Inuit returning to Igloolik from visits to southern Canadian cities have remarked how different and unfamiliar the sky seems to be in the "south." The Sun shines during midwinter days; midsummer nights are dark; twilight is shorter; the stars are in strange positions, seem closer, often brighter and more numerous. Taken together and compared with the celestial sphere above Igloolik, these observations are fair comment on the way the sky and its contents vary in accordance with changing latitude.

Due to the proximity of the polar regions to the Earth's axis, as one journeys into higher latitudes the visible portion of the celestial sphere decreases while its various luminaries appear to take on increasingly eccentric itineraries. *Dutton's Navigation and Piloting* affords a concise summary of astronomical conditions at that most extreme point of northerly latitude, the North Pole:

> At the pole the sun rises and sets once a year, the moon once a month. The visible stars circle the sky endlessly, essentially at the same altitudes; only half the celestial sphere is visible. . . . The planets rise and set once each sidereal period (from 225 days for Venus to 29.5 years for Saturn). A day of 24 hours at the pole is not marked by the usual periods of daylight and darkness, and "morning" and "afternoon" have no significance. In fact, the day is not marked by any observable phenomenon except that the sun makes one complete circle around the sky. [Maloney 1983:838]

While Inuit do not quite experience these extreme conditions (their most northerly range, in the Thule region of Greenland, being at latitude 76°N), there is no question that the north polar celestial regime would be far more in keeping with their view of astronomical succession than that seen in either the temperate or the equatorial regions of Earth.

Theoretically, an observer at the equator, over the course of a year, would see all the stars on the celestial sphere while one at the North Pole would see only half of them. At Igloolik, which is situated in latitude 69°22'N, all stars having southerly declinations approaching or exceeding 20° are always below the horizon. Thus, major constellations such as Scorpius, Sagittarius, Canis Major, and much of the "Milky Way," so familiar to those who live in more southerly regions, are never seen in their entirety at the latitude of Igloolik. An example of the effect of latitude on Inuit star lore is provided by a comparison of two versions of essentially the same legend involving the Moon-man and the "Entrail Snatcher," one collected from Greenland's Thule region (see page 265), the other from Igloolik (see page 223). The latter account contains a reference to the star Sirius which is absent in the Greenlandic version, a predictable omission as Sirius is always below the horizon at the latitude of Thule.

Another important aspect of latitude, also stressed in the passage quoted above from *Dutton's Navigation and Piloting*, is its apparent effect on the behaviour of the Sun and the Moon. Edward Weyer has discussed this question, intent on dispelling false impressions about the "long darkness" of Arctic winters. He points out that on balance the north enjoys more sunlight, moonlight, and twilight than the equatorial regions of Earth:

> Defining daylight as the amount of light enabling one to read newspaper print out of doors under a clear sky, there are 32 weeks of continuous daylight at the Pole and over eight weeks more during which there is at least some twilight all the time. This leaves only about 80 days of real night. Where the northernmost Eskimos live, the sun is below the horizon continuously for only a little over 16 weeks each year. Of this period only 11 weeks are without any twilight. And during these 11 weeks, the landscape is brightened much of the time by the moon, which behaves in a way that seems odd to people who live in lower latitudes. Among these northernmost people the sun shines continuously for about 18 weeks in the summer. [Weyer 1956:1]

At Igloolik the Sun is below the horizon for forty-six days between 29 November and 14 January and above the horizon for sixty-six days between 19 May and 24 July (U.S. Naval Observatory, 1990). This so-called light period is further extended by a continuous twilight beginning around mid-April and ending in the latter part of August. During this time the sky is too bright for any stars to be seen with the naked eye. At higher latitudes this effect is even more pronounced. Robert Peary attributes the "necessarily limited" astronomy of the Polar Eskimos "to the fact that the movements of the stars can be observed during only three months of the year" (Peary 1898, I:494).

The unfavourable viewing conditions of the Arctic's spring and summer skies are in no way balanced by the region's comparatively long, dark winters. The winter skies above Igloolik are frequently obscured or dimmed by a variety of atmospheric conditions including snow, blowing snow, cloud cover, ice-fog, the aurora borealis, and moonlight. Even the stars, through their reflected light, contribute significantly to their own dimming. Vilhjalmur Stefánsson estimated that the light produced by Arctic stars is "between two and three times as effective as that of the stars in other zones" (Stefánsson 1944:69).[1]

These very real practical drawbacks to stargazing in Arctic regions during winter are easily overlooked. Birket-Smith does exactly this when he tries to contrast the apparent paucity of star lore among the Inuit with his assumption that Arctic winters provide optimum conditions for celestial viewing: "The astronomical knowledge of the Caribou Eskimos is not great in consideration of the opportunity which the open prospect and the long, starlit, arctic nights give for observation. Probably the explanation is that the stars, apart from serving as a guide and a certain approximate division of the night, have no significance to the Eskimos" (Birket-Smith 1929:156).

Even on seemingly clear nights the sky is not wholly available to the observer, a fact eloquently noted by Parry when he complains of rarely seeing the Milky Way:

> This . . . beautiful feature of the heavens very seldom appeared here, for notwithstanding the notion generally entertained of the extreme clearness of the atmosphere under a polar sky, we have always found the reverse to be the fact. . . . There is scarcely one night in twenty when the heavenly bodies, if viewed through the telescope, do not appear surrounded with more or less haze. Indeed it very seldom happens that a considerable disposition of minute snow may not be observed to take place, even in the clearest nights in these regions. [Parry 1824:142][2]

Charles Francis Hall, travelling in the same region some years later, makes a similar complaint: "Tried my best to make observations for latitude of Jupiter, but *though not a cloud in the heavens,*[3] yet the stars shine dimly and fine snow is falling. Usually the sky is called hazy when it is really diffused aurora" (Nourse 1879:366).

The overall effect of Arctic conditions on the would-be stargazer thus tends to be one of relative impoverishment. The limitations placed by high latitude on the celestial sphere, coupled with extreme atmospheric conditions, which discourage any unnecessary lingering in the open, may have restricted the development of a more elaborate astronomy. This said, it must be emphasized that the celestial knowledge of the Inuit and its application to their technical, literary, and spiritual needs became an indispensable part of their world view, a worthy tribute to their remarkable powers of observation, imagination, and inventiveness.

★ ★
"Shamans, in
their spirit flight,
visit otherwise
inaccessible
regions,
both above and
below the Earth,
returning with
illuminating
accounts of their
explorations."
See page 19.

Sculpture of Human-Animal Transformation. Stone. By Tivi Paningajak. Tarramiut.
Ivujivik, Quebec, c. 1982. Royal Ontario Museum. Gift of Richard C. Martin.

★ ★ ★

Stars and Constellations: Naming

*In the course of the pursuit they at last rose up
into the air and were transformed into Aagssuk.
Thus people are wont to tell of those two,
who were transformed into stars.*

(Pualorssuaq, in Holtved 1951)

Sun, Moon, and the planets excepted, the astronomy of the Iglulingmiut settles on approximately thirty-three individual stars, two star clusters, and one nebula. Of the stars only six or seven have individual names, the remainder being incorporated into some sixteen or seventeen named constellations depending on a variety of possible groupings. Several stars hold two designations: an everyday "common" name and a "literary" name reserved for use when the star serves as the personification of a mythic character.

With the possible exception of the constellation *Tukturjuit*, in Ursa Major, variously designated as a single caribou or as a herd of caribou, only single stars are used by Inuit for the personification of humans and animals. This practice seems consistent with a widespread Inuit view that all stars were once animate beings on Earth, possessed of single souls, which in transformation logically retained their individual identities. Inanimate objects, on the other hand, are represented by groups of stars which, by their particular arrangement on the sphere, are more or less suggestive of the objects they are deemed to be. Interestingly, the basic conditions governing the naming of Inuit stars match precisely the astronomical naming system said to have been used by ancient Arab peoples:

> The archaic nomenclature of the Arabs . . . in one respect is unique. They did not group together several stars to form a living figure, as did their Western neighbours. . . . Single stars represented single creatures, a rule that rarely seems to have been deviated from—although the case was different in stellar counterparts of inanimate objects. Even here they used

★ 14 ★

but few stars for their geographical, anatomical, and botanical terms; their tents, nests, household articles, and ornaments—all of which they imagined in the sky. [Allen 1963:vii]

Inuit designations for stars and star groupings fall into several categories. The two principal ones are, first, human and animal personifications such as hunters, polar bear, caribou, dogs, and wolves, and second, "intrinsic" designations derived from some specific quality of the stars in question including colour, distance of separation, whether the star is leading or trailing, the order of its appearance in the night sky, and, in the case of Polaris, its apparently fixed position on the sphere. Humans personified as stars are typically accompanied by one or more companions, usually close relatives, who, propelled by the momentum of a desperate pursuit following some social transgression, ascend with them into the sky.[4] The well-known Sister-Sun/Brother-Moon myth typifies this kind of personification.

Two important groupings have anatomical designations—the "breast-bone" and "collar bones"—again deriving from a perceived arrangement of the stars, while another category includes familiar material objects such a soapstone lamp stand, a blubber container, or a sled. Stars with roles to play in Inuit mythology simply cross from one category to the other as circumstances require, with or without changing their names. Vega, for example, whose common designation in Inuktitut is *Kingulliq*—"the one behind" or "the next one," becomes *Ningiuraaluk*—"the old woman," when appearing in legend. By contrast, Sirius, named *Singuuriq* in Inuktitut for the characteristic flickering or pulsating of its light—an apt description of this brightest of stars—uses this same name when appearing on stage, so to speak.

Inuit assign more importance to those major stars in their sky which rise and set, than they do to the so-called circumpolar stars which constantly rotate above them. Stars of the former variety, perhaps due to the apparent animation bestowed by their rising, setting, and progressively shifting appearance in the sky, are more apt to be personified as human beings and assigned parts in legends. In addition, this class of stars, especially those in the constellations of Aquila and Orion, when making their first appearance of the year in designated parts of the sky, were important for Inuit in the calculation of seasonal time.

Birket-Smith (1929:157) complains that "in many cases it is impossible to get statements from one's informants to agree, because very often the names [of stars] are quite confused." Igloolik's Hubert Amarualik appears to support Birket-Smith's claim, explaining that "People are different and so their interpretations of the stars also tend to be different. There was never a consensus on stars. . . . They would have the same names but the names would be assigned to different stars depending on where the person made his home, so it was common for people that resided in different places to have differing names [for the stars]" (Amarualik 1992, IE-212).

On the basis of interviews and observations made with Igloolik elders, the claims of Amarualik and Birket-Smith are not entirely supported. At Igloolik the "common" names given to particular stars by various Inuit elders are essentially consistent and, differences of regional nomenclature aside, there was usually agreement on the non-literary Inuktitut designations for all major identified stars and constellations.[5]

This consistency, however, did not always extend to the assignment of stars used as *dramatis personae* in some of the myths. Here, the requirements of the narrative often take precedence, settling comfortably on whatever appropriate set of stars happens to be available. Thus, in the hands of various narrators, the legend of *Iliarjugaarjuk,* the orphan boy, attached itself as easily to the three stars of Orion's belt as it did to the stars Muphrid, Vega, and Arcturus. In Northwest Greenland the same story is linked to the stars Altair and Tarazed, which comprise the Inuit constellation *Aagjuuk.*[6] Such flexibility doubtless accounts for much of the apparent inconsistency in the designation of Inuit stars and may have been partly responsible for Birket-Smith's conclusion.

A number of Inuktitut star names, particularly those designated as animals or inanimate objects, end either with the suffix *-juk-* (pl. *-juuk-, -juit-*) or *-ttiaq-* (pl. *-ttiat*), implying that the star is a "likeness" of, or more correctly, "has the spirit"of, the animal or object it is said to represent. The usage of these suffixes is shared with many of the names given by Iglulingmiut and other Inuit groups to their string-figure depictions, suggesting some ancient conceptual link between the two systems. The relationship between astronomy and string figures will be touched on later.

Inuit learned the names of stars at a young age, usually in a rather casual fashion, in conjunction with some more immediate activity. As we have seen, night travel by dog-team and the associated camp-making stops provided ideal opportunities for pointing out the stars and relating their significance, lore, and legends. Some of the stars, as Noah Piugaattuk says, have legends behind them "to pinpoint their exact locations" (Piugaattuk 1988, IE-040). In Ava's [Aua's] account of a shamanistic journey to the "land of the dead," Rasmussen provides an interesting description of a collective approach to the learning and recollection of star names. At the very moment the shaman's soul leaves the igloo on its spirit flight, "aided by all those stars which were once human beings . . . a rushing, whistling sound" is heard. Ava continues: "'Pfft—pfft—pfft!' That is the stars whistling for the soul of the shaman, and the guests in the house must then try to guess the human names of the stars, the names they bore while living down on earth; and when they succeed, one hears two short whistles: 'Pfft—pfft!' and afterwards a faint, shrill sound that fades away into space. That is the stars' answer, and their thanks for being still remembered" (Rasmussen 1929:130).

Most of the prominent bright stars seen in the skies above Igloolik are accounted for in local astronomy either as separate entities or as members of a constellation. A notable exception is the star Deneb, which does not seem to be included in present-day Iglulingmiut celestial lore.[7] Other Inuit groups, including the West Greenlanders, have recognized Deneb as one of a number of "guiding stars" *(nalerqat)* in the constellation Cygnus (Birket-Smith 1924:436).

★ ★ ★

Myth and Nature

Science explains nothing. . . . It can only reduce to simpler and more concise terms our crude descriptions of phenomena which in the last analysis, are perhaps inexplicable.

(R. G. Smith, 1962)

Among many indigenous peoples vestiges of the so-called mythic view of the world still persist, but their expressions, particularly in a cross-cultural context, are all too easily characterized and dismissed as mere superstition. Rather, they should be seen as the residues of complex patterns of belief and knowing which defined for generations the interrelationship between mankind and the universe. Laurens van der Post, paraphrasing the psychologist Carl Jung, puts the matter forcefully: "The word 'myth' in common usage was the label applied to what the rationalist in command of the day dismissed as illusion, non-existent, apocryphal, or some other of the proliferating breed of reductive words the cerebral norms of our time produce for dismissing the existence of any invisible and non-conceptual forms of reality" (van der Post 1975:119).

The popular mythologist Joseph Campbell unwittingly exemplifies van der Post's complaint by suggesting that Inuit shamans when recounting their feats "have had a tendency to pull the long bow . . . or perhaps, rather, to confuse dream reality with daytime events" (Campbell 1991:244–45). The mythic view in fact admits no such confusion. This point was well understood by A. F. Anisimov, a Russian ethnographer who worked among the Chukchis of northeastern Siberia—a people whose cosmology has much in common with that of the Inuit. With particular reference to transformation—a major element of Inuit celestial myths—Anisimov writes: "In the views of the Chukchis such transformations appeared possible at one time. They supposed that nature was endowed with life, analogous to the life of man, and its transfer from one state to another constituted a natural phenomenon of this general creativity of life. Every material object can act according to its own will" (Anisimov 1959:217).

A compelling example of the gulf between mythic and "rational" views of nature occurred in Igloolik a number of years ago. Government biologists, intent on introducing legislation to limit the number of polar bears killed in the area, met with community representatives. One old hunter strenuously objected to their proposals, pointing out that polar bears had intelligence matching or exceeding that of humans and, as such, could be "taken" only when they wanted to "give themselves." By way of explanation the hunter told of a time he followed fresh bear tracks across the island of Qaggiujaq in the Northern Foxe Basin. The tracks suddenly ended, and there, on the tundra, was a rectangular block of ice. Clearly, the polar bear, not wanting to be taken, had transformed itself into ice. The government biologists were bemused at this explanation, whereupon the old hunter told them that if they did not, or could not, believe him, then they knew nothing about polar bears. (A. Innuksuk, 1995, IE-324; Georgia 1982:151)

At one level mythology is often seen as a device for the explanation of otherwise inexplicable natural phenomena and events.[8] Arthur Koestler's views on the complementary purpose of science and religion, the fruitful mingling of the rational and the intuitive, although intended to characterize the uneven progress of

European astronomy, are just as apt when applied to Inuit views of the universe. In common with all cosmologies the Inuit system strives to provide "reassurance by explanation, by reducing threatening, incomprehensible events to principles familiar to experience . . . [thereby] appeasing cosmic anxiety" (Koestler 1959:531). Thus, with Inuit many celestial objects are assigned terrestrial origin. They are given names, and therefore souls, and in some areas even accorded biological function, as evidenced in mushrooms being termed "star feces," and a certain variety of lichen "the Sun's urine." In parts of Greenland even dietary attributes were extended to stars—the red ones were said to subsist on liver, and the white ones on kidney (Birket-Smith 1924:436).

The existence of other worlds in the sky, more or less analogous to Earth, are confirmed periodically by animal tracks found on fresh snow which appear to start from nowhere. The inference is that the animal has fallen from the sky. In particular the "collared" lemming *(Dicrostonyx groenlandicus)* is said to originate in this way. Rachel Uyarasuk of Igloolik recalled seeing such tracks, on more than one occasion, spiralling out from a single point in the snow.[9] In her view they "were the tracks of the *Amiqlak* [the collared lemming] whose claws are usually formed in layers.[10] They used to say that these were the lemmings that had fallen from the heavens" (Uyarasuk 1990, IE-076). Inuit of the Coronation Gulf area held a similar tradition about lemmings with "double claws" which they appropriately call sky-lemmings—*"avingait qilangmiut"* (Rasmussen 1932:23).

But why should human beings or their personifications be found in the sky? It seems that the notion of cosmic creation, like so many other facets and conditions of Inuit reality, is a product of human frailty and transgression. Nâlungiaq, Rasmussen's main source on Netsilik (Nattilingmiut) cosmology, importantly attributes the existence of many celestial and atmospheric phenomena to "evil actions and taboo-breakings." She points out that "the sun and the moon murdered their mother, and though they were brother and sister, they [incestuously] loved each other. For that reason they ceased to be humans" (Rasmussen 1931:209–10).

The events leading up to the placement of humans and animals in the sky are carefully explained by myths in terms true to Inuit experience. Shamans, in their spirit flights, visit otherwise inaccessible regions, both above and below the Earth, returning with illuminating accounts of their explorations. The relationship between humans and all the other creatures and spirits of the universe is regulated by complex sets of taboos, enforced by the Moon spirit, which in their breach or observance, can explain virtually any happening, untoward or fortuitous. In this way, cause and effect are established, the unknown becomes known, the inexplicable explained. A powerful affirmation of this view is found in Ava's evocative response to Rasmussen's persistent question, "What do you believe?" Ava's answer—as paraphrased by Rasmussen—"We do not believe, we fear," often advanced as proof of the dearth of spiritual belief in traditional Inuit society is, at least at the cosmic level, as much a statement about belief as about fear. Indeed, most of Ava's fears are given context and mercifully circumscribed by his cosmology:

> We fear the weather spirit of the earth, that we must fight against to wrest our food from land and sea. We fear Sila. . . . We fear Takanakapsaaluk, the great woman down at the bottom of the sea, that rules over all the beasts of the sea. We fear the sickness that we meet with daily all around us; not death, but the suffering. We fear the evil spirits of life, those of the air, of the sea and the earth, that can help the wicked shamans to harm their fellow men. We fear the souls of dead human beings and animals we have killed. [Rasmussen 1929:56]

Years before, Rasmussen had posed the same question in Northwest Greenland. The replies were much more positive and emphasized the necessity of belief and the observance of taboos in maintaining life and cosmic order: "We believe our *Angákut* [shamans] and we believe them because we wish to live long. We believe, in order to make our lives and our food secure. . . . We observe our old customs, *in order to hold the world up, for the powers must not be offended*"[11] (Rasmussen 1908:123–24).

Janet McCrickard, author of a study on solar mythology, assigns the status of hypothesis to those early mythic ponderings on celestial matters which are, as she says, "based on observations [and share] common roots with scientific inquiry" (McCrickard 1990:138). For Birket-Smith, at least where traditional Inuit culture is concerned, science, mythology, and religion merge to form a single system of knowledge: "Science and mythology cannot . . . be separated at a primitive stage and, if we are to consider the geographical and astronomical knowledge of the Caribou Eskimos, it would be logically correct to do so in combination with an examination of their myths and their religious view of life. Where definite knowledge has its boundaries, there the myths begin" (Birket-Smith 1929:153).

Perhaps no better expression of this process can be found than in the elegant logic used by Sorkrak, a shaman, to explain an unusual absence of polar bears in his Northwest Greenland neighbourhood: "No bears have come because there is no ice, and there is no ice because there is too much wind, and there is too much wind because we mortals have offended the powers" (Steensby 1910:364).

Myth was also used to account for unusual geographical and botanical reality. An interesting example of this relates to Greenland's Disko Island. This large island on the northwest coast of Greenland is host to a number of plant species normally associated with the more southerly regions of the country. In particular the large herb angelica *(Archangelica officinalis)* grows here and is a delicacy valued by the Inuit of the area. Both the occurrence of angelica on Disko Island and the island's supposed geographical beginnings are explained in Jorgen Fleischer's delightful version of this local legend:

> Disco originally lay further to the south, but, because it took up too much space on the hunting grounds, it was decided to move it. Two hunters, Niffiffaarssuk and Nivingasilernak, towed it behind their kayaks to its present position using a single hair as a tow-rope. The hair, which was from the head of a baby, was bewitched and the whole journey took just one day.
>
> Kiviaritajak, another legendary figure, did not want the island moved. He stood on the mainland and encircled the island with a [leather] belt and pulled in the opposite direction. But the baby's hair was so strong that the leather belt broke. The proof of this story, or so people say, is the fact that Disco island is the only place in north Greenland where wild angelica grows. [Fleischer 1990:2][12]

Nearer home, myth is invoked to explain Igloolik Island's unique demographic past, as well as the origin of death. Evidence of Igloolik's ancient human population is everywhere provided by the numerous archaeological sites scattered throughout the island. While archaeologists hold that these sites are in fact cumulative—the tangible signs of successive occupation over the past four thousand years—local mythology views the sites as having been occupied at a single time in the distant past by the island's first people:

> In Igloolik the first people were known as Aakulukjuusi and Uumarniittuq. There were no other people. . . . Aakulukjuusi was given a

name, Nunaliurti (creator of earth). Aakulukjuusi and Uumarniittuq were made so that they were able to bear children. At this time the land never experienced winter.

The children born to Aakulukjuusi and Uumarniittuq never died and so the population of Igloolik became great and the entire island was overrun with people. This is the reason why the island has many signs of occupation, especially on top of every hill where you will see tent rings. Indeed, so crowded was the island that it became harder and harder to find a place to live . . . and the people started to push each other to the limits of the beach. Food, however, was readily available because the winter never set in and the people knew nothing of cold. . . .

One man who found himself without a place said, *"Tuqu! Tuqu! Tuqu! Unata! Unata! Unata!"* ("Death! Death! Death! Fight! Fight! Fight!") He wanted death, because there was no more room: the land was overcrowded.

As soon as he had said these words, one that overheard him replied thus: *"Tuqujuunatigllu, unatajuunatigllu!"* ("No death should occur, no fighting should occur!") But he did not prevail because he had spoken after the one who had first called for death. And so people started to die, and they also became susceptible to sickness, and winter came about. From that time on the Island of Igloolik was no longer overcrowded. [Kappianaq 1995, IE-329]

Accounts of Inuit mythology in the anthropological and historical literature, particularly where they relate to celestial and atmospheric phenomena, are replete with examples upholding the "hypothesis" aspect of myth. Eclipses, the phases of the Moon, shooting-stars, and the aurora are among the many phenomena convincingly accounted for by specific elements of Inuit mythology. Unfortunately, most of the legends offered by Igloolik elders in the course of this study stopped short of explicitly linking relevant details in the narrative to an explanation of some specific phenomenon. What in earlier times seems to have been an integral part of each story, a sort of explanatory codicil, is now largely omitted or forgotten. The few explanations that were gathered are included where appropriate and are augmented by additional material drawn from various published sources.

CHAPTER 2
The Universe

It was related that the first missionaries at Barrow told of the creation according to the Biblical account. Many people, it was said, refused to accept this and were reported as having said, "Very well, God made the world, but Raven made it first."

(Robert Spencer, 1959)

★ ★ ★

THE EARTH—*NUNARJUAQ*

Inuit everywhere tended to regard the Earth as being at the centre of the universe. Multiple celestial realms, sometimes up to four or five in number, were layered horizontally or spherically above the Earth, each supporting its own distinct world often associated with a particular heaven or "land of the dead."

Temptingly reminiscent of a Platonic universe delineated by "perfect concentric spheres," the Eskimos of the Bering Sea area have graphically represented their various celestial worlds by incorporating circular hoops of wood, known as *ellanguat* ("models of the universe"), into some of their ceremonial masks (Fienup-Riordan 1988:257). This geocentric view of the universe is also implicitly supported as an obvious and indisputable condition of the natural world: clearly, the sky and all its contents encircle the Earth. For the Nunamiut of Alaska, the proof of this fact is found in observing the apparent motion of the Sun: "The sun moves around the sky in a circle during July and June when it never sinks below the horizon. During the months when the sun sets, it was thought to travel all the way under and around the earth, since any other explanation would not make sense in view of what one could see" (Gubser 1965:193).

In the Inuit view, the Earth was thought to be stationary while all the observable celestial bodies revolved above or around it. An amusing but revealing demonstration of this truth is related by Alex Spalding. On a summer's day in Aivilik (Repulse Bay, NWT) he and his companion, Kuviiq, were painting the roof of the Hudson's Bay Company store when Spalding was suddenly moved to expound on the heliocentric view of the universe:

> Taking a break from our painting . . . we got to talking about the sun and the moon and the earth and heavenly bodies in general, and I thought that I would try to explain simply—perhaps I was a little presumptuous from being so high up in the air—the nature of the earth's movements, both elliptically about the sun and also its revolutions about its own axis. When [Kuviiq] heard this from me, I think he thought I was talking nonsense, and he replied somewhat disdainfully, *"Aulajjaaqquunngitturli manna!"* ("I think it's very unlikely that this thing moves though!") I had to agree with him that the movement of the earth was not at all perceptible to the senses. Since I didn't believe I knew how to explain it to him convincingly, I let the matter drop. [Spalding 1993:182]

Spalding might have fared better with Maurice Arnatsiaq of Igloolik, who rather preferred to believe that the Earth revolves while the stars remain fixed. He reasoned that if the celestial sphere were in fact revolving then *Nuutuittuq*, the

Pole Star, would also appear to move just as the other stars do, but as the Pole Star never moves nor, by extension of this logic, the sky, then the apparent motion of the heavens must be attributed to the movement of the Earth (Maurice Arnatsiaq, pers. comm., 1990). Whatever the merits of this argument, it does demonstrate some current Inuit speculation about the nature of celestial movement.

In form, the Earth was assumed to be a large, flat disk of some considerable thickness—an assumption supported by Inuit observation of the way water behaves on various surfaces. As Gubser reports, the Nunamiut, when they first heard of a round Earth, "pointed out that the water would run off if the earth were not flat" (Gubser 1965:193). Similar arguments were advanced by several Igloolik elders. In particular Eli Amaaq recalls the difficulty he had in accepting the concept of a spherical world:

> I have heard that Sila is round. . . . When I was first told this I thought to myself, because of my absurdity, that if the Earth were indeed round there would be no water as it would run off. I knew for a fact that the water would spill if the Earth was round. At that time it was evident that I was a non-believer! Then I was told: "You know a pail filled with water will not spill if you rotate it around at an even speed." . . . And from that moment on I believed that the Earth was round. [Amaaq 1989, IE-074]

The notion of a flat Earth was widely held by Inuit. An unusual version of the Sun/Moon myth, told to Frederick Cook by his companion, Etuq, has the protagonists racing across a flat Earth and beyond: "The chase continued for a long time. At last they arrived at the end of the earth. She stepped off into space and winged the air. He still followed. In time she became the sun and he became the moon. The chase is still on. This proves to us that the earth is flat" (Cook 1951:282).

Spencer records that in North Alaska "lost hunters were said to have fallen off the edge of the world" (Spencer 1959:257). By contrast, such accidents, in the view of the Labrador Inuit, were prevented by the flat Earth being "bounded by high precipitous sides, shelving outward or sloping inward to prevent anything living from going to the region beyond" (Turner 1894:267).[1] Flatness of form was also attributed to the Sun and the Moon. In parts of the Eastern Arctic, for example, the Moon was considered to be "a thin round disk of ice which follows the sun and turns about itself" (Fleming 1928:58), while in East Greenland the Sun is portrayed as being almost without substance, her back virtually skeletal, the result of being flayed by men with sharp instruments attempting to prevent her descent below the horizon in the winter time (Holm 1914, *in* Thalbitzer 1914, part 1:105).

Speculation about the size of the Earth is demonstrated in a number of legends from different areas of the Arctic. In Northwest Greenland's Thule District it is told how two young men set out in different directions to travel around the world. The journey lasted most of their lives. When they at last met again they could barely walk and had to be guided by their children. Of their musk-ox horn drinking-cups nothing but the handles remained, "so many times had they drunk on the way. . . . Yes the world is large" (Rasmussen 1908:103). The same conclusion is reached in an epic from Alaska:

> We started out to go round the world, but we had only been walking two nights and three days when we went into a house that seemed to be without end. The air and the sea and the earth seemed to have gone, and for fear of getting lost we had to walk round and round, along by what we thought were the house walls. We could not turn back, and we walked and kept on walking. We grew beards, we got white hair, we got wrinkles in our skin, and my friends died of old age; I am the only one to come back. All I am able to tell you is that the world is enormous, and that it is round; the earth is round like the inside of an *igdlo'*. This is what the old man said, and then he fell down and died. So great, so enormous, is the earth. [Ostermann 1952:194]

Another tale, well known in the Canadian Arctic, also illustrates Inuit notions about the Earth's dimensions. Johnny Annanack of Kangiqsualujjuaq, Northern Quebec, gives the following version:

> A man called Atunga and his wife began a journey around the world, leaving their young daughter at home. They travelled by dog-team and boat. The journey took many, many years. Atunga and his wife even passed through the land of the qallunaat [the white man] where they acquired some beads as a gift for their daughter.[2] When they at last returned to their home they found their daughter had become a very old woman while they themselves remained relatively young. The daughter scorned Atunga's

gift, saying, "What need does an old woman have of beads?" Atunga's footprints can be seen in the bedrock near Kangiqsualujjuaq.[3] [J. Annanack, pers. comm., 1992]

There are very few Inuit legends remaining that refer in any detail to the mystery of universal creation. A remarkable exception, however, must be a story given to Knud Rasmussen by Arnaruluk, an old woman from the north of Greenland. After stating that "old women do not carelessly waste words," Arnaruluk continues:

At that time, long, long ago, when earth was to be, it fell down from above; soil, mountains, and stones fell from the sky. Thus the earth was. After the earth was created men came. It is told that men came from the soil. . . . The soil gave them their food. . . . But the men increased; they became more and more. They did not know death at that time, long, long ago. . . . Neither did they know the sun; they lived in darkness; day never dawned. Only in the houses had they light. They burned water in their lamps. . . . But the people who did not understand how to die became far too many; they overcrowded the earth—and then a mighty flood came. Many were drowned. . . . Now the people were fewer and two old women began to talk. "Let us be without day," one of them said, "if at the same time we may be without death!" . . . "No," said the other one, "we will have both light and death." And as the old woman had spoken these words so it came to pass. Light came, and joy and death. . . . Now, when the people had light they were able to go out hunting, and were no longer forced to eat from the soil. And with death came the sun, the moon and the stars. For when the people die they rise to the sky and become radiant. [Rasmussen 1921:28–29]

About the Earth's beginnings little information was gathered through the Igloolik interviews. Even in Rasmussen's time Inuit of this area, when questioned on the subject, would generally answer that they "know nothing about the creation of the earth; they know it simply as it is and as they have seen it for themselves." Rasmussen, nevertheless, was able to gather two Nattilingmiut versions of a creation legend, which he later found to be "generally known . . . among the

Iglulingmiut." One version was given by the shaman Unaliq, the other by Unaliq's wife, Tuuglik. Tuuglik's version follows: "There once was a world before this, and in it lived people who were not of our tribe. But the pillars of the earth collapsed, and all was destroyed. And the world was emptiness. Then two men grew from a hummock of earth. They were born and fully grown all at once. A magic song changed one of them into a woman, and they had children.[4] These were our earliest forefathers, and from them all the lands were peopled" (Rasmussen 1929:252–53).

Other peoples with whom the Inuit were to come in contact originated in quite another way. The well-known legend of *Uinigumasuittuq* ("She who never wants a husband" (see page 237) relates how Indians and Europeans were created as the result of a marriage between an Inuk woman and a dog.

A Greenlandic account offered by Cranz, and also alluded to by Rasmussen, suggests that a reccurrence of the kind of cosmic collapse described above by Tuuglik is, in Greenland at least, prevented by the frequent and active intervention of shamans: "They think the globe of earth stands upon posts, which are so rotten with age that they often crack; and they would have sunk long ago, if they had not continually been kept in repair by the angekoks [angatkuit], who sometimes bring back a piece of rotten wood as proof of their important service. Their astronomy makes their firmament to rest on a lofty pointed hill in the north, and it performs its revolutions on that centre" (Cranz 1767, II:230).

Far to the west, among the people of Coronation Gulf, the notion of posts as part of the cosmic structure fit for the attention of shamans was also entertained, but in this case it applied to supporting the sky rather than the Earth. Diamond Jenness relates a story told to him by his friend Uluksak:

Now Uluksak's father-in-law, who was one of the principal shamans in the settlement, had a grudge against the other people because they had killed one of his relatives, so with the aid of his familiars he knocked down one of the two poles that were erected by men in the earliest times to hold up the heavens. The sky fell and many of the Eskimos were killed. The man then left the settlement and went east to Bathurst Inlet. After he had departed the Akulliakattak shamans divined that the pole had been knocked down by some shades of the dead, so with the help of their familiars they erected it in place again. [Jenness 1922:196]

An account of somewhat more substantial terrestrial creation, though not of the entire Earth, comes from the Nunivak Eskimos and concerns, not surprisingly, the creation of Nunivak Island. Two brothers, kayaking far from shore, are caught in a violent storm, but luckily they are able to find temporary safety on a large iceberg. The younger brother, however, not convinced that they are out of danger, begins to cry loudly. The story continues: "Down comes the Sky Woman [Sila] singing that she will marry both of them. In her lap she carries a few handfuls of earth which she spreads around the two kayaks, whereafter the earth expands into an island, Nunivak, and the iceberg becomes petrified into the island's mountains. The brothers hunt everywhere and collect berries, roots and plants. Everything is idyllic" (Sonne 1988:122).

The Earth, as previously mentioned, is connected to a number of other regions, both above and below its surface, in which are said to dwell the spirits of the dead. The soul's eventual placement in one or other of these regions primarily depended on the particular mode of death suffered by the individual. George Kappianaq explains:

It was believed that when people died they used to go up to the heavens, particularly to the area of the Moon, and there were some that went to an area half-way between the sky and the Earth. People who had been murdered would go to the region near the Moon. It is said that people who had been killed in this way only momentarily feel pain and then afterwards would never feel pain again. When we were told about death we were told that there is nothing to fear should someone kill us; a person would only feel the pain of the wound, which is nothing considering they will go afterwards to a place where they will always be happy and jubilant. As for victims of drowning, they were said to go to the underworld. For the others who die, they go to a place below the area set aside for the murder victims where they are happy, but not so much as the ones above them. Here they wait for something to happen, something that I have no knowledge of. This place, I suspect, is something like purgatory for the Christians. There are different layers in heaven so each layer is occupied accordingly. It is said that the underworld is a world on its own where there is a sky such as one would see in our world. Shamans on a journey which we would call nakkaajut can visit the underworld by penetrating the Earth. Once they have passed through the Earth into the region below, they come out into another world complete with sky and all. [Kappianaq 1990, IE-155]

We leave the Earth with George Kappianaq's vivid account of a journey to the underworld made from time to time by shamans to ensure the availability of sea-mammals through the atonement of broken taboos:

It is said that the surface of the ground appears to be thin. When one was going through the ground it was semi-dark yet there was enough light for one to see. This was the path that one followed when the shamans were penetrating the ground. Once through the ground they would come out into another world. When they made their journey to the one known as *Kannaaluk,* they would come to a *qarmmaq*—a sod house—without any roofing. The interior of this *qarmmaq* has lining made from skin. Old clothing leads the way to the entrance. It is said that this clothing used to be worn by people who had drowned. At least that was the interpretation given to this clothing. When the shaman is about to enter the house he sees a dog gnawing a human skeleton. . . . The dog at the entrance is fierce but the shaman passes without being attacked. It is said that this dog belongs to Uinigumasuittuq.

Meanwhile Uinigumasuittuq herself is lying at the right side of the sleeping platform covered in a sleeping bag while, on the other side of the platform, is her daughter, also covered in a sleeping bag. Uinigumasuittuq's hands will start to come [out of the sleeping bag] and stretch towards the shaman who has entered. Her hands look as if they are old caribou antlers—so old, in fact, that they have cracks in them— and long finger nails. The daughter will tell Uinigumasuittuq that the one who has entered is a *pullaalik*—one with bubble—meaning that he who has entered is someone who returns a body. At that moment Uinigumasuittuq's hands are drawn back into the bed covers. The reason that Uinigumasuittuq stretches out her hands thus is because the one who enters [that is, the shaman] bears too many faults.

The shaman will then ask what has caused these faults, and the reasons will be told by Uinigumasuittuq. Then a *turngaq*—a spirit—will slap the lining of the *qammaq* and, at that moment, one will hear a splashing sound.

This sound is made by the release of all the sea mammals and animals which Uinigumasuittuq had withheld.[5] The cause [of Uinigumasuittuq withholding the animals] would be a breach of taboo: one who ate something that was not allowed; a miscarriage; or breaking a taboo during menstruation. Such were the main causes for periods of scarcity. When taboos were broken the availability of animals was taken away. [Kappianaq 1990, IE-096]

★ ★ ★

THE SKY–*QILAK*

The celestial sphere, or the sky, in which the Sun, Moon, and stars are placed is called *Qilak*. In form, *Qilak* is a solid, arching canopy, "an immense dome, of hard material, reared over the earth, long from east to west and shorter from north to south" (Turner 1894:267). In the regions of *Qilak* live the various genres of souls mentioned by George Kappianaq in the foregoing passage, as well as the personifications of the Sun and the Moon. Nowadays *Qilak* has the additional connotation of the Christian heaven.

It was to this region, for instance, that the Moon-man, in an account of the *Ululijarnaat* legend (see page 223), brought his guest, an abused woman from Earth, whom he was intent on helping. An excerpt from Zipporah Innuksuk's version of this legend confirms the view of the celestial canopy as a solid but penetrable substance: "One day when the woman from Earth had settled down in Taqqiq's igloo they lifted from the floor a scapula (of a walrus or whale) which was covering up a hole. Peering down through the hole they could see igloos and people on the Earth below" (Z. Innuksuk 1990, IE-088).

The penetrable qualities of *Qilak*, along with the characteristics of at least one of its regions, are further illustrated by Inugpasugjuk of Pikiulik in a tale told to Knud Rasmussen:

Two men came to a hole in the sky. One asked the other to lift him up. If only he would do so, then he in turn would lend him a hand. His comrade lifted him up, but hardly was he up when he shouted aloud for joy, forgot his comrade and ran into heaven.

The other could just manage to peep over the edge of the hole; it was full of feathers inside. But so beautiful was it in heaven that the man who looked over the edge forgot everything, forgot his comrade whom he had promised to help up and simply ran off into all the splendour of heaven. [Rasmussen 1929:255]

The view of a penetrable sky through which one could have access to other spheres was most highly developed among the Bering Sea Eskimos where up to five celestial realms above the Earth were envisioned. A vivid account of these more-or-less self-contained celestial regions comes from Nelson in a passage describing the origin of the "Doll Festival":

One fine, warm day the unmarried shaman went up on the hillside back of the village and sat down. As night came on he fell asleep, and as he slept he saw the air fill with falling stars, and then that the sky was sinking toward him until finally it rested upon the hilltop so close that he had barely enough room to move about below it. Looking around, he saw that every star was in reality a round hole in the sky through which the light from above was shining. Raising himself up, he put his head through the nearest star hole and saw another sky with many stars shining above the first one. As he looked, the sky sank slowly down until he could put his head through one of the star holes in it, and above this were shining the stars in still another sky. This, too, sank slowly down, and standing up he found himself breast high above the third sky, and close by was a kashim surrounded by a village like the one in which he lived. [Nelson 1899:495]

During the Doll Festival, elements of this reverie were enacted using wooden hoops and rods decorated with feathers (the above-mentioned *ellanguat*—"models of the universe") suspended from the roof of the kashim in a manner that allowed them to be lowered and raised as the script required. "[The] hoops and rods represented the heavens arching over the earth, and the tufts of feathers were the stars mingled with snowflakes" (Nelson 1899:496).

Elsewhere in Alaska, a shaman on his travels to the Moon discovered *Qilak* to be "a land like the earth, only that the grass grew hanging downwards and was filled with snow" (Nelson 1899:515). Wind, acting on this snow-laden grass, caused snowstorms on the Earth below.

That many stars are in fact holes in the celestial sphere is a widespread concept. For the people of Nunivak "stars were not spirits but big holes in the sky world [through which the shaman went] whenever he journeyed to the sky" (Lantis 1946:197). Among the Chukchi and the Koryak peoples of northeastern Siberia, the star Polaris was called "hole in the sky" (Therrien 1987:39).[6] Another example from the Bering Strait region involves the star Sirius. In the Raven creation myth, Raven takes Man to a star which was "a round hole in the sky, around the border of which grew a ring of short grass, glowing like fire" (Nelson 1899:458).[7]

Farther to the east, among the Utkuhikhalingmiut, Rasmussen learned from his host, Ikinilik, that when people die "they are carried by the moon up to the land of heaven and live there on the eternal hunting grounds. We can see their windows from on earth, as the stars" (Rasmussen 1927:197). Among the Pallirmiut, Rasmussen had the stars explained to him in this way: "Heaven is a great land. In that land are many holes. These holes we call stars" (Rasmussen 1930a:79). Similarly, in the Canadian Eastern Arctic, Bishop Archibald Fleming was told that "stars are little holes in the floor of the upper world and the reason why they twinkle is that the spirits of the upper world are passing and repassing or that the wind is blowing" (Fleming 1965:153).

A different characterization of stars is suggested in some versions of the *Ululijarnaat* legend. Here stars are represented as people wearing parkas with fur-trimmed hoods. This legend relates how an abused woman was taken up to the Moon by Taqqiq, the Moon-man. When they reached their destination people came out to meet them. "These people . . . had very thin fur-trimming around their hoods; [they] were whipped by Taqqiq and sent home" (Z. Innuksuk 1990, IE-088).

The concept of stars as actual spirits of the dead seems to have been prevalent in Northwest Greenland: "She [Anahway] pointed out to me a bright star that she told me was her mother's spirit, and explained to me how, when people die, their spirits pass from the body to become stars in heaven to watch over those they have left behind. Eskimos are few, stars are innumerable, so she reasoned that

See page 236.

★ 33 ★

the vast numbers of these stars were the spirits of white folk who had died in far-away lands of which she knew nothing" (Whitney 1910:244). Among the Caribou Eskimos "stars were said to be equal to a sealskin in size"; agreement on this measurement comes from areas as disparate as the west coast of Hudson Bay (Birket-Smith 1929:157) and East Greenland, where the stars "are as large as a Greenland seal skin" (Holm, *in* Thalbitzer 1914, part 1:106).

The notion of *Qilak* as a place inhabited by the souls of the dead is now thoroughly intermingled with a Christian view of heaven. However, from George Kappianaq's information cited above, *Qilak* is just one of several regions set aside for the afterlife, although there is a considerable variety of opinion as to its conditions and the kind of souls it received. The manner of death, itself often the result of the kind of life one led on Earth, determined the particular region to be inhabited by the soul in the afterlife. The souls of women who had died from loss of blood during childbirth, for example, or those who had been murdered, were placed among the Northern Lights, a region considered more within the bounds of *Sila* than *Qilak*. Niviattian Aqatsiaq recalls:

> The woman I heard about was placed in the Northern Lights; she had died from the loss of blood. She was not placed in *Qilak,* nor was she placed underneath us where the people who steal are placed. The people who die from illness are placed with the ones who die as a result of sickness caused by their habit of robbing of others. They are placed underneath us in a place that has been made for them. I suppose they too are waiting for the judgment day. [Aqatsiaq 1990, IE-079]

Aqatsiaq's reference to "judgment day," clearly a Christian concept, recalls Rasmussen's comments on the Umingmakturmiut's views of life and death. He had been told of places of light and dark, analogous to heaven and hell and with similar entrance requirements, to which the spirits of dead Umingmakturmiut were taken. Rasmussen thought these views untypical, and concludes: "I believe [missionary teachings] are at the bottom of what they told me, that 'they who know how to feel pity' go up to a bright land after death, whereas those who are not good to the lonely and orphaned go to a dark land where there is no food or drink. For a punishment after death is quite un-Eskimo"(Rasmussen 1932:33–34).

★ ★ ★

The Environment—*Sila*

The region below *Qilak,* which encompasses the Earth, its atmosphere, the air, the weather, and various other environmental phenomena such as rainbows and the aurora, is known as *Sila* or, in its all-encompassing sense, *Silarjuaq.* The concept of *Sila* is a complex one with far-reaching significance and, perhaps more than any other, forms the basis of the Inuit world view. Alex Spalding provides an informed summary of the term:

> *Sila* can be used in three principal ways: as an indicator of environment, an indicator of locality, and an indicator of intelligence or spirit. . . . In a word like *silajjuaq.* . . . we have a synthesis, one might say, of all these: that which supports life and physical being, that which defines horizons and limits, and that which regulates and clarifies mind and spirit. In this concept, one feels a unity of microcosm and macrocosm, near and far, inner and outer, that is, one living physical and spiritual unity of being. These are the outlooks and values of all peoples who are wise from their contact with the air, earth and water. [Spalding 1972:102]

The contiguous spatial concepts, *Sila* and *Qilak,* were also distinguished by the form of shamanistic spirit flights that took place in their respective realms. George Kappianaq explains:

> The spirits of the shamans used to visit the skies, possibly at the level of the clouds, but whether above or below them, I am not absolutely sure. It is certain, however, that when they were on a kind of flight known as *ikiaqqijut* [between layers] they did not go high in the heavens, but rather travelled somewhere below the level that aircraft fly today. This had to be so for they would travel long distances to places such as Qatiktalik and Aivilik [Repulse Bay]. . . . If they had a powerful spirit they could reach these places in a matter of moments. As for the shamans who took *ilimakturtuq* flights, they would go up to the heavens [*Qilak*] or to other regions closer to Earth where people dwelled. Certainly to the Moon or perhaps the stars or the Northern Lights.[8] [Kappianaq 1990, IE-155]

Manifest as spirit, *Sila* was one of the most powerful, complex, and constant forces confronting Inuit in their day-to-day existence. Rasmussen depicts *Sila* as a "great, dangerous and divine spirit" that "lives somewhere 'up in the air,' out in the universe, between sky and sea, hovering over earth; from there it threatens mankind through the mighty powers of nature, wind and sea, fog, rain and snowstorm. Among the Iglulingmiut and the Aivilingmiut this spirit is regarded more than all else as a personification of weather" (Rasmussen 1929:71).[9]

Sila commanded immense respect and was not to be provoked in any way. An unusual provocation of *Sila* was doubtless perpetrated by ethnologist Christian Leden's use of a sextant during a gale-plagued voyage along the Keewatin coast in 1913. His Inuit companions were so persistent in their objections to the use of the sextant that Leden thought it wise to limit the instrument's use: "They disapprove of the sextant most of all. . . . It seems advisable never to use [it] except in cases of extreme emergency" (Leden 1990:69).

Among the Iglulingmiut the power of *Sila* was said to mark certain people at birth: those born on fine days were known as *silatiariktut* ("carriers of good weather"), while others, whose births happened to coincide with a period of bad weather, were called *silaluktut* ("carriers of bad weather") (A. Innuksuk 1989, IE-068). People designated in this way could apparently work their influence on the weather by deliberately going outdoors in a state of partial undress. Piugaattuk gives an account of one such incident:

> In Tunnunirusiq [the region around Arctic Bay, NWT] there was once an older hunter who lived in a camp with others. As the winter approached the snow was late in coming, so the people had no choice but to continue living in tents in spite of the temperatures. . . . The tents were [now] becoming harder and harder to heat even with added coverings. [One day] when the hunters were returning from their sealing, the old hunter . . . mentioned that he possessed bad weather, . . . adding that he very much wanted to have snow in order that they might build an igloo. He said he had decided to do something about it. So when they reached the camp he took his outer garments off and started to walk where there was no one around. The others, meanwhile, were putting away their hunting gear and sleds. . . . The old hunter began to remove his footwear and after that his upper clothing. All this time the temperature was severe. . . . He

now started to walk around, crying out: *"Silaga nauk, Silaga nauk, ungaa, ungaa."* ("Where is my weather, where is my weather, *ungaa, ungaa.*") Finally he got down on the ground and rolled around. The others in the camp now came to see him, so he got dressed again, put his boots on and went back home. That very night the snow started to fall, becoming heavy as the clouds increased. At the same time the wind began to pick up, blowing throughout the night with such ferocity that a blizzard ensued. When the people of the camp woke the following morning they found that some of the snowdrifts had already hardened. And thus [the old hunter] succeeded in getting enough snow to build an igloo. [Piugaattuk 1990, IE-148]

The preeminent identification of *Sila* with weather continues today. All of the Igloolik elders interviewed about *Sila* immediately began knowledgeable and detailed discourses about weather in all its forms. *Sila*, personified as weather, is still to be respected and, above all, carefully watched. Eli Amaaq suggests that the ability to observe and understand *Sila* is a mark of the real Inuk: "For us true Inuit it was like this. We were told always to observe [*Sila*] and be alert. The reason why this was important was so that we did not endanger ourselves unnecessarily. The life of a human was treasured and so that it not be lost because of carelessness we were told to be on the alert at all times" (Amaaq 1989, IE-074).

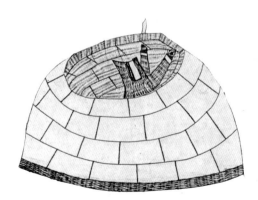

Building a Snowhouse. Copperplate Engraving. By Kovinatilliah. Sikosuilarmiut.
Cape Dorset, Baffin Island, NWT, 1964. Royal Ontario Museum.
Gift of Mr. and Mrs. E. W. Vanstone.

CHAPTER 3

Stars, Constellations, and Planets

★ ★ ★

STARS

While some stars were traditionally perceived as small apertures in the celestial sphere and others as mythic transformations of earthly humans and animals, in parts of the Canadian Eastern Arctic and Greenland they were considered to be the eyes of spirits looking down from the sky, their twinkling appearance "due to the winking of an eyelid" (Fleming 1965:153). In Kotzebue, Alaska, it was thought that numerous small, round lakes in the sky shone at night to make the stars (Nelson 1899:515). A more physical explanation of the stars' formation, albeit from mythic beginnings, is found in both Lucien Turner's (Northern Quebec) and Gustav Holm's (East Greenland) versions of the ubiquitous Sun-Moon legend. Here stars are created as a result of the Moon-Brother's desperate attempt to relight his smouldering torch during the skyward pursuit of his Sun-Sister: "When the Moon's lighted stick is about to go out, he blows on it, so that sparks fly out in all directions; it is these that turn into stars" (Holm 1911, *in* Thalbitzer 1914, part 1:253).

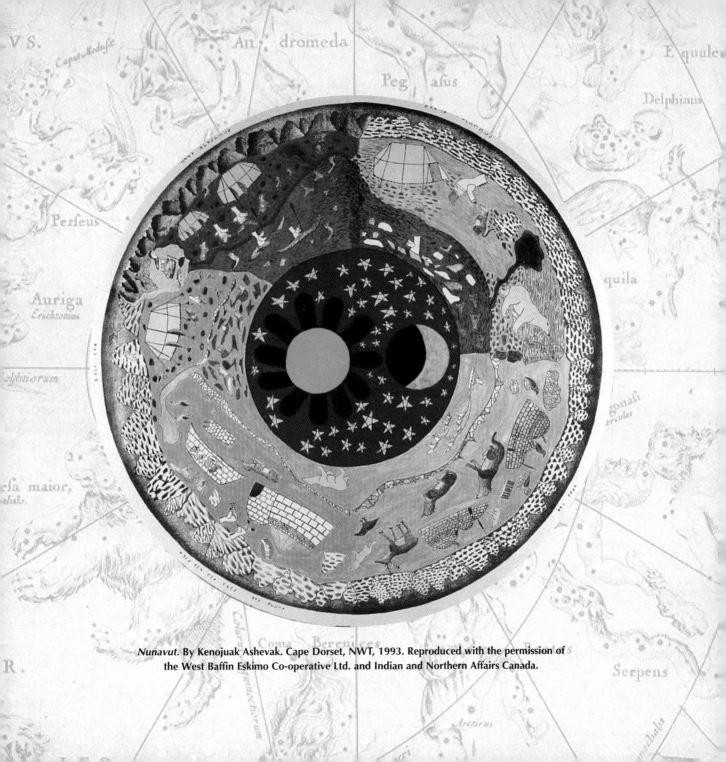

Nunavut. By Kenojuak Ashevak. Cape Dorset, NWT, 1993. Reproduced with the permission of the West Baffin Eskimo Co-operative Ltd. and Indian and Northern Affairs Canada.

A southerly view of the morning sky over Igloolik, NWT (69°22'N, 81°48'W),
as seen around the time of the winter solstice.
(Note: only those stars and constellations named by Iglulingmiut
are shown; see key on the opposite page.)

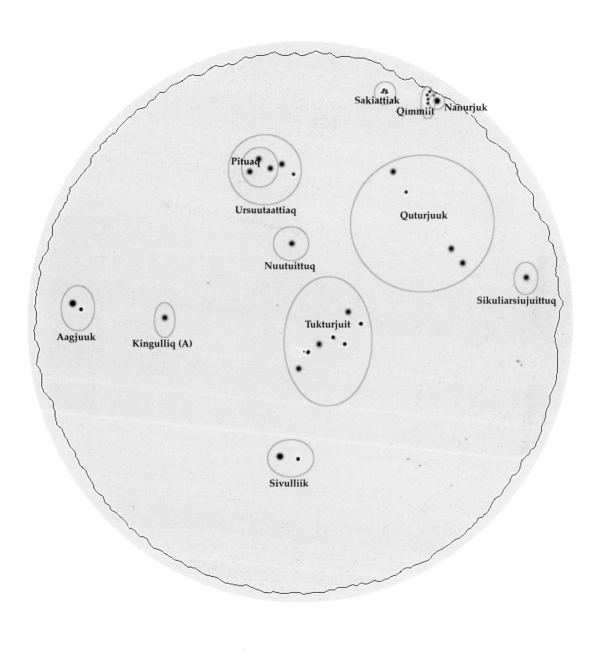

Sakiattiak

Qimmiit

Nanurjuk

Pituaq

Ursuutaattiaq

Quturjuuk

Nuutuittuq

Sikuliarsiujuittuq

Aagjuuk

Kingulliq (A)

Tukturjuit

Sivulliik

A southerly view of the late-night sky over Igloolik, NWT (69°22'N, 81°48'W),
as seen around the time of the winter solstice.
(Note: only those stars and constellations named by Iglulingmiut
are shown; see key on the opposite page.)

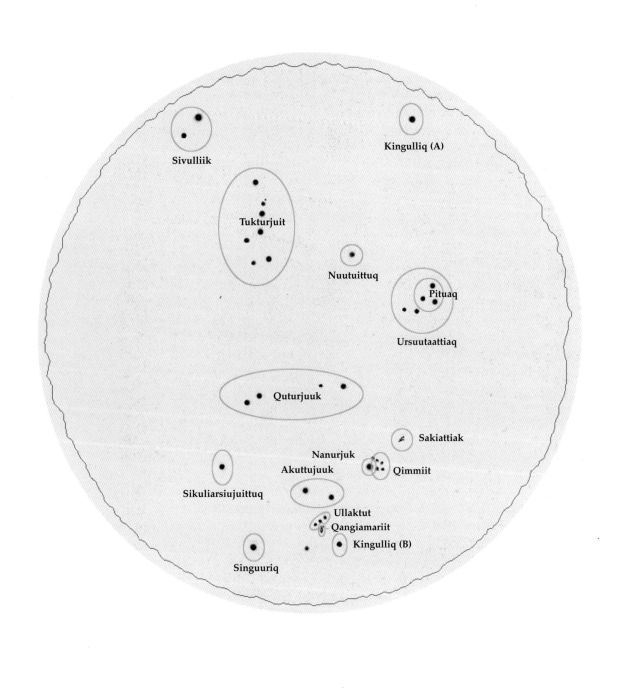

Besides their mythological and literary roles, stars had some purely practical uses for Inuit, particularly in the calculation of seasonal and diurnal time in the days before calendars and clocks. Stellar movement, position, and progression were carefully observed, especially in the months preceding and following the winter solstice. There was a widespread Inuit view that, as spring approaches, stars move across the sky faster and so "catch up with the daylight," as many of the Igloolik elders put it.[1] Stars used for telling time, particularly the coming of dawn, were known as *Qausiut*—"indicators of daylight" (Ulayuruluk 1992, IE-211).

To a somewhat lesser extent stars were used in navigation, mainly for keeping on a set course when landmarks or other clues were unavailable. The apparent variation in the size of stars and the intensity of their blinking were used in some areas for weather prediction.

Finally, the stars, in common with other celestial entities, were a major source of shamanistic power. Ulluriaq, a woman renowned in the Igloolik area both for her abilities as a shaman and for the great age to which she lived, was apparently able to invoke magical power from the stars. In one such instance, vividly recalled by Mark Ijjangiaq, Ulluriaq used this power to ensure the safe return of her grandson, Pittiulaaq, who, while walrus hunting, had accidentally been caught by the outgoing tide and carried out to sea on the moving ice. Ijjangiaq continues:

> Towards late afternoon when there was still some daylight [Ulluriaq] came outside . . . apparently to perform an incantation—not a proper shamanistic incantation but one [called] *"quunasiuttuq."* Her hood was tied in the middle, and her *aku*[2] was also tied by the mid section. She went to the porch of the igloo and, after a few attempts, managed to climb on to the roof of the porch. Once up, she stood there and cried out a number of times, gesturing with her right arm as if motioning someone to come forward. This is what she said:
>
> *"Ho, ho! ullirijaat ilaattaa! quunasiutinginniik aturpungaa! Jaru! Jaru! Jaruu!"* ("Ho, ho! with one of the stars, with its power of *quunaq* I use! *Jaru! Jaru! Jaruu!"*) These words have stayed with me ever since that day.
>
> As it turned out, Ulluriaq was doing [this] because her grandson had been carried out on the moving ice. She was asking for supernatural intervention to get him safely back to solid ground. That night, when it was

already dark, we could hear him [Pittiulaaq] coming with his dog team from the direction of Alanniq, where he had landed safely due to his grandmother's *"quunasiurut."* [Ijjangiaq 1991, IE-203]

★ ★ ★

STARS AND CONSTELLATIONS—*ULLURIAT*

The following section gives individual descriptions of the stars and constellations specifically identified and named by Igloolik Inuit elders during the winters of 1989 through 1993. Orion's nebula and the Milky Way are included as the last two items. Inuktitut names are given first, followed, where possible, by their meaning in English and the equivalent European nomenclature for the particular stars and constellations involved. The information contained under each entry also includes references made by Igloolik elders to the star's quality, position, and significance and, where useful for comparative purposes, appropriate references from a variety of other sources. The star descriptions should be used in conjunction with the detailed star maps situated between pages 38 and 40.

Except where otherwise noted, each of the stars and constellations described in this section was empirically verified by eight or nine Inuit elders during several formal outdoor observation sessions.[3] These sessions, in addition to accurately establishing equivalences between Inuktitut and English nomenclature, were especially productive in eliciting the names of other, lesser known stars and related gems of lore. As one elder put it: "When I am not looking at the stars I cannot tell you all their names." But others seemed to carry in their mind's eye a detailed map of the heavens. By way of example, Hervé Paniaq guides us through a number of his constellations:

> The stars [comprising] *Ullaktut* usually appear towards the east when the days are short and as the days get longer they start to appear further to the south. Above the *Ullaktut* there are two stars set apart from each other. When the days are shorter they will appear to be climbing and, with the start of longer days they seem to descend; these two stars are known as *Akuttujuuk.* Further to the right there is the big star we call *Nanurjuk,* which is not shining like the others but looks reddish in colour. It is situated between the group of stars called *Sakiattiak* and the *Ullaktut.* To the

left of *Nanurjuk* there are two stars, placed vertically, and another two, not far away and almost identical, but lower. This group is called *Quturjuuk*. As we move towards the left, there are a number of stars of about equal size, with some of them pointing in another direction; these are known as *Tukturjuit*. Well below *Tukturjuit* there are two stars that are late in appearing when the daylight is short. The one on the right is smaller than the one on the left; these two stars are known as *Sivulliik*. If we go to the stars which I referred to as *Tukturjuit*, and take a line from that section which points away, and follow it into that area where there appears to be a lesser concentration of the stars, we come to one that stands out from the rest; this star is called *Nuusuittuq*.* In the winter, during the dark period, there is always a big star towards the north wind; this one we call *Kingullialuk*.** Towards the west there are some stars that are known as *Ursuutaattiaq*. As the days were getting longer we see a set of stars towards the daylight which we call *Aagjuuk*. The one on the top is smaller and the bottom one, which is lower and to the left, is larger. The only time *Aagjuuk* appears is in the morning. [Paniaq 1990, IE-126]

Note: In this section, as an aid to star identification, an idealized illustration accompanies each of the stars or constellations described. In these illustrations, the star or stars in question are highlighted and shown in approximate relationship to some well-known constellation such as Orion or the Big Dipper. Star magnitudes are from Chartrand's *Sky Guide: A Field Guide to the Heavens*.

* Also rendered as *Nuutuittuq.*
** Also rendered as *Kingulliq.*

STARS AND CONSTELLATIONS

Entry	Inuit Name (Igloolik)	European Constellation	Principal Star(s)
1	*Aagjuuk*	Aquila	Altair, Tarazed
2	*Akuttujuuk*	Orion	Betelgeuse, Bellatrix
3	*Kingulliq (a)*	Lyra	Vega
4	*Kingulliq (b)*	Orion	Rigel
5	*Nanurjuk*	Taurus	Aldebaran
6	*Nuutuittuq*	Ursa Minor	Polaris
7	*Pituaq*	Cassiopeia	Schadar, Caph, Cih
8	*Qimmiit*	Taurus	Hyades
9	*Quturjuuk*	Gemini and Auriga	Pollux, Castor, Capella, Menkalinan
10	*Sakiattiak*	Taurus	Pleiades
11	*Sikuliarsiujuittuq*	Canis Minor	Procyon
12	*Singuuriq*	Canis Major	Sirius
13	*Sivulliik*	Boötes	Arcturus, Muphrid
14	*Tukturjuit*	Ursa Major	Dubhe, Merak, Phecda, Megrez
15	*Ullaktut*	Orion	Alnitak, Alnilam, Mintaka
16	*Ursuutaattiaq*	Cassiopeia	Schadar, Caph, Cih, k Cassiopeia
17	*Qangiamariit*	Orion Nebula	M42
18	*Aviguti*	Milky Way	

★ 1. Aagjuuk ★

A constellation comprising the stars Altair (mag. 0.77) and Tarazed (mag. 2.72) and, possibly, in some regions, Alshain (mag. 3.90). These stars form part of the European constellation Aquila. While the stars Altair and Tarazed can be seen during the fall months, late in the evening to the southwest, they are only recognized as *Aagjuuk* by Inuit following their first morning appearance on the northeastern horizon, usually around mid-December. Throughout January, February, and March they are seen during the pre-dawn hours but thereafter are rapidly taken over by sunlight as the days lengthen.

Alternative spellings and names for *Aagjuuk:*

Agru-la-wik—Point Barrow, Alaska (Bockstoce 1988:351)
A.gru—Point Barrow, Alaska (Ray 1885:56)
Aaguruk—North Alaska (Spencer 1959:258)
Aagruuk—North Alaska (Etalook 1983)
Agguk (aagzuuk)—Noatak River, Alaska (Jenness 1924:183B)
Agyuk (aagjuuk)—Coronation Gulf, NWT (Jenness 1922:197)
Ag.zu.k (aagjuuk)—West Hudson Bay, NWT (Birket-Smith 1929:157)

Aajjuuk (aa'juuk)—East Hudson Bay, NWT (Qumak 1988:54)
Agsuk (aaksuuk)—Labrador (Richardson 1852:483)[4]
Aagssuk—Northwest Greenland (Holtved 1951:20)
Aagssiit (aassuutit)—West Greenland (Schultz-Lorentzen 1927:3)
Augsuutit—West Greenland (Birket-Smith 1924:436)
Asiit—Angmagsalik, East Greenland (Holm 1914, *in* Thalbitzer 1914, part 1:105)
Aavssit—East Greenland (Ostermann 1938:50)

In addition the *Comparative Eskimo Dictionary* (Fortescue et al. 1994:1) gives the following:

aaɣzuuk   [proto-Inuit term]—"constellation of two stars appearing around winter solstice."

aayɣuk   [Yup'ik]—"pair of stars seen at dawn (Altair and Tarazed in the Eagle?)."

aaɣzuuk   [North Alaskan Inuit]—"constellation consisting of two stars."

aayɣuuk   [Western Canadian Inuit]—"Altair and Beta Aquilae in the constellation Aquila."

ayyuuk   [Eastern Canadian Inuit]—"two stars appearing early in the morning and disappearing during last part of winter (December)."

aassu(u)tit   [Greenlandic Inuit]—"constellation appearing on the shortest day of the year."

aaxxuuk   [Northwest Greenland]—"a large and a small star Canis Minor appearing in a northerly direction."[5]

By all accounts, *Aagjuuk* was for Inuit everywhere one of the most important constellations. It seems to have been known by this name, or a variant of it, across the entire Arctic. An early reference to the constellation is found in Rochfort Maguire's 1854 Point Barrow journal: "Vega and two other stars not visible [are called] *agru-la-wik* . . . from rising at certain seasons just before daylight" (Bockstoce 1988:351).[6] The linking of *Aagjuuk*'s stars with dawn and solstice were the characteristic features of this constellation recognized as well by other Arctic peoples, in particular the Chukchis: "The stars Altair and Tarazed of the constellation Aquila are singled out by the Chukchis as a special constellation, *Peggittyn*. This constellation is considered to bring the light of the new year, since it appears on the horizon, just at the time of winter solstice" (Michael/Anisimov 1963:212).

The meaning of the term *Aagjuuk* is not clear. Etymologically, Fortescue has postulated a link between the *aayɣuk* and the Yup'ik term for arrow, "as if the dual of *aayɣu*, 'arrow'" (Fortescue et al. 1994:1). Birket-Smith (1924:436) for Egedesminde (West Greenland) mentions two stars called *Augsuutit* which appear on the horizon "about Christmas"—a clear reference to *Aagjuuk*. He translates *Augsuutit* as "plethoric," seemingly on the mistaken assumption that the name derives from the Inuktitut *auk*—"blood."

An emphatic and, in our context, attractive explanation of the constellation's name is found in a legend from Noatak, Alaska. Here *agruks (Aagjuuk)* are said to be "the two beams of light cast by the sun when it first reappears above the horizon in late December" (Hall 1975:PM45). The legend (see page 283) then goes on to recount how these two sunbeams were transformed into stars and so confirms, from the Inuit point of view, the various and widespread connections between the *Aagjuuk* stars, winter solstice, daylight, and the return of the Sun.

For the Iglulingmiut, and probably for most other Inuit groups, *Aagjuuk* was a distinctly seasonal constellation which took on significance only after its first appearance of the year in the northeastern sector of the morning sky, usually during the second week of December. Most published descriptions of *Aagjuuk* tend to leave the impression that it suddenly appears on cue as if out of nowhere. Schultz-Lorentzen, for instance, conveys this view in his West Greenlandic dictionary which defines *Aagssiit (Aagjuuk)* as the "constellation appearing on the shortest day of the year" (Schultz-Lorentzen 1927:3).

This definition is somewhat misleading because throughout the autumn and winter months at latitudes above the Arctic Circle *Aagjuuk's* principal star, Altair, is one of the brightest and most visible stars in the south and western sectors of the sky. But so completely is *Aagjuuk* identified with mid-December and the winter solstice that one Igloolik elder, invited to point to the constellation in early November, firmly replied that we would not see it until around Christmas, and this in spite of the fact that Altair was at the time in full view to the southwest. It would be no contradiction then to claim that *Aagjuuk*, appearing outside its respected position in the winter morning sky is, in a real sense, seen but not noticed.[7]

Aagjuuk was one of the principal constellations used by Inuit for the reckoning of time, particularly during the winter dark period. Its appearance in the morning sky indicated the proximity of dawn or twilight in those more northerly regions where the sun did not rise above the horizon: "These stars [which form *Aagjuuk*] come out when the daylight is going to return. They were important to determine the time of the morning. They were comparable to the clock when they were used to mark time. When the daylight was returning they would appear to get bigger" (Paul and Martha Quttiutuqu, 1990).

Many of the elders interviewed recalled as children being sent outside in the dark winter mornings to see if *Aagjuuk* were visible. The term *"aagjuliqtuq"* ("it is making the sign of *Aagjuuk"*) implied that the day's activities should begin: "These stars were used to determine the passage of time. Before the break of dawn we would visit our elder and he would ask if it was *'Aagjulirtuq.' Aagjuuk* are located above the daylight" (Ijjangiaq 1990, IE-081).

Kunuk recalled: "Our elder, Iqipiriaq, when he had gone outdoors, upon his return used to say *aagjulirtuq*, which means the beginning of a new day as these stars appear just before the daylight" (Kunuk 1990, IE-087).

Among the Inuit of Northern Quebec the practice regarding *Aagjuuk* was identical. Markusie Iyaituk of Ivujivik recalls: "I was asked to go out in the dawn to see if the two stars called *'aarjuuk' [Aagjuuk]* have appeared. I knew where they were and could tell the time with them. I have asked people today if they know what *'aarjuuk'* are and most don't. I don't blame them for not knowing" (Markusie Iyaituk, 1985 interview, Avataq).

Salomonie Alayco of Akulivik continues in the same vein but brings in an additional constellation, *Quturjuuk* (entry 9), comprising the stars Capella, Menkalinan, Pollux, and Castor: "Every single morning, I was asked to go and check if the constellation *'Quturtuuk' [Quturjuuk]* was in view before the constellation *'Attuuk' [Aagjuuk]* appeared" (Salomonie Alayco, 1985 interview, Avataq).

Among the Inuit of Coronation Gulf, the constellation's universal association with dawn is enshrined in one of their formal incantations. These *irinaliutit* or "magic words," as Rasmussen calls them, are a form of prayer or supplication uttered at dawn by those going hunting:

By which way, I wonder the mornings—
You dear morning, get up!
See I am up!
By which way, I wonder, the constellation *Aagjuuk* rises up in the sky?
By this way—perhaps—by the morning
It rises up![8]

In some areas the constellation was also used to designate the calendar "moon," corresponding approximately to mid-December. Moses Qumak of Akulivik, Quebec, for example, mentions that this month will "have a name other than December. It is called *Arjuliut*" (Moses Qumak, 1992 interview, Avataq). The same term was used for December on the east coast of Ungava Bay (Johnny Annanack, Kangiqsualujjuaq, pers. comm., 1992), and for Labrador *(Aaksulliut)*. Peck (1925:25) lists similarly for the Paatlirmiut of the west coast of Hudson Bay the "moon" in which the *Aagjuuk* stars made their first appearance of the year was named *Aagjulervik* (Birket-Smith 1929:159).[9]

In Igloolik many of the older Inuit still associate the first appearance of *Aagjuuk* with the arrival of the winter solstice. On 19 December 1990, for example, Jacobie Avingnaq announced over Igloolik's community radio that, in his view, the shortest day of the year had arrived because he had seen *Aagjuuk* in the morning sky for the first time of the season.

For Iglulingmiut the appearance of *Aagjuuk* also marks the time when the bearded seals *(Erignathus barbatus)* start to migrate from the open sea towards the land-fast ice and can be hunted on the *uiguaq,* the newly formed ice lip extending out from the floe-edge (Kupaaq 1991, IE-187). The *Aagjuuk* stars also signalled the time for the midwinter celebration known as *tivajuut.* Symbolically complex and involving masquerade, partner exchange, and shamanistic ritual, this festival was usually held in a *qaggiq*—a large igloo specially built for the purpose: "[The celebration] was held when the *Aagjuuk* stars are seen for the first time in the season. This time was said to be the middle of winter when the daylight hours [were beginning] to return, so the people were made to celebrate it with a *tivajuut.* Here they would gather in a *qaggiq.* This celebration was made in order to strengthen the land—*nunagiksaqtut*" (Kappianaq 1991, IE-174).

Gustav Holm's information shows the East Greenlanders also making use of *Aagjuuk* in their reckoning of seasonal time. (In the Angmagsalik dialect, *Aagjuuk* is rendered as *Asiit,* which Holm equates exclusively with the star Altair when in fact the constellation should also include the lesser star Tarazed):

The East Greenlanders divide the year according to the new moons; they take as their starting point the first new moon which occurs after *Asiit,* i.e., the star alpha aquilae [Altair] has been seen for the first time in the morning twilight. In former times their starting-point was the first new moon after the shortest day, and as in certain places they still keep up the former mode of reckoning, there is some uncertainty with regard to the number of months. The moons are named solely according to their number after the first new moon.

The Angmagsaliks are not only able to tell by the position of the sun when the shortest day has arrived, but they also can tell its arrival with precision, when they have seen *Asiit*'s position in the morning twilight. [Holm 1911, *in* Thalbitzer 1914, part 1:105]

Talking also of *Aagjuuk* and the East Greenlanders, Rasmussen notes that "they had a winter feast, which was celebrated when two stars, *agtit* and *avssiit*, appeared in the northeast, a sign . . . that the days would grow longer" (*in* Ostermann 1938:50).

In Igloolik no legends are attached to the *Aagjuuk* stars. Among the Nattilingmiut, however, the constellation is personified as "the entrail snatcher"[10] who "[stood] outside the house of the sun" (Rasmussen 1931:238)—an association that coincidentally affirms the unique relationship between the Sun and *Aagjuuk* in Inuit astronomy. From the Thule region of Greenland, Erik Holtved collected a version of the "Orphan Boy" story (see page 284) both of which centre on the constellation *Aagjuuk*, or *aagssuk* as he terms it (Holtved 1951:20–21). By contrast, this tale in Igloolik involves one or the other of two sets of stars: either Vega, Arcturus, and Muphrid, or the three stars of Orion's belt. A number of versions of the "Orphan Boy" legend are found in Chapter 10.

From Alaska's Noatak area, Jenness records information linking the *Aagjuuk* stars with string-figure games. He was given the following story at Harrison Bay (70°30'N, 152°24'W) by Alak,[11] a North Alaskan Eskimo who had lived on the Noatak river during his youth.

I knew of two men who lived in another settlement on the Noatak river. They did not believe in the spirit of the string figures, but said they originated from two stars, *agguk,* which are visible only when the sun has returned after the winter night. One of these men was inside a dance-house when a flood of mist poured in. . . . His two companions rapidly made and unmade the figure "Two Labrets," an action intended to drive away the spirit of the string figures, uttering the usual formula . . . but the mist kept pouring in. [Jenness 1924:183B]

Again, in a diary entry dated 18 December 1913, Jenness notes the same Alak telling him that "they never played cat's cradles while two stars called *agruk* were visible, just before the long days of summer. . . . They played other games then, like whizzer [a noisemaker]" (Jenness 1991:89). This contradicts the more probable claim, made by Jenness in the previous passage, that *Aagjuuk* are visible only when the Sun is returning after winter solstice—hardly the harbinger of summer. That he misunderstood the season of *Aagjuuk*'s appearance is also implied by the date of Alak's comments, for by 18 December, at the latitude of Harrison Bay, *Aagjuuk* would be making itself increasingly obvious in the dawn sky. We may reasonably surmise that Alak had recently observed *Aagjuuk* and was trying to communicate this information to Jenness.

Alak's comments indicate that, for the Noatak area at least, the appearance of *Aagjuuk*, rather than the Sun, signalled the end of the string-game season.[12] And the opinion, expressed in the first passage, that string figures came from, and are therefore related to, *Aagjuuk* may have given rise to the prohibition against playing them after the solstice appearance of these stars. It is also possible that the string game mentioned by Alak—"Two Labrets"—rapidly made and unmade in an attempt to drive off the "string figure spirit," was intended to symbolize *Aagjuuk*'s two stars and so confound the constellation with its own likeness or spirit.

"Arctic" John Etalook's 1983 testimony on the significance of the *Aagjuuk* stars in this part of Alaska closely matches that given to Jenness by Alak seventy years earlier. Interestingly, Etalook refers to the "*aagruuk*" as "labrets,"[13] giving them, it seems, an alternate name, *ayaqhaagnailak*, "they prohibit the playing of string games":

> They [the *aagruuk* stars] are the ones that discourage playing a string game. . . . That's what they're called, *ayaqhaagnailak*, those two stars. . . . When the two stars come out where there is no daylight, people are advised not to play a string game then, but [play instead] with *hii, hiii, hii* . . . toy noisemakers of wood or bone and braided sinew. . . . Our parents tell us not to play the string game anymore. [Etalook 1983]

Robert Spencer (1959:258) equates the Inuit constellations *Aagjuuk* (which he terms *Aaguruk*) and *Sivulliik* (see entry 13) with the "evening" and "morning" stars respectively, presumably meaning the planet Venus as seen in its evening and morning appearances. However, given the almost universal correspondence in the Inuit world of *Aagjuuk* with the star Altair, and *Sivulliik* with the star Arcturus, he is likely mistaken. Interestingly, Nicholas Gubser states that the Alaskan Nunamiut base the "starting point for the year . . . on the first appearance of the planet Venus above the horizon shortly after the first of January" (Gubser 1965:191), implying a time-keeping role for Venus similar to that given *Aagjuuk*. From year to year, however, the itinerary of Venus appears erratic and, compared with the constancy of Altair, seems an unlikely choice for a seasonal marker.[14]

For Inuit, *Aagjuuk* was clearly the most important and most widely recognized constellation. We have seen references and allusions made to it throughout the entire Inuit world from Point Barrow, Alaska, to East Greenland, from Thule to Northern Quebec.[15] *Aagjuuk* doubtless owed its revered position in Inuit culture to its ancient role as an unfailing herald of daylight.[16] Its welcomed appearance on the northeast horizon meant that the darkest days of winter were almost over, that the Sun was now again beginning her slow journey north. Thereafter *Aagjuuk* would proclaim the coming of each day's dawn until, its seasonal usefulness spent, it faded into the morning twilight of early spring. Something of the constellation's profound significance is perhaps captured in Duncan Pryde's lines:

> And have you felt the bitter chill of calm days
> Under a naked sky
> Or hoped for the two stars
> That rise above the dawn of spring
> And promise sunlight.[17]

★ 2. AKUTTUJUUK ★

A constellation comprising the stars Betelgeuse (mag. 0.80) and Bellatrix (mag. 1.63), in the constellation Orion. Beginning in early September *Akuttujuuk* are seen in the pre-dawn sky to the southeast. Thereafter they rise increasingly earlier and by the New Year have become one of the dominant features of the mid-evening sky's southern sector. *Akuttujuuk* means "those (two) placed far apart" and refers to the spatial separation between Betelgeuse and Bellatrix, a designation occurring principally in North Baffin Island and Melville Peninsula, although also reported for the Bathurst Inlet area of the Central Arctic (Duncan Pryde, pers. comm., 1996). In the Thule region of Greenland, Betelgeuse and Bellatrix are referred to as *Akuttuut* (Jens Qaavigaq, pers. comm., 1994), strongly suggesting that the term was introduced to this area following the Qitdlarssuaq migration from North Baffin Island in the 1860s.

Among the Iglulingmiut *Akuttujuuk,* like *Aagjuuk,* were used for telling the passage of time:

> There are two stars known as *Akuttujuuk*. These stars will show up after twilight during the dark period. . . . When you see them during the [evening twilight] it is an indication that the days are getting longer. The

Akuttujuuk are located towards the daylight, the daylight is starting to appear towards the stars. There are two stars, that is why the constellation is called *Akuttujuuk*. [Ijjangiaq 1990, IE-081]

Iqipiriaq used to say that *Akuttujuuk* "had caught up." What it means is that after the winter dark period the *Akuttujuuk* will appear while there is still daylight, whereas during the dark season they appeared only before the dawn. So the saying goes: "*Akuttujuuk* has caught up" when the two stars are seen while there is daylight, a sure indication that the days are getting longer" (Kunuk 1990, IE-087).

In Pelly Bay, NWT, while the collective designation of Betelgeuse and Bellatrix as *Akuttujuuk* is apparently known, Betelgeuse, according to Quttiutuqu, is individually recognized: "There is a star that in your region is called *Akuttujuuk* but in our region it is called *Ulluriajjuaq*" (Paul Quttiutuqu, 1990). *Ulluriajjuaq* means "large star," an appropriate designation for Betelgeuse, which in Arctic latitudes appears as the brightest star in Orion, its ruddy colour and higher altitude making it much more noticeable than the technically brighter Rigel.

No myths are associated with the *Akuttujuuk* stars in the Igloolik area. Boas (1888:636–37), in his version of the *Ullaktut* legend, assigns, probably erroneously, the role of the polar bear, *Nanurjuk*, to the star Betelgeuse. In Pelly Bay the constellation is linked to the *Iliarjugaarjuk* legend (see page 230) where the "old man" becomes personified as Betelgeuse and the "orphan boy" as Bellatrix, appropriate assignations, given the relative size of these two stars: "So the little boy became afraid of the old man and fled. The old man kept following him around the igloo and they soon ascended into the sky and there became stars. The stars are known as *Akuttujuung [Akuttujuuk]*. The old man is behind while the orphan boy is in front (Paul Quttiutuqu, 1990).

A song, well known in Igloolik but probably originating in the Pond Inlet area, celebrates *Akuttujuuk*'s special relationship with the returning daylight. Depending on latitude, this song refers to a time in late February or early March when the *Akuttujuuk* stars are seen to the south in the lengthening evening twilight:

> *Akuttujuuk* appear! Yonder the day light
> It is a joyous feeling that
> I will go on living . . .[18]

Considering the prominence of Bellatrix and Betelgeuse in the Arctic sky, it is strange that they are rarely mentioned in the ethnographic literature. It is possible, however, that references may have been made to them unwittingly. In West Greenland, for instance, Poul Egede's two unidentified stars which he calls *Inerfuk*—"two persons that contend with songs or verses in taunting one another"—possibly refer to Bellatrix and Betelgeuse. Egede places this pair in Taurus rather than Orion, but the former constellation, with the exception of Aldebaran, appears to lack stars of appropriate magnitude and positioning. That Bellatrix and Betelgeuse are in fact *Inerfuk* is made even more likely when Egede explains that the Greenlanders call Aldebaran *Nenneroak*—"a light, which lights those who sing and dance" (Birket-Smith 1924:436). Thus an illuminated dancing scene involving Aldebaran as the lamp and Bellatrix and Betelgeuse as singers, is satisfactorily rendered.

★ 3. KINGULLIQ (A) ★

The star Vega (mag. 0.04) in the constellation Lyra. At the latitude of Igloolik, Vega is a circumpolar star. In the fall and early winter *Kingulliq* is the brightest star in the south and southwest evening sky. In the early months of the year it is seen high in the pre-dawn sky to the south and southeast.

Alternative spellings and names for *Kingulliq*:

Kingullialuk—"[big] one behind." Igloolik (Paniaq 1990, IE-141)
Kiudleq—"one behind." Repulse Bay area, NWT (Mathiassen 1928:233)
A.gru.la.bwuk—Point Barrow, Alaska (Ray 1885:56); Nelarsik,
    East Greenland (Holm 1911, *in* Thalbitzer 1914, part 1:85)

In an Igloolik version of the *Iliarjugaarjuk* legend (see page 230) Vega is also known as *Ningiuq* or *Ningiuraaluk*—"old woman" (Paniaq 1990, IE-141).

Kingulliq means the "one behind" or "the second one." This name may derive from *Kingulliq*'s association with the star Arcturus which, generally across the Arctic, is known as *Sivulliq* (the "one in front," "the first"), or in its dual form, *Sivulliik* when viewed with its small companion star, Muphrid. At certain times of the year Arcturus *(Sivulliq)*, the fourth brightest star in the sky, is often the first to be seen in the evening's twilight and is followed soon after by the slightly less brilliant Vega *(Kingulliq)*; hence the designations implying "first" and "second," in accordance with their order of nightly appearance. It is also possible that *Kingulliq* and *Sivulliq* are named for their apparent relative positions in the night sky, where, in the westerly procession of stars across the sphere, Arcturus is seen to be ahead of Vega.

The relationship of *Kingulliq* (Vega) and *Sivulliik* (Arcturus and Muphrid) is further confirmed in the *Iliarjugaarjuk* legend already mentioned. The story ends in a desperate chase involving the old man *(Utuqqalualuk)*, the orphan boy *(Iliarjugaarjuk),* and the boy's grandmother *(Ningiuraaluk)* in which all three ascend to the sky and are transformed into stars. *Iliarjugaarjuk* and *Uttuqalualuk* become *Sivulliik,* while *Ningiuraaluk,* trailing behind in the pursuit, becomes *Kingulliq*.

The three stars are actually known by other names. The first two are known as *Sivulliik* and the one behind is called *Kingullialuk* ("the big one behind"). In the legend, this one is known as *Ningiuq* (or *Ninguraaluk*)—the old woman. Of the *Sivulliik* stars, the smaller one is known as *Iliarjugaarjuk* ("the little orphan") and the bigger one *Uttuqalualuk*. These names are given to the stars when telling the legend (Paniaq 1990, IE-141).

According to Gustav Holm, Vega is also the subject of a legend in East Greenland: "Vega, who is called *Nelarsik,* is, like the moon, the brother of the sun. As to how it got into the sky a similar legend is told with regard to the moon. It does great service to the human race, indicating the time when it is dark, just as the sun does when it is light. Besides that there are many other ways in which it assists man" (Holm 1911, *in* Thalbitzer 1914, part 1:85).

Holm also records that in Angmagsalik tradition *Nelarsik* (Vega) is said to have shot, with his bow, one of the women who caused thunder thereby reducing the frequency of that phenomenon. Thunder is indeed a relatively rare occurrence in Arctic regions.

★ 4. KINGULLIQ (B) ★

The star Rigel (mag. 0.11) in the constellation Orion. In the early months of the year it is best seen in the south during the mid and late evening hours. In Igloolik, when mentioned at all, this star is designated *Kingulliq*, a reference to its role in the *Ullaktut* legend (see page 226). Here *Kingulliq*, "the one behind," is said to represent a hunter who, to recover his dropped mitt, leaves his three brothers (the Orion "belt" stars—entry 15) in pursuit of a polar bear (Aldebaran—entry 5).

The term *Kingulliit* or *Kingulliik* (dual form) can also be applied to the stars Dhube and Merak in the constellation Ursa Major when these were considered to represent the hind legs of the caribou in the Inuit constellation *Tukturjuk* (entry 14) (Emil Imaruittuq, pers. comm., 1990).

★ 5. Nanurjuk ★

Usually the star Aldebaran (mag. 0.85) in the constellation Taurus. *Nanurjuk* is best seen in the early months of the year. Appearing late in the afternoon to the north-east, its route traces a wide arc across the sky to the northwest where it sets in the pre-dawn sky of the next day. For some Igloolik elders, mainly those with links to Aivilingmiut traditions, *Nanurjuk* is Alcyone, the principal star in the Pleiades cluster (entry 10). *Nanurjuk* means "like, or having the spirit of, a polar bear."

Alternative spellings and names:

Pa-chukh-lu-rin—"sharing out of food"? Point Barrow, Alaska
    (Simpson 1875:271)
Agleoryuit—"pursuers." Coronation Gulf, NWT (Jenness 1922:179)
Kajorjuk—"reddish." Murchison River, NWT [Netsilik]
    (Rasmussen 1931:211)[19]
Kajorssuk (kajurzuk)—"reddish." Repulse Bay, NWT
    (Mathiassen 1928:233)
Nanuqdjung (nanurjuk)—"polar bear." Cumberland Sound, NWT
    (Boas 1888:636)

Nenneroak (naniruaq)—"a light." West Greenland
  (P. Egede, *in* Birket-Smith 1924:436)
Nelikatek—East Greenland (Holm 1914, *in* Thalbitzer 1914, part 1:106)

In a version of the *Ullaktut* polar bear hunting legend given by Franz Boas *Nanurjuk* is said to be the star Betelgeuse—a claim apparently not made elsewhere—while the faint stars of "Orion's sword" represent a sled, *Kamutiqdjung* (Boas 1888:636). More commonly, *Nanurjuk* settles on either Aldebaran or Alcyone where it is taken to represent a large polar bear held at bay by a pack of dogs. When *Nanurjuk* is Aldebaran, then the dogs, *Qimmiit*, are represented by the stars of the Hyades (entry 8). However, with Alcyone as the bear, the dogs are considered to be the remaining visible stars in the Pleiades (entry 10). In most versions of the legend the running hunters (*Ullaktut*—entry 15), trailing behind their dogs, are supplied by the three stars of Orion's belt: "In the legends they are known as *Ullaktut* (the runners). There are three of them and they are slanted upwards; they are evenly separated and most visible. Directly in front of these stars there is a big star with many smaller stars around it. That star is called *Nanurjuk*" (Piugaattuk 1988, IE-040).

In Point Barrow, Alaska, Aldebaran is also considered a polar bear, but one which has been killed and is on the point of being butchered and distributed. The star Aldebaran with the cluster of the Hyades and other smaller ones around, are called Pa-chukh-lu-rin,[20] "the sharing-out" of food, the chief star representing a polar bear just killed, and the others the hunters around, preparing to cut up their prize and give each hunter his portion (Simpson 1875:271).

In the Coronation Gulf, Jenness was informed that Aldebaran, together with its neighbouring stars, presumably the Hyades, represented a hunter and his dogs (collectively termed *Agleoryuit*, "the pursuers") while the object of their pursuit, a polar bear, was the Pleiades star cluster. Jenness also points out that "the more usual name for the Pleiades is *Agietat* (Jenness 1922:179). This is not necessarily a contradiction for in some regions where the Pleiades are known as *Agiattat* (entry 10) the major star of the cluster, Alcyone, is designated the bear.

Aldebaran, although a bright and distinctively coloured star (Mathiassen's "Iglulingmiut" term for it is, fittingly, *kajorssuk*—"the reddish one"), was not mentioned by any of the Igloolik elders as having particular significance either in the telling of time or in navigation. However, its role as the polar bear, *Nanurjuk,* in the preferred version of the Igloolik *Ullaktut* legend (see page 228) is undisputed.

Among the Arviligjuarmiut of the Pelly Bay area Aldebaran is also given a part in the *Ullaktut* legend, but as *Kajuqjuk,* an old, lame, reddish dog unable to keep up with its team mates, the lesser stars in the Pleiades:

> The star that rests between the *U'lakturjuit* [Orion's belt stars] and *Aggiattaan* [the Pleiades] is what we call *Kajurjuk* [Aldebaran]. It is said that this was one of the dogs pursuing the polar bear [the star Alcyone in the Pleiades]. This dog was limping so he could not keep up with the rest of the dogs. It is said that if *Kajurjuk* had been able to keep up with the rest of the dogs they would have been able to stop the polar bear. [Simon Inuksaaq 1990]

★ 6. Nuutuittuq ★

Polaris, the Pole Star (mag. 1.99) in the constellation Ursa Minor. At the latitude of Igloolik *Nuutuittuq* appears to be almost overhead. It is easily located by extending an imaginary line through the stars Merak and Dubhe (of Ursa Major) towards the centre of the sky. *Nuutuittuq* means "never moves" and refers to the apparently fixed position of Polaris on the celestial sphere. In Igloolik it is also referred to, by some, in the plural form, *Nuutuittut,* thus incorporating two other stars from Ursa Minor: Kochab and Pherkad.

Alternative spellings and names for *Nuutuittuq*:

Agyarrlak—"major star." Yup'ik Eskimo, Alaska (Jacobson 1984:48)
Qitirarjuk (qitiraarjuk?)—"spinal cord"? Caribou Eskimo, west coast of
    Hudson Bay, NWT (Birket-Smith 1929:157)
Nutuitsoq (nuutuittuq)—"never moves." Repulse Bay area, NWT
    (Mathiassen 1928:233)
Turaagaq—"something to aim at." Northern Quebec (Schneider 1985:424)
Nikitsuituq—"unmoving." Northern Quebec (Schneider 1985:202)
Nikkisuitok—"unmoving." Northern Quebec (Peck 1925:154)
Suqusuittuq—"unchanging." Northern Quebec (Schneider 1985:380)
Nikkisuitok (nikisuittuq)—"unmoving." Labrador (Peck 1925:154)
Nuusuittuq—"never moves." Kangiqsualujjuaq, Northern Quebec
    (Johnny Annanack, pers. comm., 1992)
Avangnâta uvdloriâ (avannaata ulluriaa)—lit. "north star."
    West Greenland, (Bugge et al. 1994:387)

Nuutuittuq, well known as the guiding star in more southerly latitudes, was also mentioned in this context by some of the Igloolik elders, but there was considerable disagreement as to its ultimate usefulness in navigation. Eli Amaaq, while being familiar with constellations such as *Tukturjuk* (entry 14), *Sakiattiak* (entry 10), and *Quturjuuk* (entry 9) had this to say about *Nuutuittuq:* "It was pointed out to me once, but now I am unable to show anyone where it rests. I have no knowledge of that star. I have seen it once but now I do not spend much time out of doors so I have no clear knowledge of where it might be" (Amaaq 1989, IE-074).

George Kappianaq, on the other hand, has quite a different view of *Nuutuittuq:*

There is a star that seems to be directly above us but a little to the north. I think it is right in the middle of *Sila* for it does not move like the rest. It has always been used as a navigational object at night. It could be used when one was carried away on moving ice at the floe edge. You can use it to determine the position of the land or the land-fast ice. It is also known that the *Qallunaat* used it when they sailed across the great ocean. It is said that this star was their only means of navigation. This was the time when only sails were used. It is said that this star helped them to go on one course rather than travelling blindly. I have heard this from Nakungajuq, my father's step-father. As Inuit, we have used this star for ages as a help in navigation. It is the star that does not move, *Nuutuittuq*. [Kappianaq 1986, IE-071]

Abraham Ulayuruluk of Igloolik remembers when he was first told about *Nuutuittuq* and how he set about to discover for himself the stationary quality of this star:

> I became curious about this star . . . called *Nuutuittuq*. . . . So, on the lee side of our *uquutaq* [a snow windbreak] I positioned a harpoon pointing directly at this particular star to see if it would move. In the morning I checked it and discovered that the *Tukturjuit* [Ursa Major] had changed their position completely but the harpoon still pointed at this star. . . . I had discovered the stationary star—*Nuutuittuq!* [Ulayuruluk 1992, IE-211]

Generally, *Nuutuittuq* was considered to have too high an altitude at Igloolik, almost 70°, to be used as a star by which one could comfortably maintain a heading. Western navigational practices also reject the use of Polaris at these latitudes for much the same reason (Greenaway 1951:67). The diminished usefulness of Polaris at higher latitudes is doubtless reflected in Robert Peary's claims that the Polar Eskimos had no knowledge of Polaris: "Less observant than were the Arab shepherds, they have not noticed that one star is the centre about which all the others move" (Peary 1898:494). Similarly, among the Inuit of Coronation Gulf, Duncan Pryde found no word for the Pole Star (pers. comm., 1991). By contrast, Inuit living in more southerly areas valued Polaris and, in some parts of Northern Quebec, around latitude 60°N, the star is referred to as *Turaagaq*, ("something to aim at"), where indeed the star's altitude is low enough to be used as a "target."
For Niviattian Aqatsiaq of Igloolik *Nuutuittut* (the plural form of *Nuutuittuq*) is a constellation which, in addition to Polaris, includes other members of Ursa Minor,[21] presumably the stars Kochab and Pherkad: "There are three stars that are known as *Nuutuittut*. As *Sila* turns, the rest of the stars move around but the

Nuutuittut are stationary" (Aqatsiaq 1990, IE-079).

    Nuutuittuq's bearing, in European tradition considered the first cardinal point, "north," is assigned no special importance by Inuit, its position simply being referred to as *"uangnaup kanangnaullu akuningani"* or *kanangnaqpasik*, an intermediate point between two wind directions, *uangnaq* (northwest) and *kanangnaq* (northeast).

    In Igloolik there are no legends associated with *Nuutuittuq*.

★ 7. PITUAQ ★

A constellation comprising the three brightest stars from the Western constellation Cassiopeia: Schadar (mag. 2.22), Caph (mag. 2.26), and Cih (mag. 2.50). Circumpolar at the latitude of Igloolik, *Pituaq*, with its distinctly triangular shape, can be found on any clear, dark night opposite *Tukturjuk*, both endlessly revolving around *Nuutuittuq*. *Pituaq* means "lamp-stand" and refers to the three stones, or posts made from wood, stone, or bone, placed upright in the floor of a dwelling in the form of a triangle upon which rests a soapstone oil lamp. Note the cross-references between this entry and entry 16 *(Ursuutaattiaq)*; both constellations are formed from combinations of the major stars in Cassiopeia.

Alternative names and spellings for *Pituaq*:

Ibrsk-si-sin (ivzuqsisit)—"the house builder." Point Barrow, Alaska
    (Bockstoce 1988:351)
Ikurraattiaq—"a structure on which something is raised." Arctic Bay,
    NWT (Charlie Inuaraq, pers. comm., 1995)
Nikurrautiit—"lamp-stand" or "pot-stand." Clyde River,
    NWT (Uyarasuk 1990, IE-076)
Nihhovgautet (nikurrauttat)—Labrador (Peck 1925:154)[22]
Pitoohen (pituaq)—"three stones supporting a lamp." Northwest
    Greenland (Kroeber 1899:319)

For the Point Barrow area, John Simpson (1875) gives Cassiopeia as *Ibrsk-si-sin* which he translates as "the house builder" due to "some fancied resemblance to a man in a working attitude" (Bockstoce 1988:351). More than likely Simpson is attempting to express the term *Ivruqsii* (Spearman 1988), meaning the triangular-bladed "sod tool" used to cut turf for the construction of winter houses. In this case Simpson's glossing ("house builder") might refer more to the instrument for making houses—an *Ivruqsii*—than to a person building a house.

In Northwest Greenland the designation *Pituaq* is also associated with Cassiopeia—Robert Peary gives it as *Pitoohen* (Kroeber 1899:319). This particular name for the three major stars in Cassiopeia was almost certainly introduced to Northwest Greenland in the 1860s by Inuit from Baffin Island, members of the so-called Qitdlarssuaq migration.[23]

An alternative designation, *Nikurrautiit,* also meaning "lamp-stand" or "pot-stand," was given for these same stars by Rachel Ujarasuk of Igloolik: "*Nikurrautiit* are . . . two stars side-by-side and one star up front. We used to have pot-holders like that for our *qulliq* [lamp]" (Uyarasuk 1990, IE-076).

The term *Nikurrautiit* is not widely known in Igloolik either as a reference to Cassiopeia's stars or, indeed, to "pot-stands." The word appears to come from the Clyde River area of Baffin Island where Rachel Ujarasuk spent many of her formative years.

In Igloolik there was not always agreement on the designation of Cassiopeia's stars. Some elders preferred to combine all of the constellation's six brightest stars into a grouping which they called *Ursuutaattiaq* ("sealskin oil container") (entry 16). Those favouring this arrangement did not seem to know or recognize the three-star *Pituaq* constellation. On the other hand, some who did recognize *Pituaq* also knew of a set of stars named *Ursuutaattiaq* but these they placed well outside Cassiopeia, near the star Scheat (constellation Pegasus). The exact location of this particular *Ursuutaattiaq* was never empirically verified.

Mathiassen, in *Material Culture of the Iglulik Eskimos*, records that the stars of Cassiopeia are called *Amarotjuit (Amarujuit)*—"wolves" (1928:233). Information provided by Qaggutaq of Pelly Bay, NWT (pers. comm., 1990) and Birket-Smith (1929:157), however, suggests that *Amarujuit* were more likely associated with some stars in the constellation Boötes, excluding, of course, the major star Arcturus (see entries 13 and 14).

☆ 8. QIMMIIT ☆

The Hyades star cluster in the constellation Taurus. *Qimmiit* means "dogs" and refers to the stars in the vicinity of Aldebaran (*Nanurjuk*, entry 5). On a clear night *Qimmiit* can be seen in a "V-like" formation to the right of *Nanurjuk*. The Hyades (*Qimmiit*), along with Aldebaran (*Nanurjuk*) and the belt stars of Orion (*Ullaktut*, entry 15) provide, in Igloolik at least, the preferred cast for the legend of the polar bear hunters (see pages 227–28). Among the Nattilingmiut, if Rasmussen's interpretation is correct, some of the stars in the Hyades may have been identified:

"Beside *Kajurjuk* [entry 5, Aldebaran] are two small stars that we call *Qanngiamariik* ["the relatives who are very fond of one another"[24] (Rasmussen 1931:211). As previously mentioned, in Point Barrow, Alaska, the Hyades are considered to be hunters sharing out the meat of a freshly killed polar bear, Aldebaran, and are termed *Pa-chukh-lur-in* (see entry 5).

★ 9. QUTURJUUK ★

A constellation comprising four stars arranged in two pairs as follows: Pollux (mag. 1.15) and Castor (mag. 1.97) in the constellation Gemini; and Capella (mag. 0.08) and Menkalinan (mag. 1.90) in the constellation Auriga. *Quturjuuk* means "collarbones." *Quturjuuk* is a circumpolar constellation at the latitude of Igloolik. During the winter months its distinctive form is seen moving from the east to the south during the night. In the early morning hours it is seen to the north or northwest.

Alternative spellings and names for *Quturjuuk*:

Ko-tog-eu-in (quturzuk)—"collar-bones." Point Barrow, Alaska
(Bockstoce 1988:351)

Kuttoryuk (quturjuk)—"collar-bones." Coronation Gulf (Jenness 1922:179)

Qitortjuk (quturjuk)—"collar-bones." Repulse Bay area, NWT
    (Mathiassen 1928:233)

Kuttorsuk (qutuqsuk)—"collar-bones." Labrador, Northern Quebec
    (Peck 1925:132)

Killab Kuttuk—"collar-bones." But Cranz gives it as "heaven's breast-
    bone." West Greenland (Cranz 1767, I:232)

Quturjuuk is a widely known Inuit constellation recognized from North Alaska through the Central Arctic to West Greenland. In Igloolik *Quturjuuk* was used as an indicator of both time and direction. Mark Ijjangiaq of Igloolik describes the constellation precisely:

> These are the stars underneath the *Tukturjuk* (Ursa Major) known as *Quturjuuk*. There are two sets of stars, four stars in total, and they are brighter than others. They are shaped like *qutu* (the collar bone) and it is from this appearance that their name is derived. As we would travel at night heading for home after a hunt, with my father, I tried to make a habit of observing the stars as we trekked along, this was so I would know how late at night it was. [Ijjangiaq 1990, IE-081]

From Northern Quebec, Salomonie Alayco recalls: "My father asked me to go and check whether the constellations *Quturtuuk* and *Attuuk* were in sight at dawn before the first light of day. That's how we used stars to tell the time in the morning (Salomonie Alayco, 1985 interview, Avataq).

In the following recollection, the stars that signalled the start of each late winter day for Thomas Umaok of the Mackenzie Delta are almost certainly a pair from the *Quturjuuk* group, namely Pollux and Castor, setting to the northwest shortly before dawn: "Look like maybe February time. Start early in the morning before light. Suppose clear—watch two bright stars. When they look like start to go down, everybody start out" (Marsh 1991:118).

Like *Aagjuuk* (entry 1), *Quturjuuk* was recognized over a large portion of the Inuit world. The earliest and most accurate description of the constellation in North Alaska is given by John Simpson who spent the winters of 1852–1854 at Point Barrow: "*Ko-tog-eu-in* "The Collar bones" are the Twins, Castor and Pollux, with two others Capella [and] a small star which are placed in pairs slightly inclined to each other thus having a fanciful resemblance to the slope of those bones or rather the shoulders in the human frame" (Bockstoce 1988:351).[25] Jenness mentions it from the Coronation Gulf as *Kuttoryuk* (Jenness 1922:179) but was unable to identify it in terms of European nomenclature. Cranz, in West Greenland, does slightly better, correctly linking *Quturjuuk* with the constellation Gemini: "They call Gemini, *killab kuttuk*, heaven's breast-bone" (Cranz 1767, I:232). Cranz is mistaken in translating *Kuttuk* as "breastbone."[26] As well, he may have missed the fact that *Quturjuuk*, even in Greenland, likely comprises, in addition to Pollux and Castor, the two brightest stars from Auriga.

This point is well noted by Mathiassen who records that the constellation is "formed of Castor, Pollux, Kapella and Beta aurigae [Menkalinan]" (Mathiassen 1928:233). Peck's *Dictionary* also lists *Kuttorsuk (Quturjuuk)* as comprising four stars, Pollux and Castor, and Sectatrix and Capella; the latter pair he mistakenly places in the constellation "Charles's Wain" (Ursa Major) (Peck 1925:123). In Northwest Greenland, Pollux and Castor, according to Robert Peary, "are two stones at a house entrance" (Kroeber 1899:319); the Greenlandic term is not given.

In Igloolik no legends are connected with *Quturjuuk*. The constellation's appropriate anatomical designation, "collar-bones," makes it easy to identify in the night sky.

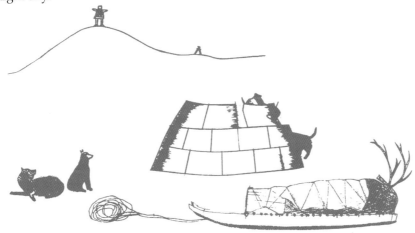

Caribou Hunt. Copperplate engraving. By Kananginak. Sikosuilarmiut.
Cape Dorset, Baffin Island, NWT, 1964. Royal Ontario Museum.
Gift of Mr. and Mrs. E. W. Vanstone.

★ 10. Sakiattiak ★

The Pleiades, an open star cluster in the constellation Taurus. Circumpolar at the latitude of Igloolik, *Sakiattiak* is typically seen as a patch of light to the right of and high above *Nanurjuk*. On any clear midwinter night the constellation will be in the eastern or southern sectors of the sky. *Sakiattiak* means "breast bone," a name suggested by the apparent arrangement of the stars in this cluster.

Alternative names and spellings for *Sakiattiak:*

Kaguyagat (kagguyat)—"red fox." Norton Sound, Alaska (L. A. Zagoskin, *in* Michael 1967:314)

Kavyagat (kavyagak)—"red fox." Lower Yukon River, Alaska (L. A. Zagoskin, *in* Michael 1967:314)

Kaviaret—"little foxes." Yup'ik, Western Alaska (Jacobson 1984:193)

Siqupsiqat (siqupsiqqat)—"shattered." Nunamiut, Alaska (Spearman 1988)[27]

Pa-chuk-tu-rin (paachuktyyzat)—"sharing." Point Barrow, Alaska (Bockstoce 1988:351)[28]

Pituktutin—(= ?). Point Barrow, Alaska (Ray 1885:56)

Sakopsakkat—"ones that close their eyes." Point Barrow, Alaska (Jenness 1922:179)

Siqupsiqqat—"fragmented ones." Point Barrow, Alaska
    (Pryde 1995)

Amihuaruit—"many." Coppermine, NWT (Duncan Pryde,
    pers. comm., 1990)

Agietat (agiattaat)—(= ?). Coronation Gulf (Jenness 1922:179)

Nannorjuit—"polar bears." Victoria Island, NWT (Jenness 1991:529)

Agjaatat (agiattaat)[29]—(= ?). West Hudson Bay (Birket-Smith 1929:157)

Agiacait (agiattaat)—(= ?). Pelly Bay, NWT (Mary-Rousselière 1969:95)[30]

Agiattat (agiattaat)—(= ?). Repulse Bay area, NWT (Mathiassen 1928:233)

Sakiaciat (sakiattiak)—"breast-bone[s]." Igloolik, NWT
    (Mary-Rousselière 1969:95)

Sakietaun (sakiattiak)—"breast-bone." Baffin Island, NWT (Boas 1888:643)

Sakiassiat (sakiattiak)—"breast-bone[s]." Northern Quebec (Qumak 1985)

Sakkiaitsiet (sakiattiak)—"breast-bone[s]." Labrador (Peck 1925:200)

Qillugtussat (qiluttuusat)—"baying dogs." West Greenland
    (Schultz-Lorentzen 1927:96)

Tartututut (taqtutuqtut)—"those who eat kidneys." West Greenland
    (Birket-Smith 1924:436)

Killukturset (qiluttuusat)—"baying dogs." West Greenland
    (Egede, *in* Allen 1963:397)

Qilugtuussat (qiluktuusat)—"baying dogs." Northwest Greenland
    (Holtved 1951:16)

Kilugtut—"baying dogs." East Greenland (Holm 1914, *in* Thalbitzer
    1914, part 1:105)

Kuukiaujat—"dogs." East Greenland (Ostermann 1938:203)

Knud Rasmussen in his *Intellectual Culture of the Iglulik Eskimos* mistakenly designates the Pleiades as *Uvdlaktut*. This confusion is discussed under *Ullaktut* (entry 15).

The Pleiades were for Inuit an important and widely recognized star cluster. The names given to this cluster by various Inuit groups reflect, to some extent, the role played by the Pleiades in their legends. Frequently the cluster is said to represent a bear surrounded by baying dogs.

Kroeber is only partly correct in noting that "the dogs and bears which in Angmagsalik, Greenland[31] and Smith Sound form the Pleiades, in Labrador and the Central Regions are transferred to Orion" (Kroeber 1899:319). In fact, "in the

Central Regions" the "dogs and bear" motif is typically applied to the Hyades and Aldebaran respectively, while the belt stars of Orion are the bear hunters. There is evidence that as far west as Coronation Gulf the Pleiades were sometimes associated with polar bears and bear hunting.

In most parts of Greenland the name given to the Pleiades is usually a dialectal or orthographic variation of the West Greenland term *Qillugtussat* and refers to the particular sound made by dogs holding a polar bear at bay.[32] Thus in West Greenland "the seven stars are so many dogs, *Kellukturset*, that are hunting a bear"[33] (Cranz 1767, I:232). In Northwest Greenland "the Pleiades [are] dogs and a bear" (Kroeber 1899:319) and in East Greenland *"Kilugtut"* are the "barkers" (Holm 1914, *in* Thalbitzer 1914, part 1:105). Alternative names for the Pleiades in East Greenland, according to Rink and Rasmussen, are *Kuukiaat* and *Kuukiaujat* respectively, meaning "dogs" (Thalbitzer 1914:215; Ostermann 1938:203). Thus the general Greenlandic association of this cluster with a pack of hunting dogs is maintained.

Among some of the Inuit groups to the west of Igloolik the Pleiades are known as *Agiattat* and, as in Greenland, are often designated as dogs encircling a polar bear. From Pelly Bay we have the following: "There is a set of stars that are in line. The one in the middle is the largest and is known as *Kajurjuk*, which is situated between the stars we know as *Ullakturjuit* and *Aggiattaat*. In *Aggiattaat* there are a number of dogs. The largest star in the group is called *Nanurjuk*" (Paul and Martha Quttiutuqqu, 1990). Here *Kajurjuk* is Aldebaran; *Ullakturjuit,* the "belt stars" of Orion; *Aggiattaat* the Pleiades; and *Nanurjuk,* Alcyone, the largest star in the Pleiades cluster.

For the Coronation Gulf, Jenness records in his diary that "the Pleiades are *nannorjuit* polar bears, [and] Aldebaran below them is *ugleorjuit* because it follows them" (Jenness 1991:529). Elsewhere, however, in giving details of the associated bear-hunting legend he mentions that a more common name for the Pleiades in this area is *Agietat*:

> Long ago a polar bear was being hunted by a man and his dogs. It fled into the sky and its pursuers followed after it. We can still see the bear, *Nannoryuk,* in the sky, and behind it the hunter and his dogs, always pursuing but never overtaking it. One native pointed to the Pleiades and called them the bear, while Aldebaran and some stars near it were the hunter and his dogs, *Agleoryuit,* "the pursuers," but the more usual name

for the Pleiades is *Agietat;* the meaning of which I did not discover."
[Jenness 1924:179]

In the above passage, the first of the two names given to the Pleiades, *Nannoryuk,* may simply acknowledge the star cluster's literary role and so distinguish it from its "everyday," common name, *Agietat*—a feature of Inuit star classification already mentioned.

By the time one reaches the Bering Strait area the Pleiades have become foxes: "they [are] called the 'Little Foxes' and are said to be a litter of fox cubs"[34] (Nelson 1899:499). Ray, meanwhile, notes that the word used for the Pleiades in Point Barrow is *Pituktutin* (Ray 1885:56).

In Igloolik, where the descriptive designation *Sakiattiak* (breast-bone) is used for the Pleiades, the bear and dogs are usually represented respectively by Aldebaran (*Nanurjuk*—entry 5) and the Hyades (*Qimmiit*—entry 8). The term *Sakiattiak* has been less widely used for the Pleiades than either *Qillugtussat* or *Aggiattaat* and was probably confined to those parts of the Canadian Eastern Arctic, including Northern Quebec and Labrador,[35] where the Hyades and Aldebaran were personified respectively as the dogs and bear of legend. Nevertheless, even in Igloolik, *Sakiattiak* is not easily dissociated from thoughts of polar bear hunting. Abraham Ulayuruluk, for example, mentioned that his father, Siniqkak, called the Pleiades *Sakiattiak,* but also used the term *nanniqijut*—"those engaged in killing a bear"—to describe how the star cluster should be thought of. This, Ulayuruluk explained, made these stars more interesting and helped one to remember that they were, in fact, called *Sakiattiak.*

Sakiattiak was mentioned by several Igloolik elders as being particularly useful as a navigational guide. This star cluster also appears to have been widely used for telling time.[36] Among the Kobuk River Eskimos, for instance, its appearance in a certain position, would mark bedtime (Giddings 1961:43), invoking, perhaps, the term used for the cluster in Point Barrow, Alaska—*Sakopsakkat*—"the ones who close their eyes" (Jenness 1922:179).[37] On Kodiak Island, where the Pleiades are not circumpolar, the cluster's first appearance above the horizon in August indicated the start of a new year (Hrdlicka 1944:70).

Detail from *Esquimaux in the Bear Lands.* Ink on paper. By Enooesweetok. Sikosuilarmiut. Baffin Island, NWT, 1915. Royal Ontario Museum. Gift of Mrs. Robert J. Flaherty.

The star Procyon (mag. 0.35) in the constellation Canis Minor. During January and February *Sikuliarsiujuittuq* is best seen in the early evening rising reddish in the east or southeast. Meaning "the one who never goes onto the newly formed sea-ice," *Sikuliarsiujuittuq* is in Igloolik a local personification of a legendary character bearing the same name. According to the story, *Sikuliarsiujuittuq* was a grossly oversized man whose sheer weight prevented him from going on to the sea-ice. To survive he stole the catch of other hunters. Eventually persuaded that the ice was thick enough to bear his weight, *Sikuliarsiujuittuq* went out hunting and was brutally murdered by his companions. A complete version of this story, given by George Kappianaq, is on pages 211–18.

Of the Igloolik elders interviewed, many knew of the legend of *Sikuliarsiujuittuq* but only George Kappianaq mentioned its connection with a star. While we were unable to identify the star empirically, George Kappianaq's indication of its approximate position relative to Pollux and Orion's belt, his description of its coloration, and his identification of it on a computer-generated star map allow reasonable certainty that the star in question is Procyon. In midwinter *Sikuliarsiujuittuq* bears a distinctly reddish hue, at times tinged with green, as it begins to rise over the sea-ice. George Kappianaq explains that the star's ruddy coloration is equated with blood because *Sikuliarsiujuittuq* was a victim of murder.

The star Sirius (mag. −1.45) in the constellation Canis Major. At Igloolik *Singuuriq* is best seen late at night in mid-January, low on the southern horizon. *Singuuriq* means "flickering" or "pulsating" as, for instance, a flame affected by a draft.

Alternative names and spellings for *Singuuriq*:

I-gha-lum ki-mukh-ti—"the Moon's dog." Bering Strait area, Alaska
    (Nelson 1899:458)
Kajuqtuq Tiriganniaqlu—"red fox and white fox." Coppermine area,
    NWT (Peter Kamingoak, pers. comm., 1994)
Singoreq (singuuriq)—"pulsating." Repulse Bay area, NWT
    (Mathiassen 1928:233)
Ubluriakjuak (uvluriarjuaq)—"big star." West coast of Hudson Bay
    (Spalding 1960:A10)
Udluriaralu (ulluriaraaluk)—"big star." East coast of Hudson Bay
    (Spalding 1960:A10)
Nelleraglek—a Greenlandic proper name. West Greenland
    (Egede, *in* Birket-Smith 1924:436)

At Igloolik, Sirius, the brightest star in the sky, reaches a maximum altitude of about 4° and is above the horizon for only slightly longer than five hours each day. It is visible only during the midwinter months. The combined effects of refraction, extremely cold temperatures, and atmospheric absorption causes the star's light to behave in the manner which earned it its Inuktitut name, "the flickering one." The spectacular performance of *Singuuriq* in Arctic latitudes is breathlessly described by Parry: "Sirius, which was nearly on the meridian at this time, exhibited the most beautiful violet and blue colours that can be imagined—the Aurora was playing about at this time. I thought I had never before seen anything so brilliant; the play of prismatic colours that can be imagined in a cut diamond comes nearest to it" (Parry 1824:141).

The intensity of Sirius's flickering could for some Inuit be used to forecast the weather: "I know that *Singuuriq* was used to predict the weather and the severity of the temperatures. When the weather is going to be extremely cold the star turns reddish. If the star does not twinkle, milder weather will come. And when the wind is going to blow the star behaves like a flame exposed to a draft (Amarualik 1992, IE-212).

According to Usuittuq (Cape Dorset area, South Baffin Island) the appearance of *Singuuriq* on the horizon was, like the *Aagjuuk* stars, a sign of lengthening days. Usuittuq adds that, by holding one's breath, *Singuuriq* seems to change colours (Norman Hallendy, pers. comm., 1992).

The "flickering" characteristic of Sirius is explained in one of the Igloolik versions of the *Ululijarnaat* legend (see page 223). In this story *Singuuriq* is personified as an old woman dwelling near the route taken by those travelling between the Earth and the Moon:

> They [the Moon-man and the woman from Earth] were passing many houses with windows. In one of these houses sat a woman who was making a window. A draft from the door was causing the flame of her *qulliq* (a seal-oil lamp) to flicker and change colours. This woman looked up and muttered: "passers-by, passers-by," expressing her annoyance at those who went by her house causing a draft. Her name was *Singuuriq*. [Z. Innuksuk 1990, IE-088]

In parts of the Western Arctic, the rapid, animated colour changes of Sirius earn it the name "fox star," *Kajuqtuq Tiriganniarlu* ("red fox and white fox"). It is said that the "red fox" and the "white fox" are fighting together, each trying to gain access to a single foxhole (Peter Kamingoak, pers. comm., 1994).

Pauli Kunuk of Igloolik recalls a fragment of a legend relating how a group of hunters, caught on moving sea-ice, tried to use stars to guide them to safety. The story illustrates the consequences of following the wrong star and is principally an exhortation to "know your stars" before using them for navigation. *Singuuriq* (Sirius) and *Kingullialuk* (Vega—entry 3) are the particular stars mentioned:

> There is a story about men who were marooned on the moving ice. I believe the story is a legend but there might be some truth connected to it as well. I am not sure how many there were . . . two, possibly more. It is said that they set out for the land-fast ice using stars to guide them. One followed the star *Singuuriq* and was never seen again. His companions followed *Kingullialuk* and eventually made it back to the land-fast ice. [Kunuk 1990, IE-087; 1991, IE-171]

Pauli Kunuk's story may well have some factual basis considering the relationship of the two stars involved. In the Igloolik area, the short, midwinter appearances of Sirius invariably occur in a southerly direction at a time when Vega is seen to the north. Vega and Sirius are of similar brilliance and both are subject to spectacular colour variation when near the horizon. Vega, of course, has a considerably higher altitude on its northern meridian than has Sirius on its southern meridian (18° to 4°) but given a mix of unfavourable weather conditions, moving ice, and no other known points of reference, it would not be difficult to confuse these two stars. Pauli Kunuk's story infers that by following Sirius the doomed hunter was led further to the south and so on to more treacherous ice while Vega guided the surviving hunters northwards to the safety of the land.

It is curious that Sirius has not been mentioned more often in the anthropological literature. This fact raises the possibility that some of the various Inuit names for Sirius may have been erroneously attributed to one or other of the planets, in particular to Venus or Jupiter, by ethnologists who did not have the opportunity or inclination to make empirical observations. On the other hand, Spalding's (1960) west coast of Hudson Bay term for Sirius, *Udluriakjuak* ("big star"), if correct, suggests that the generic use of the designation "big star" could in some regions be extended to include Sirius, and even Arcturus,[38] as well as the planets: "We might also note that Nelson, for instance, specifically equates the North Alaskan Eskimo's "Moon-dog" star *[I-gha-lum ki-mukh-ti]* with Sirius (Nelson 1899:449, 458), while Fitzhugh and Kaplan link it to "the Morning Star," presumably the planet Venus (Sonne 1988:101–2).[39]

★ 13. Sivulliik ★

A constellation incorporating the stars Arcturus (mag. –0.06) and Muphrid (mag. 2.69) in the constellation Boötes. Beginning early in September *Sivulliik* is a prominent feature of the western evening sky. By mid-December the constellation is making pre-dawn appearances above the southern horizon. *Sivulliik* means "the first ones" or "the [two] in front." The term *Sivulliik*[40] is often used when referring to Arcturus alone whether or not the lesser star of the pair, Muphrid, is visible. In Igloolik, as elsewhere, it can also be rendered in the singular form, either as *Sivulliq,* or *Sivulliaaluk,* in which case Arcturus alone is implied.

Arcturus is one of the stars most visible during the midwinter period. Edward Parry used this star to illustrate the extent of daylight, or more accurately, twilight, occurring at Igloolik during the winter solstice: "On the 21st

[December] . . . with the sky clear overhead, Arcturus was discernible to the naked eye till forty-seven minutes after eleven, A.M., apparent time; and at half an hour past noon it was again visible, and stars of the second magnitude could be distinguished at three-quarters past one o'clock" (Parry 1824:385).

Alternative names and spellings for *Sivulliik*:

Sibwud.li (sivlliq)—"one in front." Point Barrow, Alaska (Ray 1885:56)
Sivolliik (sivulliik)—"two in front." North Alaska (Spencer 1959:258)
Sivuglėt (sivulliik)—"two in front." Mackenzie Delta
      (Ostermann 1942:78)
Sivulik (sivulliq)—"one in front." Coronation Gulf, NWT
      (Jenness 1922:179)
Hivulik (sivulliik)—"the leader." Victoria Island, NWT (Jenness 1991:529)
Siudleq (sivulliq)—"one in front." Repulse Bay area, NWT
      (Mathiassen 1928:233)
Siugdlît—"those who walk in front." Egedesminde, West Greenland
      (Birket-Smith 1924:436)
Hiulliit—"the ones in front." Qaanaaq, Northwest Greenland
      (Jens Qaavigaaq, pers. comm., 1994)

Kroeber, on information received from Robert Peary, mentions that in Northwest Greenland Arcturus is a "personification" but fails to give the Greenlandic name for it (Kroeber 1899:319).

The *Sivulliik*, in Igloolik, are principally associated with the *Iliarjugaarjuk* ("Orphan Boy") legend (see pages 230–31) where the constellation's two stars, Arcturus and Muphrid, are personified respectively as *Uttuqalualuk* ("old man") and *Iliarjugaarjuk* ("orphan boy") who are racing out in front of *Ningiuraaluk* (Vega), the legend's third character.[41] Details of this legend and of the relationship between the stars involved are included under *Kingulliq* (entry 3). An Inuit song which forms part of the narrative of the *Iliarjugaarjuk* legend, and is well known among the Igloolik elders, is given on page 239, transcribed, translated, and rendered in musical notation.

The name *Sivulliik*, having connotations of "leading," can refer to the early appearance of the star at certain times of the year. As the days shorten in the fall,

Arcturus is often the first star to appear in the evening twilight.[42] The term *Sivulliik*—"first"— also implies the existence of a "second" quantity which, in this case, is appropriately furnished by Vega (*Kingulliq*, entry 3), often the second star to come out. The sequential relationship between Arcturus and Vega, established so clearly in the *Iliarjugaarjuk* legend, is further supported by their relative positions on the sphere where Arcturus, being more westerly than Vega, gives the impression of leading Vega across the sky.[43]

The Inuit of Coronation Gulf, while also referring to Arcturus as *Sivulliq*, offer a rather different explanation: "Arcturus when high in the heavens ushers in the sealing season, and hence has been given the name *Sivulik* 'The Leader'" (Jenness 1922:179).

Spencer is probably mistaken in his view that for the North Alaskan Eskimo "the morning star [presumably Venus[44]] bore the proper name *Sivolliik [Sivulliik]*" (Spencer 1959:258). Nowhere else in the literature is this association made although Rochfort Maguire in his Point Barrow journal cites John Simpson as thinking the term *Si-vud-liu* "ought to be applied to some of the planets from their passing between *[si-vud-lia]* and the other stars" (Bockstoce 1988:351). In the same passage Simpson also links *Si-vud-lia* to Arcturus while Lieutenant P. H. Ray, whose expedition to Point Barrow in 1881 included an astronomer, equates, without qualification, "*sibwud.li*" *(Sivulliik)* to Arcturus (Ray 1885:56).[45]

For the Egedesminde District of West Greenland, Birket-Smith mentions "*Siugdlît*" *(Sivulliik)* as a group of two stars possibly involving "Boötes and Arcturus" (Birket-Smith 1924:436). However, as "Boötes" is a constellation incorporating many stars, including Arcturus, the identity of the second star is in doubt unless we proceed on the reasonable assumption that Birket-Smith intended to specify Boötes "*Eta*"—Muphrid.

In Igloolik, the term *Sivulliik* is also applied, on occasion, to the stars Megrez and Phecda in Ursa Major when these stars are considered to form the front legs of caribou in *Tukturjuk* (entry 14) (Emil Imaruittuq, pers. comm., 1990).

Untitled Sketch. Pencil on paper. By Enooesweetok. Sikosuilarmiut. Baffin Island, NWT, 1913–1914. Royal Ontario Museum. Gift of Mrs. Robert J. Flaherty.

A constellation involving various arrangements of the principal stars in the European constellation Ursa Major, particularly the seven stars of the "Big Dipper" or "Charles's Wain" (Dubhe, Merak, Phecda, Megrez, Alioth, Mizar, and Alkaid—ranging in magnitude from 1.79 to 1.86). At the latitude of Igloolik *Tukturjuit* is circumpolar. Its distinctive form can readily be seen on any clear, dark night. *Tukturjuit* expresses "caribou" (plural); *Tukturjuk,* "caribou" (singular).

Alternative names and spellings for Tukturjuit:

Tuntoyuk—"caribou." Norton Sound, Alaska
    (L. A. Zagoskin, *in* Michael 1967:314)
Tutoyuk—"caribou." Lower Yukon River, Alaska
    (L. A. Zagoskin, *in* Michael 1967:314)
Tu-ts-eu-in—"caribou." Point Barrow, Alaska
    (Bockstoce 1988:351)
Tuktuotuin—"caribou" (pl.). Point Barrow, Alaska
    (Ray 1885:56)

Tunturyuk—"caribou." Bering Strait area, Alaska
  (Jacobson 1984:48)

Toktoyok (tukturjuit)—"caribou." Mackenzie River, NWT
  (Yerbury 1984:507)

Panngnirjuit—"bull caribou." Holman Island, Coronation Gulf, NWT
  (Pryde 1995:33)

Tuktuyuin (tukturjuit)—"caribou" (pl.). Coronation Gulf, NWT
  (Jenness 1922:179)

Tugtortjuit—"caribou" (pl.). Repulse Bay area, NWT
  (Mathiassen 1928:233)

Tuktuqdjung (tukturjuk, tukturjuit)—"caribou." Baffin Island, NWT
  (Boas 1888:643)

Iksivautarsuit (iksivautaqsuit)—"seat," "stool." Northern Quebec and
  Labrador (Peck 1925:59; Peacock (n.d.:372)

Tutturuit—"caribou" (pl.); *Qallutik,* "dipper." Akulivik,
  Northern Quebec (Moses Qumak, 1985)

Tuttujuit (tuktujuit)—"caribou" (pl.). Ungava, Northern Quebec
  (Schneider 1985:430)

Tukturuit (tutturuit)—"caribou" (pl.). Povungnituq, Northern Quebec
  (Qumaq 1991:224)

Tuktujuk—"caribou." Labrador (Peacock 1974:548)

Tukto—"caribou." West Greenland (Cranz 1767, I:232)

Nalerqat—"marker." West Greenland[46] (Schultz-Lorentzen 1927:150;
  Birket-Smith 1924:436)

Tooktoksue (tuktuqsuit)—"caribou" (pl.). Northwest Greenland
  (Kroeber 1899:319)

Tuktuhuit—"caribou" (pl.). Qaanaaq, Northwest Greenland
  (Jens Qaavigaaq, pers. comm., 1994)

Asalûsat (asaluusat)—"kayak stand." West Greenland
  (Birket-Smith 1924:436)[47]

Kalîp Qamutai—"Kale's sled." West Greenland (Le Mouël 1978:33)

Asalut—"kayak line rack." East Greenland (Ostermann 1938:202)

Pisidlat—"lamp foot." East Greenland (Holm 1914, *in* Thalbitzer 1914,
  part 1:105)

Except for East Greenland, where by various accounts the constellation was named either *Pisidlat* ("lamp foot") or *Asalut* ("kayak line rack"), Ursa Major's particular association with caribou appears to have been recognized in most parts of the Inuit world.[48] Even in West Greenland where the "Big Dipper" is now known as *Asaluusat* ("kayak stand"), in earlier times it was taken to represent a caribou. Both Poul and Hans Egede, followed by David Cranz, have recorded the terms *Tugto* or *Tukto* to designate Ursa Major (Robert Petersen, pers. comm., 1991; Cranz 1767, I:232).

In spite of this seemingly consistent representation of Ursa Major, there are widely differing views concerning the actual stars in the constellation deemed to represent *Tukturjuit* or *Tukturjuk*. In Igloolik the first point of debate centres on whether to give the constellation a singular or a plural designation. Generally, the more senior the elder the more likely the constellation was taken to represent a group of caribou rather than a single animal. This dichotomy is also reflected in the references to *Tukturjuit* found in historical record which, to the extent that the orthographies can be deciphered, attach both plural and singular endings to the root *tuku-*.[49] From Point Barrow, via the journal of John Simpson, there is also the suggestion that a single star, "the lower one in the tail of Ursa Major," presumably the star Alkaid, was used to represent a caribou (Bockstoce 1988:351).

Even among those in Igloolik who considered Ursa Major to be a single caribou, *Tukturjuk,* there was little agreement on which stars constituted the various parts of the animal. For some, particularly the younger observers, Dubhe and Merak, Phecda and Megrez represented, respectively, the back and front legs of the caribou, while Alioth, Mizar, and Alkaid were seen to be the neck and head (Emil Imaruittuq, pers. comm., 1990). Others preferred to invert this arrangement, making Megrez, Alioth, Mizar, and Alkaid the back and body of the animal, its antlers being represented by Dubhe, Merak, and Phecda (M. Ijjangiaq 1990, IE-081). A delicate refinement of this latter arrangement has the caribou's tail represented by the faint star Alcor which, together with Mizar, forms a "double star" (N. Qamaniq, pers. comm., 1990).

Those in Igloolik, particularly George Kappianaq, who used the plural designation *(Tukturjuit)* tended to consider each of the "seven stars" in Ursa Major as individual caribou. On the other hand, Paul and Martha Quttiutuqu of Pelly Bay were rather more particular, *Tukturjuit* for them comprising only three stars in Ursa Major, probably Dubhe, Merak, and Phecda. Also associated with their *Tukturjuit* is a lesser formation of stars known as *Amaruqjuit* (wolves), and said to be a formation of wolves in pursuit of the caribou.

"These stars are close together so the way they are placed resembles a number of caribou . . . that is why we call them *Tuktujjuit*. They stand out from the rest of the stars nearby. The stars we call *Amaruqjuit* are smaller than the *Tuktujjuin*. They resemble a pack of wolves so that is why we call them *Amaruqjuit*. They are close to *Tuktujjuit* but, I believe, a little bit behind them. They are three stars, close together, like wolves in formation. The *Tuktujjuit* also consist of three stars" (Paul and Martha Quttiutuqu 1990).

The *Tukturjuit* and *Amaruqjuit* formations of Paul and Martha Quttiutuqu share many elements with two similarly named constellations reported for the Caribou Eskimo by Birket-Smith: "The best known of them all is *(tukturjuk)* 'the Caribou' which comprises Ursa Major, the nearest star in Draco, and the clearest in the Hounds [Canes Venatici]. The 'Caribou' is pursued by the 'Wolf' *(amaruqjuk)*, which probably consists of Boötes, Gemma, and some stars in the Serpent" (Birket-Smith 1929:157).

In this attempt to equate the stars of the Caribou Eskimo's *Tukturjuk* with their European counterparts, Birket-Smith takes a rather improbable sweep of the sky, hardly typical of the manner in which Inuit construct their constellations. However, the designation of various stars in Boötes (probably Seginus, Nekkar and δ Boötis) as *Amaruqjuit* ("wolves") was empirically confirmed by Paatsi Qagutaaq during a visit to Igloolik in January 1991. Mathiassen equates Cassiopeia with *Amaruqjuit* (Mathiassen 1928:233) but this association was not confirmed by any of the Igloolik elders who instead took Cassiopeia to be either *Pituaq* (entry 7) or *Ursuutaattiaq* (entry 16).

Among the Inuit of Coronation Gulf, Jenness found that *Tuktuyuin* is represented by just two stars—Merak and "a faint star near it" (Jenness 1922:179). He makes no mention of the wolf motif. In Labrador *Tukturjuk* apparently shares Ursa Major with yet another constellation, *Iksivautarsuit* ("seat" or "stool") comprising "the three star triangle (probably Dubhe, Merak, and Phecda) of Great

Bear" (Peacock 1974:372). Peck also mentions this formation as *"Iksivautarsuit—* the stars at the forefront of the Greater Bear" (Peck 1925:59).

Tukturjuit, revolving endlessly around Polaris, is mentioned frequently as a constellation used by Inuit for estimating the passage of time. According to Moses Qumak of Akulivik, Northern Quebec, *"Tutturuit* turn upside down at dawn" (Qumak 1985), meaning that the attitude of the constellation is the reverse of its evening position. In a rather unclear passage, Knud Rasmussen seems to imply that among the Polar Eskimos Ursa Major is used to predict the return of the Sun. When the constellation is seen at dawn "men are filled with great delight; for then it will not be long till the light comes again" (Rasmussen 1908:174). The implication here is that the Great Bear rises and sets and, in the fashion of *Aagjuuk* (entry 1), is the Sun's harbinger. But at the latitude of Thule, Ursa Major is a circumpolar constellation, always visible given favourable conditions, and therefore could not be used as a seasonal marker in the manner suggested by Rasmussen.

Ursa Major is doubtless the most recognized constellation in the northern hemisphere. Its "Big Dipper" form has been, and still is, used as a symbol by various organizations and institutions in the North including, for example, the Anglican Church's Diocese of the Arctic. In Greenland, the "Dipper" is, as well, represented on postage stamps and Christmas seals.[50] The very familiarity of this constellation renders it susceptible to the encroachment of European star lore and may already account for some of the uncertainty surrounding its Inuit designation. Moses Qumak for example mentions that *"Tutturuit* is sometimes called *'Qallutik'"* (Qumak 1985). Meaning "dipper," this is an obvious translation from the English term.[51] From West Greenland we have another example. Jean-François Le Mouël (1978:33) finds that Ursa Major is "enigmatically" called *Kalîp Qamutai* ("Kale's sled"). The name, however, appears less enigmatic if we consider it merely a borrowing from the Scandinavian designation for Ursa Major—"Karl's Wagon"—sometimes called in English Charles's Wain.

Many Igloolik elders mentioned using *Tukturjuit* for wayfinding and time estimation.

A constellation comprising the three major stars in Orion's belt: Alnitak (mag. 1.79), Alnilam (mag. 1.70), and Mintaka (mag. 2.19), in the European constellation Orion. *Ullaktut* is most obvious on midwinter late evenings, high in the southern sector of the sky.

Alternative names and spellings for *Ullaktut*:

Chshakhkuakhtlit—(= ?). Norton Sound, Alaska
    (L. A. Zagoskin, *in* Michael 1967:314)
Uujuzat—"linked ones." Kobuk River (?), Alaska (MacLean 1980:96)
Ta-rout-san—"the travellers." Point Barrow, Alaska (Bockstoce 1988:351)
Tuatsan—(= ?). Point Barrow, Alaska (Ray 1885:56)
Tubatsiat—"sealers." Point Barrow, Alaska (Jenness 1922:179)
Tuvirrat—"those who hunt seals at breathing holes on the sea ice."
    Barrow, Alaska (Pryde 1995:36)
Tuatsiät (tuvaassiat)—"the hunters." Mackenzie River, NWT
    (Ostermann 1942:78)
Tupigat—"sealers," or *Tubaryuit*—"early risers"? Coronation Gulf, NWT
    (Jenness 1922:179)

Nukatpiarjuit—"younger siblings" or "younger brothers."
 Sachs Harbour, Banks Island (Pryde 1995:26)

Tuvaaturjuit—"those who hunt seals at breathing holes on the sea ice."
 Coppermine, NWT (Pryde 1995:37)

Hiäktut—"in a row." Caribou Eskimo, inland from the west coast of
 Hudson Bay (Birket-Smith 1929:157)

Uklätut (siaktut)—"runners." West Hudson Bay, NWT
 (Rasmussen 1931:385)

Uvlagturjuir (u'lakturzuit)—"the men who are following a bear."
 Murchison River, NWT (Rasmussen 1931:211)

Uglertut—"runners," "pursuers." Repulse Bay area, NWT
 (Mathiassen 1928:233)

Uvdlaktut (ullaktut)—"runners," "pursuers." Igloolik area, NWT
 (Rasmussen 1929:263)

Udleqdjun—"runners," "pursuers." Cumberland Sound (?),
 Baffin Island, NWT (Boas 1888:643)

Ullautut—"racers." Inukjuak, Northern Quebec (Qumaq 1991:95)

Siaktuit—"standing by the side of each other." Labrador (?),
 Northern Quebec (?) (Peck 1925:209)

Ka'muti'qdjuag—"sledge." Labrador (Hawkes 1916:29)

Siektut—"bewildered men"? West Greenland (Cranz 1767, I:230).

Siagtut—"are placed in a row." West Greenland
 (Schultz-Lorentzen 1927:212)

Tummiqqan—"steps." Qaanaaq, Northwest Greenland
 (Jens Qaavigaaq, pers.comm., 1994)

Ugdlaglut, Ugsagtut—"runners," "pursuers." East Greenland
 (Thalbitzer 1914, part 1:214)

Utaliit—"runners," "pursuers." East Greenland (Ostermann 1938:203)

Ullaktut, meaning "runners," refers to the role that the three belt stars of Orion play in an Inuit legend known throughout much of Canada's Eastern Arctic, Northern Quebec, Labrador, and East Greenland (several versions of the *Ullaktut* legend are given in Chapter 8). In Igloolik, the *Ullaktut* narrative also incorporates the stars Aldebaran (*Nanurjuk,* entry 5) and the Hyades cluster (*Qimmiit,* entry 7) from the adjoining Taurus constellation.

Noah Piugaattuk and Niviattian Aqatsiaq describe the various stars involved: "In the legends they are known as *Ullaktut* ('runners'). There are three of them and they are slanted upwards, they are evenly separated and most visible. Directly in front of these is a big star with many smaller stars around it. That star is called *Nanurjuk* and the smaller stars surrounding it are known as the *Qimmiit*" (Piugaattuk 1988, IE-040).

"While they ran they started to turn into stars with the bear ahead of them, so you will see *Nanurjuk* ahead of the *Ullaktuit* and the fourth,[52] lower and behind them" (Aqatsiaq 1990, IE-079).

Consistent with the notion that people are sometimes transformed into celestial objects when taboos are breached, Nâlungiaq, a Nattilik woman, told Rasmussen that the *Ullaktut* hunters became stars "because an unclean woman, a woman who had just had a child, came out and saw them" (Rasmussen 1931:211).

In the Pelly Bay area, the *Ullaktut* legend retains a number of interesting embellishments. The three Orion "belt stars," for instance, all had names: "Each of the hunters was given a name, but the only one I can remember is *Qaqqunnilik*.[53] I cannot remember which one of the stars he is" (Paul and Martha Quttiutuqu, 1990).

From Simon Inuksaaq, also from Pelly Bay, we learn that the small stars situated directly below the *Ullaktut* trio, including Orion's "Great Nebula" (Messier 42), [*Qangiamariit,* entry 17], are said to represent the hunters' children carrying clothes to their fathers (Inuksaaq 1990). The distinct "fuzziness" of the stars in this area is indeed an appropriate representation of bundled fur clothing.

Boas, in a version of the *Ullaktut* legend deriving from the Cumberland Sound area, equates *Nanurjuk* with the star Betelgeuse, an association not made elsewhere in the literature nor indeed by any of the Igloolik elders. In addition Boas refers to the faint stars comprising the so-called "Orion's bow" as representing the hunters' sled which he terms *Kamutiqdjung* (Boas 1888:637).[54]

Rasmussen's Iglulingmiut and Nattilingmiut accounts of the *Ullaktut* legend (Rasmussen 1929:263; 1931:211) settle on the Pleiades star cluster (entry 10) rather than on the "belt stars" of Orion. While current Igloolik accounts of this tale can be found to use either the Pleiades or the Hyades and Aldebaran to represent that particular element of the legend involving dogs and a polar bear, none suggests that *Ullaktut* can be anything other than Orion's "belt stars." Rasmussen's designation of the Pleiades as *Uvdlaktut* among the "Iglulingmiut" is also contradicted by Mathiassen, who terms this star cluster *Agiattat* (entry 10)[55] and correctly

★ ★

"Nanurjuk . . . is taken to represent a large polar bear
held at bay by a pack of dogs."

See page 58.

Polar Bear and Dogs. Ivory sculptures. Pangnirtung area,
Baffin Island, NWT, 1933–1942. Royal Ontario Museum.
Dr. Jon A. and Mrs. Muriel Bildfell Collection.
Purchased through the generosity of Mr. Donald Ross.

★ ★

"She surfaced once more, still twisting her hair, which had now become long. Her hair then transformed into a spiralled tusk. And so from the old woman did the narwhals come into being."

See page 216.

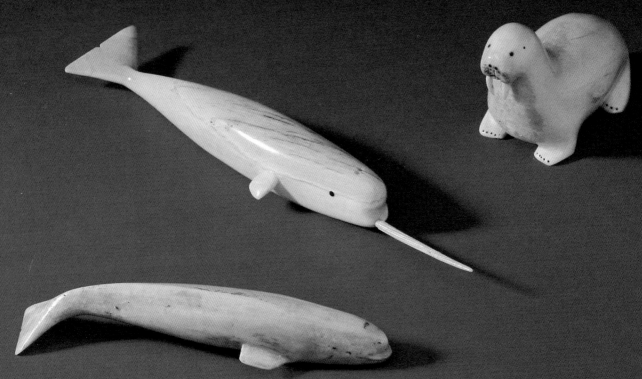

(Top) Walrus. Ivory sculpture. Pangnirtung area, Baffin Island, NWT, 1933–1942.
(Middle) Narwhal. Ivory sculpture. Pangnirtung area, Baffin Island, NWT, 1933–1942.
Royal Ontario Museum. Dr. Jon A. and Mrs. Muriel Bildfell Collection.
Purchased through the generosity of Mr. Donald Ross.
(Bottom) White whale. Ivory sculpture. Aivilingmiut. Cape Fullerton, NWT, 1928.
Royal Ontario Museum. Gift of L. A. Learmonth.

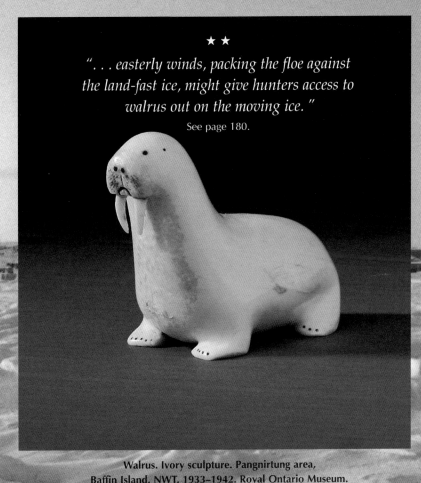

★ ★

". . . easterly winds, packing the floe against the land-fast ice, might give hunters access to walrus out on the moving ice."

See page 180.

Walrus. Ivory sculpture. Pangnirtung area,
Baffin Island, NWT, 1933–1942. Royal Ontario Museum.
Dr. Jon A. and Mrs. Muriel Bildfell Collection.
Purchased through the generosity of Mr. Donald Ross.

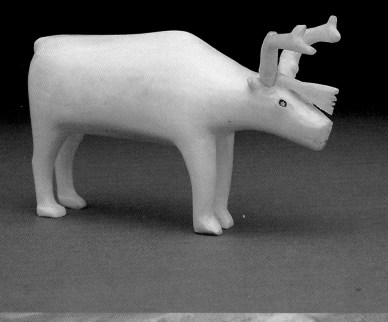

"Tukturjuit, *in Ursa Major, is variously designated as a single caribou or as a herd of caribou.*"

See page 14.

Caribou. Ivory sculpture. Southern Baffin Island or eastern Hudson Bay, early 20th century. Royal Ontario Museum.
Robert J. Flaherty Collection presented by Sir William Mackenzie.

reserves the name *Uglertut (Ullaktut)* for "the belt of Orion" (Mathiassen 1928:233).

In West Greenland, the Pleiades represent all the elements of a polar bear hunt in a self-contained narrative without reference to Orion. It is this arrangement which is doubtless the source of Rasmussen's confusion. Being familiar with the Greenlandic legend, he has simply transferred the Igloolik and Netsilik versions of the *"Ullaktut"* story to the Pleiades. Interestingly, Birket-Smith notes that for the Caribou Inuit there are four stars called *Uv,dlätut* 'the assembling ones'" (Birket-Smith 1929:157). No European terms are provided by Birket-Smith but these stars apparently are not Orion's belt which in the same passage he gives as *"Hiäktut*—the row" (Birket-Smith 1929:157). Because Orion's belt is elsewhere known by both these terms, there is a possibility that in this case Birket-Smith's *Uv,dlätut* and *Hiäktut* are one and the same, the first term a legendary designation, the second a spatially descriptive one. In this arrangement, the "fourth star" could then be either Rigel or Saiph.

The different regional Inuit designations for the Pleiades and Orion, as they relate to the polar bear hunting legend, were noted early by Kroeber: "The dogs and bears which in Angmagsalik, Greenland, and Smith Sound form the Pleiades, in Labrador and the Central Regions are transferred to Orion" (Kroeber 1899:319).

Towards the extremities of the Inuit geographical range the stars of Orion assume different identities. In the Bering Strait region, Nelson mentions that "the stars of Orion's belt are called the 'Great stretchers,' being regarded as posts on which rawhide lines are being stretched" (Nelson 1899:229).

In Point Barrow, Alaska, Orion's belt stars were called *Tubatsiat*—"seal hunters" (Jenness 1922:179). The constellation's first connection with a polar bear hunting legend seems to occur as far west as the Mackenzie Delta where Inuit recognize a group of stars "that lie close to one another" having once been hunters in pursuit of a polar bear (Ostermann 1942:78). Again, in the Coronation Gulf, NWT, these stars are, according to Jenness, "three sealers who never returned to their camp, so the Eskimos call them *Tupigat*, 'the sealers,' or *Tubaryuit*, 'the early risers'"[56] (Jenness 1922:179).

Among the West Greenlanders, Orion's belt as a representation of lost seal hunters is also mentioned. The three stars here are called *"Siektut*, the bewildered men, because they could not find their way home from seal-catching, and so were translated among the stars" (Cranz 1767, I:232). Peck gives a similar term for these same stars: *"Siaktut*—the three stars in the girdle of Orion" (Peck 1925:209)—but this term is possibly a Moravian import from Greenland via Erdmann's 1864 Eskimo-German dictionary. And finally Kroeber, on the basis of information received from the explorer Robert Peary, states that for the Polar Eskimos "the three stars of Orion's belt [are] steps cut in a steep snowbank" (Kroeber 1899:319), an observation confirmed by Jens Qaavigaq of Qaanaaq who names these stars *Tummiqqan* (pers. comm., 1994).

Ullaktut were used in the Igloolik area for the reckoning of time but apparently not to the same extent as *Aagjuuk* (entry 1) or *Quturjuuk* (entry 9). Under some circumstances they were also used to maintain direction when travelling. Among the Kodiak Island Eskimos, according to Davydov, the stars of Orion, presumably the "belt stars," were used to mark the second month of their year—September (Hrdlicka 1944:70).

✶ 16. Ursuutaattiaq ✶

A constellation corresponding to six of the stars in the European constellation Cassiopeia: Schadar (mag. 2.22), Caph (mag. 2.26), Cih (mag. 2.50), δ Cassiopeiae (mag. 2.67), ε Cassiopeiae (mag. 3.37), and κ Cassiopeiae (mag. approx. 4.50). *Ursuutaattiaq* is circumpolar at the latitude of Igloolik. Its distinctive triangular or

"W"-shaped form is clearly visible on the other side of *Nuutuittuq* opposite *Tukturjuit*. Note the cross-references between this entry and entry 7 *(Pituaq)*; both constellations are formed from combinations of the major stars in Cassiopeia, along with its lesser star κ Cassiopeiae.

Alternative names for *Ursuutaattiaq*:

Ibrsk-si-sin—"the house builder." Point Barrow, Alaska
    (Bockstoce 1988:351)
I.blusi—"sod cutter." Point Barrow, Alaska (Ray 1885:56)
Amarotjuit—"wolves." Repulse Bay area, NWT (Mathiassen 1928:233)
Pitoohen (pituaq[k])—"lamp supports."[57] Northwest Greenland
    (Kroeber 1899:319)

Ursuutaattiaq means a "seal-skin oil, or blubber container." Niviattian Aqatsiaq explains: "It is probably so named because it resembles *Ursuutit* (seal-skin blubber container). When it is set out to dry in the sun it is usually placed so that it is laid down on its side with the fore-flipper sticking out" (Aqatsiaq 1990, IE-079).

Catherine Arnatsiaq also describes *Ursuutaattiaq* and its position in the sky relative to *Tukturjuk*: "Then there is a group of stars formed like a diamond—it is across from *Tukturjuk* and is called *Ursuutaattiaq*" (Arnatsiaq 1990, IE-077).

The three brightest stars in Cassiopeia—Schadar (mag. 2.22), Caph (mag. 2.26), and Cih (mag. 2.50)—are frequently considered a separate constellation known in Igloolik as *Pituaq* or *Nikurqautit*. This constellation is noted separately under *Pituaq* (entry 7).

Niviattian Aqatsiaq suggested that *Ursuutaattiaq* can sometimes be referred as *Avatattiaq* [an inflatable seal-skin float] (Aqatsiaq 1990, IE-149) while Tatigat Arnattiaq believed that these were two distinct constellations (Arnattiaq 1991, IE-186).

In Igloolik there are no legends or stories attached to *Ursuutaattiaq* or *Avatattiaq*, these names being purely descriptive.

See page 115.

The Great Nebula (Messier 42) in Orion and the small stars in its vicinity are known to some in Igloolik, particularly by those familiar with the star names of the Nattilingmiut of northwest Hudson Bay, as *Qangiamariik* ("nephews" or "nieces") (Josiah Inuujak, pers. comm., 1993). However, Rasmussen (1931:211), on the basis of information given to him by Naalungiaq, uses this same term to refer to "two small stars" beside *Kajurjuk* (Aldebaran, entry 5), in which case stars in the Hyades cluster (entry 8) are likely indicated. Simon Inuksaaq (1990) of Pelly Bay explained that the nebula and its stars represent children carrying caribou-skin clothing to the polar bear hunters (Orion's "belt stars"—entry 15).

Detail from *Near the Flow Edge*. Copperplate Engraving. By Kovinatilliak. Sikosuilarmiut.
Cape Dorset, Baffin Island, NWT, 1964. Royal Ontario Museum.
Gift of Mr. and Mrs. E. W. Vanstone.

The Galaxy or Milky Way, is called *Avigutaa* (Amarualik 1992, IE-212), *Avigut*, or *Aviguti* (Ulayuruluk 1992, IE-211) in Igloolik. The term means "divider" or "separator."[58] In West Greenland the Milky Way carries a similar designation—*Qilaup sivdlia*—deriving from the word *sivdleq*, the "middle line on the belly of an animal where it is cut up" (Schultz-Lorentzen 1927:221). Peck's *dictionary* (1925:120) gives the Labrador–Northern Quebec word for the Galaxy as *kopput*—meaning a longitudinal "stripe" or "streak."

The Milky Way is firmly embedded in the mythology of the Bering Strait region where, according to Nelson (1899:449), it is "the track made by a Raven's snowshoes when he walked across the sky during one of his journeys while creating the inhabitants of the earth." The Yup'ik term for this feature is *Tanglurallret*, deriving from the word for snowshoe (Jacobson 1984:359). Similarly, for the Norton Sound region, Zagoskin, in the 1840s, records the term *Tangukhuatlyat* for the Milky Way. Among Alaska's Nunamiut, however, the Galaxy, according to John Etalook, was thought of as a celestial river: "the whitish area that surrounds a group of stars is considered a river when people speak of it" (Etalook 1983).

At Igloolik, the Milky Way is rarely seen with any clarity. Parry (1824:142), we recall, pointed out that "this beautiful feature of the heavens very seldom appeared here." The centre of the Milky Way, in the constellation Sagittarius, is, at Igloolik's latitude, always below the horizon and those portions of it which extend into the High Arctic are often obscured by various atmospheric conditions including the aurora, moonlight, and ice crystals. It is perhaps for these reasons that few Igloolik elders mentioned the Milky Way or, when specifically asked, had a name for it. An exception was Hubert Amarualik who recalled an old tradition about the Galaxy related to him by his father: "I have heard that it is called *Avigutaa*—a separator for the winds. It is here the winds collide . . . and where the stronger wind prevails. This cloud-like mass [the Galaxy] is not stable, so that when you see it has moved slightly towards one direction it means that, for a while, the wind will blow from that direction" (Amarualik 1992, IE-212).

⋆ ⋆ ⋆

THE PLANETS—*ULLURIAQJUAT*

Planets, unlike the fixed stars, are wanderers. Their positions in the sky are predictable only through calculations based on consistent and continuous observation—a difficult task at best under Arctic conditions. In particular, the lengthy annual period without darkness meant that, above the Arctic Circle, planets could not be given the level of scrutiny needed to reveal their fairly complex itineraries.[59] For this reason, with the possible exception of Venus, Inuit had little practical use for planets, save when they happened to move through some of their familiar constellations. Jupiter, for instance, did this in the winter of 1990 when it accompanied Gemini which, along with Auriga, forms part of the Inuit *Quturjuuk* constellation (entry 9).

As elsewhere the planets most visible in the Igloolik area are Venus, Jupiter, Mars, and Saturn but Inuit do not generally distinguish between them, appropriately calling all planets *Ulluriaqjuat*—"great stars." There is some indication, however, that the term *Ulluriaqjuaq* (singular) was especially applied to Venus, in both its "morning star" and "evening star" appearances. Venus, particularly when it is seen towards the end of the year, is for some of the Igloolik elders closely associated with the Christmas story. Referring specifically to Venus, Rachel Ujarasuk recalls: "There is *Ulluriaqjuaq*. We have heard that when Jesus was born they went to look for him using that star as a guide" (Uyarasuk 1990, IE-076).

She goes on to describe how, in some areas, the appearance of Venus was used to foretell the return of the Sun after the winter darkness. Her remarks are especially interesting because she vividly recalls her dismay at discovering that planets do not always appear when they are expected:

> *Ulluriaqjuaq* was used as a sign of the returning of daylight in the Pond Inlet area, but it was not always there. When I was a child growing up in the Clyde River area, we would hear about *Ulluriaqjuaq* appearing on the horizon shortly after Christmas when the daylight began to come back, so I would watch for *Ulluriaqjuaq*. It has always been like that for as long as I can remember. Sometimes it did not appear but, as a child, I never noticed this. It was when I was an adult and living at Agu Bay that I first noticed *Ulluriaqjuaq* was missing. It frightened me when I did not see it anymore. I thought it might be a sign that the world would end. [Uyarasuk 1990, IE-076]

Reports from other, widely separated, areas also make claims for Venus as a time-keeper. For the Polar Eskimos this planet was seen "in the west when the light begins to return after the long Dark" (Rasmussen 1908:177). Among the Nunamiut of North Alaska, Venus was known as *Uvluiaqpaq* ("the big star"), and was said to be the only star that "moves in the background of stars" (Gubser 1965:196). The start of a new year was marked by the "first appearance of the planet . . . above the horizon shortly after the first of January" (Gubser 1965:191).

Gubser's statement misleadingly implies that Venus is seen predictably each year at the beginning of January. In fact the planet's entrances and exits, although based on a regular cycle (Burch 1986:113), give all the appearance of randomness. A few calculations serve to illustrate this point.[60] Assuming that Venus is generally not seen under Arctic conditions until it is at least about 2° above the horizon, its first appearance at Igloolik in the winter of 1990–91 would be some time after 12 January. In the previous year the event would have been earlier, around 25 December, while in the winter of 1988–89, Venus, having disappeared below the horizon by 19 December, would not have been seen again until around 9 February of the following year. Given this seemingly erratic itinerary, it seems more than likely that Venus, if used to mark the start of a new year or to signal returning daylight, would be accorded these functions only when its appearance coincided with some other more reliable, but less spectacular, marker such as the pre-dawn rising of the *Aagjuuk* stars (see entry 1).

Robert Spencer, in *The North Alaskan Eskimo,* seems to be referring to Venus when he writes that the "morning star bore the proper name *Sivollik,* the evening star *Aaguruk*" (Spencer 1959:258). However, as the names *Aaguruk* and *Sivollik,* as used in the Inuit world, apply almost universally to the stars Altair/Tarazed and Arcturus (see entries 1 and 13), Spencer, if he is in fact associating them with Venus, is probably mistaken. In the same passage Spencer mentions that Mars was sometimes called *"Kayaktuq"*[61] meaning "the red fox"—a fitting designation for this reddest of planets; at other times he claims it was characterized "as a

Waiting at the Seal Hole. Stonecut print. By Henry Napartuk. Itivimiut. Kuujjuaraapik, Quebec, 1973. Royal Ontario Museum.

white fox and a red fox fighting over a single foxhole," an image more evocative of the dynamics and colour changes of Sirius than of Mars (see entry 12).[62] John Simpson for the same area has the name *Shu-ga-run* applying to both Mars and Venus (Bockstoce 1988:351).

Diamond Jenness records in his Arctic diary that, in the Coronation Gulf area, Jupiter is "*Uvloreaq ugjuk*—the bearded seal" (Jenness 1991:529). On this, however, he seems to have misunderstood his host, Ikpuk. We can be reasonably certain that Ikpuk had given the name *Uvloreahugyuk* but that Jenness, still new to the language, took the last two syllables, -*ugyuk*, as a separate word, *ugjuk* (meaning "bearded seal"), rather than as a suffix implying "largeness." Interestingly, in his monograph on the Copper Inuit Jenness makes no mention of Jupiter but instead gives Venus as *Uvloreahugyuk,* the "Big Star" (Jenness 1922:179).

For the Greenlanders, the planets seemed to have had a more extensive role in their traditions. In West Greenland, for instance, planets "in their conjunctions [were said to be] two females that visit or wrangle together" (Cranz 1767, I:230), while in the Ammassalik region Jupiter "is regarded as being the mother of the sun; it is very dangerous for the angakut to pass near it on their journey to the moon" (Holm 1914:85).

From the Thule region of Northwest Greenland, both Rasmussen (1908) and Holtved (1951) have recorded versions of a legend in which a seal hunter, the "great Naalagssartoq," rose up into the air and was transformed into Venus (Holtved 1951:19).[63] Holtved's version (see page 282) is the more detailed of the two. Kroeber, for the same region, also mentions this "star," which he terms *Naulaxssaqton,* but does not specifically identify it as Venus (Kroeber 1899:319). Other Greenlandic terms for Venus are *Nalaarteq* (Ostermann 1938:203), *Nalaarseq* and *Qaasiut* (Robbe and Dorais 1986:121), and *Seqernup maleruartâ* ("the Sun's follower"), used specifically to designate Venus as an "evening star" (Schultz-Lorentzen 1927:132).

CHAPTER 4
Sun, Moon, and Eclipses

At last . . . they began to rise upwards.
His younger sister became the Sun,
being warm and burning brightly.
But he became the cold Moon.

(Amaunalik, *in* Holtved 1951)

THE SUN AND THE MOON

A most rudimentary appreciation of the role of the Sun and the Moon in Inuit astronomy must be based on some knowledge of the great Inuit myth telling of the creation and regulation of these two essential luminaries. This myth, one of the most widespread and complex of all Inuit traditions, is often abbreviated to relate how two siblings, a sister and her brother, commit a number of grave social transgressions, including murder and incest, and then rise up to the sky to become the Sun and the Moon. In its fullest version the story is a tale of epic proportions, addressing universal concerns about creation, social and cosmic order, nourishment, retribution, and renewal. It also provides Inuit with their principal metaphors for several of nature's basic dichotomies—night and day, summer and winter, and, of course, male and female.

George Kappianaq's fluent account of the Sister-Sun/Brother-Moon legend is given in Chapter 8. For our immediate purposes the following excerpt, taken from Kappianaq's account, is sufficient. It presents the concluding portion of the tale in which the Sun and the Moon are actually created:

> At this time they would regularly hold festivities in the *qaggiq*.[1] While these celebrations were in progress, a person she [the sister] did not recognize, would sometimes come into her birthing place and extinguish the light of her *qulliq*.[2] This person would then fight and fondle her but she never knew who he was. Knowing she would be handled in this manner again, she devised a way to discover the identity of her visitor. So, during the next celebration, she blackened her nose with soot from her cooking pot and waited.
>
> She was sewing or mending something when she suddenly heard a noise and all at once her lamp was extinguished and again she was fondled. Shortly afterwards the aggressor returned to the *qaggiq* and she could hear laughter coming from that direction for the soot on the man's nose had been noticed.
>
> She put her boots on and, despite the taboo she was under, having recently given birth, went outside to see who the molester might be. It was her brother, her own flesh and blood. She was devastated by this rev-

elation. In despair she entered the *qaggiq* and exposing one of her breasts through the hood opening of her *amauti*, severed it and offered it to her brother saying, *"Tamarmik mamaqtugalunga una niriguk."*[3]

After she had said these words she took some moss, dipped it in the oil of the *qulliq* and, having lit it, ran outside. Aningaat [her brother] did the same and pursued his sister round the *qaggiq*. The flame on his moss soon went out but his sister's continued to burn brightly and so the chase around the *qaggiq* went on until eventually they both started to ascend into the heavens where she became the Sun and her brother the Moon. It is said that Aningaat can be seen at night smouldering. [Kappianaq 1986, IE-071]

The Moon was invariably represented as male, the Sun as female. There are a few accounts which suggest the reverse but these are almost certainly apocryphal.[4] Simply put, too many Inuit traditions and beliefs regarding the Sun and the Moon belie any other arrangement: the Moon's masculinity and the Sun's femininity are the very foundations of Inuit cosmology.

To claim that the Sun and the Moon held more importance for Inuit than for others might be overstating the case if we did not consider that, alone among the Earth's peoples who depend entirely on hunting for survival, some Inuit groups either lose or nearly lose the Sun for lengthy periods of time each year. During these periods the Moon substitutes for the absent Sun, its pale light sufficiently intensified by the snow-clad landscape to permit many outdoor activities including, most importantly, hunting.

In both spatial and spiritual terms the Sun and the Moon were considered to be relatively close to Earth as well as to each other; some legends have them dwelling in adjacent or adjoining igloos. Both were accessible (the Sun, however, less so) through shamanistic spirit flights, and both required the periodic observance of various rituals.

Across the Inuit world the Sun and the Moon are known by a number of different names, some of which, in conformity with the practice already noted for stars, are mythological references usually reserved for the telling of legends. There is some evidence, however, that in earlier times mythological names could be used interchangeably with their vernacular equivalents. Parry's vocabulary, for example, gathered in the Northern Foxe Basin area in 1822–1823, lists both categories—*"Anninga"* (brother) and *"Tatkuk"* for Moon and *"Neiya"* (sister) and

"*Sukkenuk*" for Sun (Parry 1824:564, 567). Elsewhere the mythological term seems to be maintained at the expense of a vernacular one, and so among the Polar Eskimos, Kroeber gives *Anningat* as the "ordinary word for the moon" (Kroeber 1899:318) while Cranz, in West Greenland, has the Sun as *Malina* (Cranz 1767, I:232), a term deriving from the word *malik*, meaning "following," a reference, perhaps, to the mythic Sun/Moon pursuit (Fortescue et al. 1994:186).

★ ★ ★

THE SUN—*SIQINIQ*

There is joy in
Feeling the warmth
Come to the great world
And seeing the sun
Follow its old footprints
In the summer night.

(Tatilgak, *in* Rasmussen 1927)

For the Igloolik area, at least, it seems fitting to begin a discussion of the Sun by first considering the period during which it is not visible. It is at this time, paradoxically, that the Sun is most obvious, for its absence has the understandable effect of stimulating an increasingly grateful awareness about its existence, together with a growing impatience for its return.[5]

The very fact of the Sun's disappearance seems to have given rise to deeply held beliefs linking its timely reappearance and maximum seasonal effect to appropriate human behaviour and intervention. These convictions are clearly revealed in the contents of various Inuit festivities, legends, rituals, and taboos surrounding the Sun's return and together express a general hesitancy to be complacent about the future and good fortune, a reminder, perhaps, that nothing should be taken for granted. Life in an Arctic environment, after all, even when equipped with the technology, skills, and knowledge of Inuit, must rank among the most precarious of existences.[6]

The language, too, may reflect something of this collective concern. In Inuktitut the root *qau-*, for example, expresses concepts of daylight, brightness, and knowledge, while the absence of *qau-* suggests darkness and ignorance. In many areas the Inuit word for "tomorrow" is *qauppat,* a somewhat tentative term literally meaning "when (or) if the dawn comes," implying, perhaps, that the coming of daylight is, in some sense, conditional. Beverley Cavanagh, a musicologist, apparently hears this same prudent theme permeating Inuit music:

> The absence of metric or rhythmic regularity, periodicity or melodic symmetry, indeed the actual defeat of symmetry and predictability by the contrariety of textual and musical structure, is astounding. Perhaps the capacity for the ironic, for the defeat of expectation, is so basic to . . . social relations and cultural expression, so ingrained in the very character of the Inuit people, that it is manifested not just in the context and imagery of songs, but in their very structure. [*in* Colombo 1981:15]

★ ★ ★

THE GREAT DARKNESS—*Tauvikjuaq*

*The sun is a great ball of fire which
moves around the hill. . . .
In winter it is greatly weighed down by the cold
and the frost and so cannot rise up into the sky.*

(Archibald Fleming, 1928)

The period in midwinter during which the Sun never rises above the horizon is known in Igloolik as *Tauvikjuaq*—"the great darkness"[7] and lasts for almost seven weeks, starting around the end of November. At this latitude the area is not quite plunged into the sort of Stygian darkness so often used to characterize Arctic winters. Around midday at the time of winter solstice, for example, the Sun is never more than 4° below the horizon, ensuring a daily period of twilight lasting for about two hours and spanning local apparent noon.[8]

In the past, *Tauvikjuaq* and the weeks surrounding it were frequently times of relative inactivity, anxiety, and privation. Survival during this period was never taken for granted.[9] Many elders, recalling this time, referred to it as a period of hardship.[10] It was a time when they were particularly vulnerable to nature's vicissitudes and so supernatural protection was invoked through the use of powerful and sacred words known as *irinaliutit:*[11]

When the winter quarters were complete, they would move into them, be it sod houses or igloos. Once they settled in and before they retired for the night, the elders, including my mother and father, would offer *irinaliutit* as a form of ritual to seek assistance and to cleanse oneself. In this particular case these *irinaliutit* were used in order that the winter might pass without any adversity, especially during the period when daylight is shortest and also the period of extreme cold. It was important to pass through this time without hardship as in these days the only means of survival was [by hunting] animals. The *irinaliutit* were offered so that the dwelling place would be satisfactory and that they would not encounter

★ 101 ★

sickness, epidemics, and starvation during the course of winter. It was not possible to keep in contact with other camps so it was difficult to know the conditions prevailing at these other locations. . . . This was the time when there were numerous camps, so *irinaliutit* were also said to protect and help the other camps. The offering of these *irinaliutit* resemble the prayers of the Christian faith—they too were used to seek help for the coming winter. They asked that no sickness befall them. Thoughts of survival were foremost. These were the reasons why *irinaliutit* were offered. [Piugaattuk 1986, IE-057]

The difficulty of communication between camps and distant kin was a constant concern, particularly during the early winter when unsuitable ice and snow conditions limited sled travel. Piugaattuk's song evokes the poignant anxiety of this period:

> *Eya*—I am anxious to hear, I am anxious to hear
> From there beyond *eya, ya.*
> The fur has gone from my boot upper.
> I am anxious to hear from there beyond.
> *Eya*—I am anxious to hear, I am anxious to hear,
> about the clothing they wear.
> I am anxious to hear, I am anxious to hear
> about their food supply, I sit idle.
> I sit idle in the confines of the igloo.
> I sit idle, I sit idle, waiting to hear.
>
> [Piugaattuk 1986, IE-070]

Ava's description of midwinter is apt. When asked why the Iglulingmiut had no particular "moon" designations for the months of December and January Ava, according to Rasmussen, "called them simply *'ukiup tatqe,'*" i.e., winter's moons. These two moon periods, he said, resemble each other in that they are dark, cold, and hunting in them is difficult, so that they did not need any special designation" (Rasmussen 1930:63).

Illness was particularly feared during the midwinter period, being at this time much more difficult to cope with, given severe weather, scarce resources, and reduced opportunities for hunting. The elders interviewed on this point, however, do not recall the winter camps being especially vulnerable to sickness; their impression was rather the opposite. Noah Piugaattuk attributes the relative absence of sickness in midwinter to the fact that there was little travel between camps during the dark period: "I have noticed that people seem to get sick much easier when they started to go from one region to another, some would carry sicknesses to other places. Throughout *Tauvikjuaq* we used to remain in one camp and there was not as much sickness as when people were moving around from region to region. I really could not say that people became sick easier during the dark period" (Piugaattuk 1991, IE-170).

Parry records that during his winter in Igloolik cases of illness among Inuit peaked shortly after the return of the Sun, in late January and early February: "About this time the number of sick as well as the seriousness of their complaints was rapidly increasing" (Parry 1824:389).[12] Perceiving his ships' sick-bays to be overburdened in their efforts to treat seriously ill Inuit—trials which included infestations of lice and "being taxed with a most perverse and thankless patient"— Parry was obliged to consider "some more systematic as well as extensive means . . . for the relief of their sick." The result was a "hospital" on the sea-ice: "[February 4, 1823] I determined on building a hospital . . . expressly for the reception of the natives . . . a plan for the building, medical attendance, and victualling was immediately settled. . . . A house was accordingly constructed with spars, turf, snow, and canvass, twelve feet square . . . and containing five convenient bed-spaces for the sick and a small warming stove in the centre" (Parry 1824:402).

In the context of seasonal illnesses mention must be made of a peculiar mental disorder loosely termed "Arctic hysteria." Many observers, including Rasmussen, Steensby, Jenness, Peary, and Malaurie, have mentioned the prevalence of this condition among various Inuit groups living north of the Arctic Circle. The disorder, which seems to have been most common in Northwest Greenland, is often said to be associated with the onset of winter darkness. Most cases are reported to occur in the late autumn just before the Sun disappears (Weyer 1956:21; 1932:386). Some of the symptoms of "Arctic hysteria" as given by Gussow include tearing off of clothing, achieving partial or complete nudity (this was frequently one of the first behavioural signs of the attack), glossolalia, mutterings, meaningless syllables, "speaking in tongues," making animal sounds, fleeing across the tundra, wandering into hills, if outdoors, [and] running back and forth in an agitated state" (Gussow 1960:226).

Harry Whitney, an early adventurer among the Polar Eskimos, gives a vivid account of an episode of "Arctic hysteria" or *pibloktok,* as the condition is called in the Inuit dialect of Northwest Greenland:

Beginning of winter, polar night coming, winds die down, quiet, feeling of impending gloom. Women felt depressed, but mainly worried about safety of hunters who had gone into interior to hunt caribou. . . . At half-past one that night I was awakened from a sound sleep by a woman shouting at the top of her voice—shrill and startling, like one gone mad. I knew at once what it meant—someone had gone *piblokto.* I tumbled into my clothes and rushed out. Far away on the driving ice of the Sound, a lone figure was running and raving. . . . At length I reached her and to my astonishment she struggled desperately, and it required the combined strength of . . . three of us to get her back to the shack where she was found to be in bad shape—one hand was frozen slightly and part of one breast. After a half hour of quiet she became rational again, but the attack left her very weak. [Whitney 1910:87]

George Borup, of Peary's 1908 Polar expedition, recalls another case of the illness, brought on, apparently, by the Expedition's celebration of the Sun's return:

About four P.M. all the Eskimos, men, women, and children, were called out on deck. Pointing towards the southern horizon, where at noon, a very faint twilight glow had appeared, and drawing out his watch, the Commander said the sun had just started back to us again. As he finished speaking, Marven began ringing the ship's bell, Henson fired six shots from a revolver, and I touched off a volley of flashlights. . . . Then they all trooped to the galley and our mess-room, where they were all given . . . musk-ox steaks, biscuits, and coffee.

Scarcely had they gone when someone sung out that young sixteen-year-old Pingahshoo had *piblokto* and was running around outside in his shirt sleeves looking for the sun. . . . Unable to locate the returning sun in the open, he hiked for the tidal igloo [where the expedition took its tidal measurements] in the hopes that it might come up through the hole. [Borup 1911:115–16]

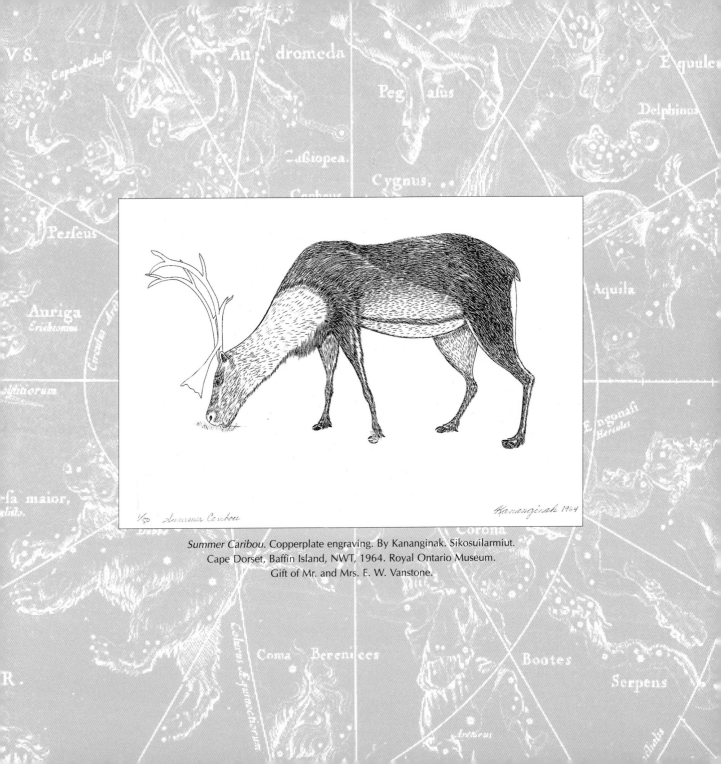

1/50   *Summer Caribou*   *Kananginak 1964*

Summer Caribou. Copperplate engraving. By Kananginak. Sikosuilarmiut.
Cape Dorset, Baffin Island, NWT, 1964. Royal Ontario Museum.
Gift of Mr. and Mrs. E. W. Vanstone.

A number of hypotheses based on cultural and environmental considerations have been advanced to explain this peculiarly northern hysteria.[13] Of these the one most relevant to our context suggests that the low sunlight levels of Arctic winters tend to inhibit the body's capacity to produce vitamin D, which in turn reduces the absorption of calcium into the bloodstream. Edward Foulks summarizes the reasoning behind this hypothesis:

> Several environmental factors . . . potentially adversely affect the functioning of the Eskimo's central nervous system. We have found that the absence of a regular 24 hour alternation of light and dark affects the circadian cycling of calcium metabolism. Calcium is an essential element in the chemical transmission of neural impulses, and it has been demonstrated that abnormalities in the physiological functioning of calcium are capable of producing a variety of mental disorders including hysteria-like behaviour.
>
> The arctic environment contributes to abnormalities of calcium homeostosis in other ways too. . . . By December the days involve only several hours of twilight. By January there is complete darkness with only several minutes of red glow on the horizon at noon. Solar ultraviolet radiation is correspondingly decreased during this time of the year. This radiation normally induces chemicals in the skins of humans to produce vitamin D, which in turn enhances the absorption of ingested calcium from the intestine. [Foulks 1972:306]

Foulks and his colleagues clinically tested this hypothesis in North Alaska but found no evidence of calcium deficiency among their sample of Inuit patients exhibiting hysteria-like symptoms, although a number of them scored on the low side of "normal." What they did find, however, was that "the shifting, external, solar synchronizer of biological rhythms [i.e., the Sun] has profound effects on the calcium metabolism of the north Alaskan Eskimos. Calcium was desynchronized relative to other electrolytes . . . throughout the year" (Foulks 1972:223). Another medical researcher (J. Bohlen) cited by Foulks has "associated this desynchronization [of calcium] with the increase in apathy, depression, and irritability generally observed among the Eskimo in winter months" (Foulks 1972:219).

Stefánsson characteristically dismisses Arctic hysteria as "auto-suggestion" or "mass hypnosis"—"real only in the sense that any trouble based upon the imagination may be real" (Stefánsson 1944:310).

RETURN OF THE SUN

At the latitude of Igloolik, slightly less than 70°N, the Sun falls below the horizon on 29 November and is not normally seen again until 14 January. Atmospheric refraction acting on light waves can often alter these dates, on the one hand, by seeming to delay the Sun's disappearance and, on the other, by hastening its return. The remarkable and unsettling effects of refraction may in fact have lent some credence to the notion that Inuit actions—such as playing "cat's cradles" *(ajaraaq)* in the late fall or "cup-and-pin" *(ajagaq)* after the Sun's return—could delay its setting or speed its rising in the sky. In extreme cases the effects of refraction can cause the Sun to suddenly appear above the horizon long after it should have set. Parry observed this phenomenon in Igloolik during the winter of 1822 and describes it with suitable wonder:

> At apparent noon, on the 2d of December, six days after the sun had independently of the effects of refraction set to us for a period of more than seven weeks, we caught a glimpse of its upper limb from the deck of the Fury, about one-sixteenth of its whole disk being visible above the low land to the southward. It is impossible not to acknowledge the benevolence as well as to admire the wisdom of the law which, among its varied and wonderful effects, displayed throughout the works of nature, contrives to shorten, by nearly a whole fortnight, the annual absence of the cheering luminary from the frozen regions of the earth, and thus contributes so essentially to the welfare and enjoyment of their numerous inhabitants.[14] [Parry 1824:383]

The sixteenth-century Dutch explorer Willem Barents, wintering on Novaya Zemlya, was even more fortunate than Parry. His expedition was blessed with the Sun's return a full twelve days ahead of schedule. Barents, who attributed the event to divine intervention, would not have warmed to Barry Lopez's informed explanation: "What they saw that January day, we now know, was not the sun but only a solar image. . . . Such images, now called Novaya Zemlya images, are common in the Arctic. They serve as a caution against precise description and expectation, a reminder that the universe is oddly hinged (Lopez 1986:24).[15]

Rituals and festivities connected with the Sun's return, or with winter solstice in those areas where the Sun did not disappear, were observed by many Inuit groups. The event seems to have been a particularly important one in West Greenland where the exuberant festivities were mentioned dissapprovingly by Cranz:[16]

The Greenlanders keep the Sun-feast at the hyemal or winter solstice about December 22d, to rejoice at the return of the sun, and the renewal of good hunting and fishing weather. They assemble together all over the country in large parties, and treat one another with the very best they have. When they have eaten so much that they are ready to burst, they rise up to play and to dance. They cannot intoxicate themselves, because they have nothing but water to drink. . . . [A performer] accompanies the music and the dance with a song in honour of seal-catching, and such kind of exploits; he extolls the noble deeds of his ancestors, and express-es his joy at the return of the sun in the hemisphere. . . . The singer sings four cantos in every act; the two first commonly consist of the *Amna Ajah* constantly repeated. . . . Taken together it is a compleat Cantata, e.g.,

The welcome sun returns again,
Amna ajah, ah-hu!
And brings us weather fine and fair,
Amna ajah, ah-hu!

Thus they continue the whole night through; next day they sleep their fill, in the evening stuff their bellies again, and then dance all night; and this round they run for several days and nights, till they have nothing more to eat, or till they are so fatigued and spent that they can no more speak. [Cranz 1767, I:176]

Parry, well aware of Cranz's account, paid particular attention to the reaction of Inuit who were visiting his ship when the Sun reappeared on Igloolik's hori-zon in January, 1823. He seems to have been disappointed by what he observed:

On the 19th, the weather having cleared up we were once more gratified with a sight of the sun, and numerous parties of walkers were seen in various parts of the bay, enjoying the novelty and splendour of this cheering and glorious sight.[17] A parhelion also appeared on each side of the sun; and exactly opposite to it near the northern horizon was a large circular patch of white light, precisely similar to that described on the 16th of November. The Esquimaux who were at the ships to-day before the sun rose, particularly said that we should see it, and apparently with great confidence. It is certain however that on this occasion no sun-dance took place, nor any other festivity of the kind described by Cranz; their only expression of satisfaction at this event being of the same general nature as our own. [Parry 1824:389][18]

Had Parry been ashore at the Inuit encampment a few miles from his ship he may well have had more to record, for it is clear that the people of Igloolik, in common with other Inuit in the Eastern Arctic, had their own way of welcoming the Sun's return. Both Noah Piugaattuk and NiviattianAqatsiaq recalled taking part in these special observances. Piugaattuk begins:

During the time when taboos were strictly adhered to, the first day that the Sun came out was marked by the belief that the whole community must start a new life, so the children of the camp would go to each household to blow out the flames of the *qulliq*. After the lamps had been extinguished the old wicks were removed and a new wick set in place and then the lamp would be relit. In order to begin life anew, the children of the camp including myself, would run to each of the dwellings hoping that we would be the first to blow out the lamps before the others did. So this was how the first day of the Sun was observed. [Piugaattuk 1990, IE-148][19]

Niviattian Aqatsiaq continues her account, adding detail about traditional fire-making methods and the need to relight the extinguished lamps from a single flame, clearly representative of the returning Sun:

I know that when the Sun was seen for the first time in the season the occasion would be observed. In these days the only way to start a fire was with flint and stones, *kasuk*. A bag containing material for lighting the fire along with a flint and a small piece of stone would be prepared well in advance.

When the sun was finally seen by those who had kept watch they would tell everyone to confirm that the Sun had returned. At this time all the *qullit* (lamps) in the village would be extinguished by blowing them out. The person who was to start the fire by flint would be in one of the igloos, ready and fully prepared for this task. When all the *qullit* in the village had been blown out, they would be refueled with new oil; a new wick would replace the old one. This whole process was so that the people would start anew. The only way to relight their *qullit,* was to use the flame from the specially made fire container. Smouldering embers placed on dry plant material would be blown on to start the new fire. From here the whole village would come and get their fire to relight their *qullit.* So from this single source all the *qullit* in the village would be relit. Only from this new fire could the others relight their *qullit.* So people were thus renewed and it was said that the Sun would be warmer in the coming spring.

The only way to create fire was from dried *urjjut* (moss) or some other flammable plants contained in a container made from *taqtuaq* (kidney membrane, usually from walrus). This would be well looked after throughout the summer making sure that it did not get wet, in readiness for the time when it was used. Throughout this period it could be used occasionally when there was no other source of fire available. They would ignite the tinder and when it began to smoulder it would be put in the fuel bag and blown on to start the fire. From this they would be able to light their *qullit.* This container and its contents were known as *suppivik.* The word we used for going to fetch fire from another household was *ingnirsijarturtut.* We had to be sure that the light did not blow out when we carried it home.[20] [Aqatsiaq 1990, IE-149]

François Quassa's recollection of this ceremony appears to date from the time when traditional practices were on the wane and not everyone subscribed willingly to having their lamps put out: "In those days they did not have anything like matches to light a fire, so some people did not like to have their lamps put out with no easy way to start them again. Someone would rush into the house, blow out the flame and leave immediately. Of course the inhabitants of the igloo would not be too pleased, but because it was the custom in these days they would have to put up with it" (Quassa 1990, IE-156).

These accounts add substantially to the information collected by George Comer around 1900 for the ethnologist Franz Boas: "Captain Comer records some interesting customs practised in Iglulik. When the sun first returns after the winter night, the children who have watched for his re-appearance run into the houses and blow out the lamps. They then receive from their mothers presents of pieces of wick" (Boas 1907:151). The practice is also mentioned by Rasmussen (1929:183).

In Igloolik the Sun's return was also attended by some important practical considerations to do with long-range weather forecasting for the coming year. The assumptions and predictions made were based on the perceived rivalry between the Sun and the Moon:[21]

> When the sun was going to return, they used to say that the moon and the sun would compete with each other so that one would come out before the other. When the sun returns before the first new moon of the year it was said that the moon had been defeated and that the spring and summer would be warm. Should the sun come out after the first new moon, then it was said that the spring and summer would not be as warm. In the past winter [1989–1990] the sun came back first and for this reason the spring was very dry, when it would normally have been rainy. So the spring was good because the sun had come out before the moon. [Piugaattuk 1990, IE-153]

Piugaattuk refers to competition between the Sun and the Moon as *ingiaqautijuuk* or *ingiaqaaqutautijuuk,* adding that in his recollection one of the two luminaries was always defeated by the other; there was never a draw (Piugaattuk 1991, IE-170).

In Igloolik another practice relating to the return of the Sun, also involving children, was the "half-smile" to be made by those who first saw the Sun rising above the horizon. Niviattian Aqatsiaq explains: "The children used to go outdoors and keep watch for the Sun and if they saw it, were to come back in with only half a smile. I remember a time when only one child saw the Sun . . . she came back in trying to give half a smile, that is smiling with only one side of her mouth. But she couldn't do this and every time she tried to she gave a full smile!" (Aqatsiaq 1990, IE-149).

Noah Piugaattuk adds: "Yes, they had to use their left side to smile.[22] They used to smile at the Sun on the first day it reappeared. They were happy and their parents were also affected by it as they were now confident that the worst was over" (Piugaattuk 1990, IE-153).

Mark Ijjangiaq suggests a reason for the smile being restricted to one side of the face. The Sun, it seems, was not given an unconditional welcome at this time of the year: "Indeed I still smile at the sun when we see it for the first time. You smile with one side of your face—the other side must be a straight face. The reason for this is that it's going to get warmer once again, so one side of the face smiles in welcome of the warmer temperatures to come, while the other side—the straight side—proclaims the reality that the cold weather will continue for some time" (Ijjangiaq 1991, IE-184).

The practice of smiling at the returning Sun survived, at least for a time, the introduction of Christianity. Michel Kupaaq remembers participating in this custom as a child:

> I used to take part in smiling at the Sun with only one side of my face. When the Sun first came back it seemed to be stretched out on the horizon. So when someone saw it for the first time we all rushed out so that we could smile at it. I never participated in going to the households to blow out the flames of the *qulliit*. With the introduction of Christianity these practices were discouraged. . . . But the practice of smiling at the Sun did not change with the new religion. [Kupaaq 1990, IE-153]

From other Arctic areas, information is scanty about Inuit observances on the return of the Sun. In the Frobisher Bay region, where the Sun is not lost below the horizon on midwinter days, Charles Francis Hall in the 1860s notes a ceremony similar to the kind practiced in Igloolik. As expected, the event at this latitude occurred somewhat earlier than at Igloolik, albeit a number of days after the winter solstice, due, perhaps, to the obscuring effect of the high hills of the Meta Incognita Peninsula or some other massive land form to the south: "At a time which answers to our New Year's day, two men start out, one of them being dressed to represent a woman, and go to every igloo in the village, blowing out the light in each. The lights are afterward rekindled from a fresh fire. When Tookoolito was asked the meaning of this, she replied, 'New sun—new light,' implying a belief that the sun was at that time renewed for the year" (Hall 1865:529).

At Tikigaq (Point Hope, Alaska), Inuit would observe the Sun's return from atop their igloos: "[They] greeted the sun's brief emergence with a barking joy shout (*qatchalaaq*). . . . A number of rites, half-remembered by the elders of the 1940s, were directed at the sun . . . [including] a ritual in which women raised boys to the newborn sun to make them strong and athletic (Lowenstein 1992:16–17). Jenness, who witnessed the return of the Sun to the Coronation Gulf region on 9 January 1915, makes no mention of any ceremonies in connection with the event except to note that "the natives heard [the sun's] hiss as it set again in the ocean" (Jenness 1922:179).

In the Back River region of the central Canadian Arctic, Heinrich Klutschak, a member of the Schwatka Expedition (1878-1880) describes "quite an insignificant surprise" one New Year's Day—the Sun's arrival:

> Not exactly in the best humour, we were sitting together in our snow houses, gloomy and silent, when around noon the sun's first ray penetrated through the ice window into the interior and aroused a feeling of grateful joy even among the Inuit. "Namakpuk mana siqiniq qaigit" (Now everything is fine; the sun has come back) was the general exclamation. . . . For the Inuit this signified the start of a new year, the beginning of a longer day, and with it the arrival of better, warmer weather. The sunless days are hated by the Inuit too. . . . The entire landscape . . . bears a peculiar stamp which is difficult to describe; one might express it as lacking a life-giving source. . . . Both we and the Inuit left our houses to regale ourselves with the full view of our New Year's gift—but it did not last long. [Klutschak 1987:159–60]

Klutschak, in this account, seems to have resorted to poetic license. At this point, his expedition was camped about 100 km south of the Arctic Circle, where, technically, the Sun on 1 January would reach an altitude of almost 2° and even at noon on winter solstice would not be lost below the horizon.[23] Nor does the event ever signify "warmer weather" for Inuit, who well know that the coldest temperatures of winter occur after the return of the Sun, a fact borne out convincingly in Klutschak's journal where, by 3 January, temperatures as low as –57°F (-49°C) were recorded.

In East Greenland, according to Holm, the winter solstice was also marked, but somewhat more elaborately than in Baffin Island: "It was formerly the custom on the shortest day that a skin was taken into the house, prepared, and sewn into a dress for the eldest child, who was to wear it on that day. On this day also a festival with entertainments, drum-dancing, and other amusements was held (Holm 1914, *in* Thalbitzer 1914, part 1:105).

Unlike the midwinter festivities of their Greenlandic cousins, observances made on the Sun's reappearance among the Iglulingmiut were minimal and mainly symbolic. They principally involved the children of the community, themselves emblematic of renewal. Life was difficult at this time of the year. In particular, hunting activities were limited both by darkness and unfavourable ice conditions, and there was often insufficient food or fuel to meet the community's daily needs, far less that of a festival. Festivities then tended to be postponed until it was clear that the worst of the winter was over and that the Sun had indeed returned and was slowly rising higher in the sky each day.

The progress of the Sun's increasing altitude was carefully noted. Three stages of the Sun's recovery, each involving measurement of its altitude at local apparent noon, held particular significance for the Inuit of Igloolik. The first was *Unaqtaniktuq*, meaning that at noon a harpoon shaft held horizontally at arm's length would appear to fit between the horizon and the lower rim of the Sun's disk. This measurement was an indication that indeed the Sun was back, but barely. The next stage, known as *Kullutaniktuq*, was determined when, with your arm extended, the thumb of your mitted hand would fill the gap between the Sun and the horizon. *Kullutaniktuq*, occurring in late January at the latitude of Igloolik, signalled the start of seal hunting at breathing holes on the land-fast ice using the technique known as *mauliq* (Kappianaq 1990, IE-155). *Pualutaniktuq*, the final and most important measurement of the Sun's progress, was determined when it had at last reached a noon altitude now equal to the full width of your mitt. Depending on variables such as latitude, arm length, and mitt size, the Sun would reach this height on a date falling between 19 February and 4 March, in any event two or three weeks before spring equinox. The equinoxes themselves seemed to have little significance for Inuit.[24] In Igloolik, however, George Kappianaq named the period around spring equinox *Ikiaqparvik*, meaning that the Sun at noon was reaching heights halfway between the horizon and its maximum altitude at summer solstice. It was also noted at this time that the Sun would set opposite its point of rising (Piugaattuk 1990, IE-147).[25]

Harpooning. Stonecut print. By Adamie Alagoo. Itivimiut.
Povungnituk, Quebec, 1961. Royal Ontario Museum.
Presented by the Povungnituk Co-operative Society.

Pualutaniktuq truly marked the end of the winter's dark period (though not of the cold temperatures) and heralded in a time of promise if not immediately of plenty. Noah Piugaattuk conveys a vivid impression of this period:

> When the sun was getting higher and higher so that it could be completely seen the [Inuit] would know that the time was returning when they would once again have sufficient game for their survival. They would measure the sun by stretching out their arm and using their mitt. The way to measure the sun was to line up the bottom of the mitt with the horizon and if the top of the mitt lined up with the bottom of the sun then it was called *Pualutaniktuq*. At first the food supply might be scarce at times but they were now confident that the worst was over so then they would start to hold a *qaggiq*.[26] [Piugaattuk 1990, IE-147]
>
> *Pualutaniktuq* marked the time when most of the marine animals were becoming available again. The bearded seals would have made their breathing holes on the newly formed ice by the floe-edge by that time. When the south winds prevailed they would hunt on the moving ice. So when *Pualutaniktuq* was at hand, it marked the period when all the animals that could be hunted from the ice were more abundant. It was a time when the sun was higher and the temperatures were still cold but the chances of catching animals were better. So in order to show their appreciation for having food available to them and their thankfulness that the sun would continue to get higher in the sky, and thankful, too, for having passed the dark period without too much hardship in a time when it was necessary to live entirely on sea animals, they would hold celebrations. The future then would look promising with the increased sunlight making it much easier to catch wildlife, so the celebrations were used for the purpose of thanksgiving. [Piugaattuk 1990, IE-148]

Niviattian Aqatsiaq's recollection of this period is similar.[27] In addition she emphasizes that the arrival of *Pualutaniktuq* also signalled that the time had come to move away from the winter camps:

> The way they measured the sun was using a mitt. When it was determined that the sun had reached a certain height then everyone made

preparations to go to another location more accessible to the hunting grounds. This they did for they knew that the sun was going to get warmer and warmer. *Pualutaniktuq* was determined when the sun was bigger than the mitt. So if you put out your arm and lined the bottom of your mitt to the horizon and the sun shows over the top of the mitt then this was the period known as *Pualutaniktuq*. [Aqatsiaq 1990, IE-149]

In the same interview Niviattian Aqatsiaq also mentions the desire to celebrate at this time. A *qaggiq*, she says, would be held "in order to get the sun to be warmer so that the spring could be good." The concept that the Sun needed encouragement of one sort or another to speed its rising in the sky was shared by other Inuit groups. Of Baffin Island's Cumberland Sound area Boas tells us that when "the sun is going south in the fall, the game of cat's cradle is played, to catch the sun in the meshes of the string,[28] and to prevent his disappearance. When the sun is returning, the game of cup-and-pin [*ajagaq*] is played to hasten his return" (Boas 1907:151). By contrast, in East Greenland on "the day after the shortest day in the year, water must be scooped from the sea into a wooden vessel and as quickly as possible poured over a mountain top. Then the sun will rise quickly in the sky" (Ostermann 1938:198).

François Quassa recalls hearing of similar games being played in Igloolik:

I have heard that when the sun was just returning they used to play a lot of *ajagaq*. When this game is played one has to throw a bone up and try to poke the stick through one of the holes in the bone. So the idea was that by throwing the *ajagaq* bone up in the air they would appear to be trying to get the sun higher in the same manner that the bone was going higher. They did this when the sun had just started to come out, and at the same time string games, *ajaraaq*, were discouraged; otherwise the sun might get tangled up in the strings and keep falling down, making its progress much slower. [Quassa 1990, IE-156]

The Inuit of Greenland's Angmagsalik region, who do not quite lose the Sun in the winter, turned to their mythology to account for this good fortune. As Holm explains:

Two myths are current to explain why the sun at midnight [midday, presumably] on the shortest day does not descend lower than the sea. According to the one myth, this happens because its hinder parts[29] are cut with sharp instruments, and it is therefore so worn out that only the skeleton is left. It is the lamp of the sun which is visible to mortals and gives warmth to the earth.

According to the other myth, when the sun is at its lowest point, it touches a land from which it is shoved up again by a man. When the natives heard that we had been far in the direction of the sun, they asked us whether we had not been in the land to which the sun travelled. "When the sun, after having stood still at its lowest point for five days, rises again, there is great joy among mortals. At first it ascends very rapidly, so that it soon gets so high up that it cannot be reached by a sling; afterwards its progress is slower. Spring begins when the sun rises at the spot where [the constellation] Asiit takes its rise"[30] (Holm 1914, *in* Thalbitzer 1914, part 1:105).

For Iglulingmiut, the month they called *Qangattaarsat* (literally "rising increasingly," perhaps a reference to the Sun's rapid gain in altitude) ushered in a general sense of well-being. It is the month in which *Pualutaniktuq* occurs and spans roughly the period between mid-February and mid-March. Given the hopeful prospects of this time it is no wonder that Rasmussen's host, Ava, marked *Qangattaarsat* as the first month of the year, "because in that month one sees the light returning and has the inner feeling that one is approaching light and spring" (Rasmussen 1930:63).

Around this time "light and spring" are also proclaimed by the stars of *Akuttujuuk* (Bellatrix and Betelgeuse) which start to appear high in the southern sky shortly after sunset. By now there is an unmistakable change in the length and quality of the daylight. The flat light of the past two months is more and more enlivened by the northward-moving Sun, and the snowy landscape, now under a bluer sky, at last takes on the hues and sharper shadows of the approaching spring. The appearance of *Akuttujuuk* is indeed cause for celebration in song. Martha Nasook (1990, IE-151) explains:

They used to be happy to see the light coming back. There is a song about *Akuttujuuk* expressing the feeling that life will go on. I used to hear it. It was a sign that life will start again and the hunters will have an easier time in their hunting. The dark period must have been so hard.

> *Akuttujuuk* appear!
> There is still the day,
> It is a joyous feeling that
> I will go on living.
> Again in the broad daylight
> Will I sleep!

With the lengthening days and hunting activities increasingly rewarded with greater success, festivities became more frequent among the Iglulingmiut. Games and celebrations would now take place regularly until families dispersed to their spring locations. Again, Noah Piugaattuk describes this period:

When the sun got higher they would have further celebrations in view of the fact that they were able to pass the winter without too much adversity. They would hold games with teams made up of *Aggiarjuit* [old squaw ducks—*Clangula hyemal*] for those who were born in tents, and of *Aqiggiit* [ptarmigan—*Lagopus mutus*] for those who were born in igloos. The idea was to outdo each other in any games that may require some competition when the temperatures were comfortable enough for people to stay outdoors. These games would include a tug-of-war using leather thongs, called *Piklirtautiju*. All this would be done with the *Aggiarjuit* on one side and the *Aqiggiit* on the other side trying to outdo each other. In addition they would hold a *Qaggiq* to entertain themselves. After the hunters had returned from their hunt each day and had eaten, they would gather in the camp's largest igloo which would serve as a *Qaggiq* (because around this area they hardly ever built a special *Qaggiq* for celebrations). Then someone would call out *"Qaggiavuut! Qaggiavuut!"* so that the men and their wives would go to that igloo after they had eaten. A *Qaggiq* was usually held early in the evening. The men would take turns to dance while the women sat on the bed platform singing *aya-ja* songs that had been composed by the dancer. When the dancer stopped he would put down the drum and another man would take it up and start to dance, meanwhile the women sang to him. It sounded wonderful as all the women participated in the song. This was the most enjoyable time! [Piugaattuk 1990, IE-147]

Piugaattuk continues, expanding on the division of people into *Aqiggiit* and *Aggiarjuit:*

In the autumn Inuit moved into igloos. The ptarmigan are winter birds, they stay throughout winter and they depend on plants for their diet. So a person who was born in an igloo would be designated *Aqiggiq*. In the spring people moved into tents and stayed in them throughout the summer, so anyone born in that period when the Old Squaw ducks had arrived was identified as *Aggiarjuit*. The *Aggiarjuit* are numerous and can be seen in all the regions of the land so it is appropriate to identify them as summer birds. As for the *Aqiggiit* they may be found anywhere in the winter and their ability to survive this period is the main characteristic used to identify people who were born in the winter time. [Piugaattuk 1990, IE-153]

Elsewhere, Piugaattuk gives us some amusing accounts of the rivalry between the *Aggiarjuit* and the *Aqiggiit:*

I am an *Aqiggiq,* yes I am an *Aqiggiq!* I was born in early winter shortly after my parents moved into an igloo, in an area beyond Akunniq where there is a place called Sarva. In this place there is usually a polynia which freezes over later than the surrounding waters. It is here I was born. At that time when the mothers were expecting to give birth, a little birthing igloo was built so I was born in one of these.

When I was younger and there was to be a football game down on the ice I would have probably joined my team mates, who would all be *Aqiggiq,* to beat the *Aggiarjuk* team. But, in my younger days, I really did not participate in big gatherings as far as games were concerned, as our family spent most of the time alone; we hardly ever spent much time with others. But should there have been a game that required a team, I would have participated without a doubt. In those days there was rivalry between those who were born as *Aqiggiq* and those who were born as *Aggiarjuk.* This would include using songs to outdo and embarrass their rivals. When they started to hold festivities and everyone was in an excited mood, they would try to embarrass their opponent by saying or singing something that was funny.

I remember there was a man by the name of Naujaarakuluk who had seriously impaired hearing. His singing was terrible and so was his voice, for he had impaired hearing. As it turned out he was an *Aggiarjuk* while my father was an *Aqiggiq.* During a *Qaggiq* at Tunnunirusiq [Arctic Bay region], he was persuaded to sing his song known as an *Aqiggiuti* (which is a song aimed at a person who is designated as a ptarmigan). So they started to sing hoping to outdo each other. My father and his younger brother were among the participants. When most of the people that had gathered to share in the feast were leaving and there were only a few others left, he, Naujaarakuluk, began to sing his song. His singing was really poor and he sang thus:

Tussa&alaurivunga aqiggimik nuliarpaktumik niaqualungminulli!
(I have heard about a ptarmigan who mated with his head!)

My father was thoroughly embarrassed and immediately said to him, "You of all people heard that?", inferring that the singer was far too deaf to hear anything! Apparently Naujaarakuluk was pretty smart to come up with that song. I think he succeeded in getting his rivals, including my father, very embarrassed over that song. [Piugaattuk 1990, IE-148]

But Piugaattuk's father, it seems, could give as good as he got, as is evident in the following passage. This passage is also significant in that the "hardship of the winter" is repeatedly stressed in a way to emphasize the sense of joy and relief at the approaching spring:

My father had a song aimed at the *Aggiarjuit.* In the winter time they used to experience a period of hardship in the days when hunting equipment was crude. Even with the hardship they had to endure during that period, they always looked to the future for they knew once the period of privation had passed, they would recover when the weather got warmer. When the temperatures were warm enough the seals would start to bask on the ice which was an indication that the time of want was coming to an end. It was at this time that the gathering of food commenced. It was also at this time the *Aggiarjuit* started to arrive, and they would appear to be so full of joy. Once they had arrived they would start to go after each other and mate. After they mated some of them would be so exhausted that they even had difficulty flying away. So my father composed a song reflecting the behaviour of these birds. The song went like this:

When we have survived the worst and the future looks promising,
the Old Squaws now return.
They return, full of joyous spirit. One Old Squaw heard of the joyous spirit,
having heard, he could not resist to join in.
His excesses made his muscles ache.
And while he rested and waited for his sore muscles to recover,
the tips of his wings fell off.
And while he rested and waited for his sore muscles to recover,
his tail feathers fell off.

As the song goes, the Old Squaw tried so hard to join in the fun of mating that he got sore muscles on account of his efforts. And the next thing he discovered was that he could not fly away because his wing tips had fallen off. [Piugaattuk 1990, IE-153]

The competition between *Aggiarjuit* and *Aqiggiit* echoes the competition between the Sun and the Moon mentioned earlier and is often seen as an metaphor for all the opposing and complementary elements of the Inuit world. Marcel Mauss, in his remarkable essay, *Seasonal Variations of the Eskimo,* notes in particular that the outcome of a tug-of-war game between the ducks and the ptarmigan would cause "either summer or winter [to] prevail." Mauss continues:

> This division of people into two great categories appears indeed to be connected with an even greater and more general division that embraces all things. Without even discussing a number of myths in which all animals and important natural events are divided into two groups—one of winter, the other of summer—we can recognize this same idea as the basis of many ritual prohibitions. There are winter things and summer things, and the Eskimo feel the opposition between these two fundamental classes so deeply that to mix them in any way is forbidden. [Mauss 1979:60]

A number of taboos and rituals did indeed have seasonal associations, some specifically involving the Sun. Among these perhaps the most widespread was, as we have seen, the prohibition against playing string figures while the Sun was above the horizon.[31] This restriction obviously could apply only in those regions well above the Arctic Circle which experienced a sunless period in midwinter. In other locations, it seems that the playing of string games was encouraged in the fall so as to "catch the sun in the meshes of the string and so prevent his disappearance" (Boas 1907:151).[32] Boas attributes this information to Captain Comer, the Arctic whaler, who links it specifically to "customs practiced in Iglulik." Comer was either mistaken about the practice itself or, as is more likely, was referring to the southern extremity of the "Igloolik" area, around Repulse Bay for example, where the Sun does not quite disappear at winter solstice. In Igloolik proper, however, all the elders who mentioned the subject agreed that string games were supposed to be played only during the dark period and that a strict taboo against them took effect immediately following the Sun's return. While Noah Piugaattuk does mention that string figures were sometimes played in the fall he believes the intention was not so much to prevent the Sun's disappearance as to speed its rising in the sky once it had returned after the solstice (Piugaattuk 1990, IE-153). So strong was the prohibition against playing string games when

Cup-and-pin game known as *ajagaq*. Bone, depilated skin.
Southern Baffin Island or eastern Hudson Bay, early 20th century.
Royal Ontario Museum. Robert J. Flaherty Collection
presented by Sir William Mackenzie.

(Left) Buzz game. Bone. Inuit. Western Arctic,
early 20th century. Royal Ontario Museum.
(Right) Buzz game. Ivory, sinew. Tarramiut. Cap du Prince-de-Galles,
Quebec, c. 1885. Royal Ontario Museum. Gift of F. F. Payne.

the Sun was back on the horizon, the special strings used for the game were destroyed to prevent their further use. Aipilik Innuksuk hints at the almost obsessive attraction of string games and the constant desire to increase one's repertoire of figures:

> They used to play a lot of string games during the period of *Tauvikjuaq*. I also noticed that when we were living at Akimaniq we used to play a lot of string games during this period. I believe there must have been some other motive than mere amusement for playing string games; there must have been something else to it. Once when I left for a caribou-hunting trip there was a camp further on, so I was told to check if they might have the string game called *Anarulluk*. I was able to bring it back home with me, but now I have forgotten how it is made though I can still picture how it looks. [The figure] has a cane and a pointed hood and the excrement [appears] to drop. I am sure someone still has it here in Igloolik. I have heard that in former times, the people would cut their *Ajaqaat* [string figures] to pieces when the Sun returned. [A. Innuksuk 1990, IE-164]

Michel Kupaaq, on the other hand, allows that string games could be resumed after it was clear that the Sun had managed to leave the horizon and was rapidly gaining in altitude: "Before the sun starts to leave the horizon . . . when it shows only on the horizon, . . . then string games were no longer allowed as they might lacerate the sun. Once the sun had started to go higher and could be seen in its entirety, string games could be resumed, if one so wished. So the restriction on playing string games was only applicable during the period between the sun's return and its rising fully above the horizon" (Kupaaq 1990, IE-153).

Among Iglulingmiut the proscription against playing string figures after the Sun had returned was explained by the notion that the strings would somehow cause lacerations on the legs of those who ignored the taboo. Niviattian Aqatsiaq is clear on this point as well as on the prohibition itself:

> During the dark period when there was no sun they use to play *Ajaqaat*, string games. It was a sort of competition to complete a predetermined figure before the next person did. It was said that when this game is played while the sun is out, those who played it would likely get cuts on

their knees. When we were children [after the Sun came back] we were no longer allowed to play string games. Instead we started to play *Ajagaq* [cup-and-pin], a game made from ivory carved in the shape of a head with holes all over it. As the sun was getting higher they would play *Ajagaq*[33] to pass the time until the temperatures were warm enough for everyone to actively participate in hunting. [Aqatsiaq 1990, IE-149]

This belief was also reflected and confirmed in the mythology where we find the Sun sustaining serious wounds because people had broken the taboo. In the Moon-man legend referred to earlier (see pages 223-25) the plight and suffering of the Sun is described by Zipporah Innuksuk:

In the nearby igloo—the one the woman from Earth had been forbidden to look at—sat a woman wearing an *amauti*. Her leggings were off and revealed many scars and wounds, some healed, others still open. The woman from Earth was wondering how this had happened when, at last, the one with the scarred legs spoke up: "I have received these wounds through suffering." This woman was actually the Sun. During her journeys around the Earth, she received her wounds as a result of people continuing to play string-figure games—*ajagaq*—after the Sun was back on the horizon. [Z. Innuksuk 1990, IE-088]

Some idea of the geographical extent of the out-of-season restrictions against string-figure games, along with some interesting related information about the consequences of disregarding the taboo, is given by Jenness:

From Kotzebue Sound, in Alaska, to Kent Peninsula, at the eastern end of Coronation Gulf, there was a taboo against playing the game except in winter, when the sun no longer rose above the horizon. . . . In Coronation Gulf [the taboo] was observed, though not very rigidly, down to the year 1916. Thus a woman showed me some new figures in the summer of 1915, but remarked that we ought to postpone playing the game until the winter. In the same summer a girl who was showing me some figures carefully closed the door of the tent in order that the sun might not shine in on us; for the

Eskimos of this region base their taboo on a legend that the sun once beheld a man playing cat's cradles and tickled him. In the autumn of 1915 my half-breed interpreter was making some figures before the sun had disappeared, and an old man accused him of causing all the blizzards that were raging at the time. Dr. R. M. Anderson informs me that while some Coppermine River natives were making string figures in his tent during the spring of 1910 a curious noise was heard outside, and the Eskimos immediately laid aside their strings and filed quietly outside. His Alaskan interpreter then told him they thought an evil spirit had come amongst them because they were violating the taboo. [Jenness 1924:181B]

Again for the Coronation Gulf area, Jenness, reflecting something of Mauss's point about the reluctance of Inuit to mix "summer things and winter things" but raising also the dangers of mingling things of the land and things of the sea, mentions a strict taboo "against sewing new deerskin clothing on the ice during the weeks when the sun never rises" (Jenness 1922:188). This practice was also widespread in the Canadian Arctic and both Noah Piugaattuk (Igloolik) and Paatsi Qaggutaq (Pelly Bay) well remember the time when the taboo was observed in their respective regions:

In those days they had to live by the taboos. . . . When the dark period was approaching the people would really concentrate their efforts in making clothing while they were residing on the land. . . . Once they had moved to their camps on the sea-ice no one would dare to make clothing as it was taboo—I mean no one would make any clothing at all at this time. I remember this happening clearly. It was believed that should someone make clothing at this particular time the men that hunted on the sea-ice by *mauliq*[34] would not be able to catch any seals. In the event of the taboo being breached, a shaman, if there was one in the camp, would perform his rituals to set the matter right. The only time women would make clothing while they were camped on the sea-ice was during the period of continuous daylight. That was the way they lived at that time. They believed that if sewing was done while they were out on the sea-ice they would not be able to catch any seals, or that the ice might break up. [Qaggutaq 1991, IE-169]

Noah Piugaattuk, recalling a similar restriction among the Iglulingmiut, gives some additional details about the practice: "It was important that outdoor garments be made before the winter set in; this was usually done in the autumn when the days were getting shorter. The requirement was connected to a taboo. It applied not so much to everyday clothing but to clothing which was to be used when hunting on the moving sea-ice. This clothing had to be completed before the dark period. . . . The practice was governed by a taboo which had to be followed" (Piugaattuk 1990, IE-147).

The Sun's movement, direction, and points of rising and setting appear to have had profound spiritual significance for many Inuit groups. Charles Merbs, examining Thule Inuit culture burial orientation, suggests that the direction in which the body points may relate to the particular "land of the dead" its soul will inhabit: "These spirit lands are not constant with regard to earthly topography, but relate instead to an extraterrestrial object, the sun" (Merbs 1969:8).[35]

In Igloolik this was most evident in rituals surrounding the burial of the dead. W. H. Hooper, an officer with Parry's expedition, witnessed the burial of Pootooalook, the wife of Takkalikkita, in Igloolik on 24 January 1823 and writes: "The frozen earth prevented digging the grave more than a foot deep, in which the body was placed by the husband's desire, on its back with its feet to the Southward, as was the custom for full grown persons. Infants are placed with the feet Eastwards, half-grown persons South-east, those in the decline of life South-west, and the very old people have their feet tend to the Westward"[36] (Hooper 1823:797).

Noah Piugaattuk could not entirely confirm this practice. He recalled, however, that adults tended to be buried with their feet facing "the day," while children were placed with their feet facing the "dawn" (Piugaattuk 1990, IE-148).

The Inuit of Etah, in Northwest Greenland, were also particular about the placement of their dead and followed a similar principle in which the age of the deceased determined the orientation of the body relative to the diurnal progress of the Sun: "Adults were always buried with head towards the east, while children were buried with head to the north" (Whitney 1910:243–44).

Some four days after the burial of Pootooalook, mentioned above, her grave was again visited by Takkalikkita. George Lyon, Parry's second-in-command, witnessed the scene: "[Takkalikkita] now began a conversation, directed entirely to the grave, as if addressing his wife. Twice he called her by name. . . . He next broke forth into a low monotonous chant, and keeping his eyes fixed on the grave, walked slowly round it in the direction of the sun, four or five times, pausing at each circuit for a few moments at the head, his song continuing uninterrupted" (Lyon 1824:383).

The ritual circling of the grave is also mentioned in Rasmussen's account of funeral practices among the Iglulingmiut.[37] The grave is circled once in the direction of the Sun at the time of burial "in order that the dead person may bring good weather," but three times on the anniversary of the death when relatives visit the grave (Rasmussen 1929:198, 201). Among the Polar Eskimos the practice was even more pronounced. Each sunrise and sunset on "the five days following upon the burial [of a relative] . . . they must go up together to the grave, and go once around it in the same direction as that of the sun's circuit of the heavens" (Rasmussen 1908:114). In the Bering Sea area similar rituals were accorded the newly born as well as the dead: "On the third or fifth day after the birth of a child in Western Alaska, the new mother traditionally emerged from confinement, marking her return to social visibility by circling the house, again in the direction of the sun's course. Finally, on the fifth day after a human death, the grave was circled in the direction of the sun's circuit by the bereaved to send away the spirit of the deceased" (Fienup-Riordan 1988:265).

The custom of walking around the outside of the house early each morning in the direction of the Sun is noted by Rasmussen for the Igloolik area. This practice is said to give one long life (Rasmussen 1929:181).[38]

Not surprisingly, invoking the Sun's mystical power through a symbolic tracing of its path also appeared in shamanistic ritual. Piugaattuk describes a ritual performed following the purging of *tupilak,* an evil spirit: "When a *tupilak* was killed by a shaman's *saka*—an incantation—the people, led by the shaman, would go around the extremities of the community, holding the shaman by a rope. This ceremony was known as *nunagiksarttut,* meaning that they were strengthening the land. They ran around the community from the place they had started, going in the direction of the sun. Those who took part in this ceremony appeared to be running a race" (Piugaattuk 1989, IE-052).

The Sun and its movement also figured in shamanistic ritual and apprenticeship as the following account from the Angmagsalik area of Greenland illustrates:

The first thing the *[angakuk]* disciple has to do is to go to a certain lonely spot, an abyss or a cave, and there having taken a small stone, to rub it on the top of a large one the way of the sun. . . . [After] three days on end, they say, a spirit comes out from the rock. It turns its face towards the rising sun and asks what the disciple will. The disciple then dies in the most horrible torments, partly from fear, partly from overstrain; but he comes to life again later in the day. [Holm 1914, *in* Thalbitzer 1914, part 1:88]

The power of the Sun could also be manifest through amulets made from red lichen, which the Angmagsalik Eskimos called the "sun's urine." Amulets of this fungus-alga plant were given to children in order to "cast a light from behind" so that spirits called *inersuaks* "which live under the sea and always have plenty of meat can see them and communicate with them, without their needing to become an Angakut" (Holm 1914, *in* Thalbitzer 1914, part 1:86).

★ ★ ★

SUMMER SOLSTICE

There is no indication that the Iglulingmiut had any formal celebrations around the time of summer solstice. In any event, their summer dispersal into small groups along the shores and islands of the Northern Foxe Basin would have precluded large gatherings.[39] They were aware, of course, that the Sun achieved her maximum altitude above the horizon in the moon month of *Manniit* (the "egg" month, bridging June and July), but no particular significance was attached to this event. For Iglulingmiut, the "height of summer," or the "turning of the year," occurred much later than the summer solstice, in fact around August, and was indicated not by astronomical markers, but by a series of biological ones. These markers, dependent on prevailing climatic conditions, were usually seen in the moon months of *Saggaruut* or *Akullirut*, and included the molting of bumblebees, the appearance of a reddish tinge on the feathers of snow-buntings, and, in particular, the uncoiling of the tasselled seed styles on the *malikkaan* (the "mountain avens"—*Dryas integrifolia*).[40]

The Inuit of Labrador, on the other hand, seemed particularly given to summer festivals, according to F. W. Peacock, a Moravian missionary, who cites early church records to support his claim:

At the Summer Festival of the Sun activities were much more strenuous. On July the 7th in the year 1771 Moravian missionaries in Nain, Labrador made the following entry in the journal: "This afternoon the Eskimos began their heathen Diversions or ceremonies. They began two or three evenings ago during a couple of hours but as the weather had not been favourable they could not go on. But today as the weather was clear they continued their Diversions for seven hours without ceasing. The Diversions had their purposes and mysteries which are too tedious to mention." [Peacock 1981:42]

Plaintively, Peacock adds: "What these Diversions . . . were one can only speculate and regret that the missionaries did not see fit to record practices which could have added valuable knowledge concerning the Summer Festival of the Inuit in former times."

★ ★ ★

Sunspots

Astronomers have determined sunspots to be relatively "cool" areas on the surface of the Sun caused by massive solar magnetic disturbances. They appear as dark patches on the Sun's disk, and, given the right conditions, can be observed with the unaided eye. Chinese dynastic records from the first century BC mention sunspots, and numerous similar "naked eye" observations have been made down to the present time (Mossman 1989:60).

An Arctic environment would seem to provide ideal conditions for such observations. The Sun's lingering, low-angle approach to the horizon, intense refraction, and an atmosphere often permeated with haze or ice-fog, are especially conducive to sunspot viewing. A few Igloolik elders questioned on the subject thought they may have seen dark spots on the Sun, but no conclusive statement was given about these, nor did there seem to be any particular significance attached to them.[41] In the anthropological literature, however, there is mention of sunspots being given an Inuit mythological explanation, and a convincing one at that: they are said to be the scars resulting from the Sun's self-mutilation—from the severing of her breasts when she discovered her Moon-brother's incest (McCrickard 1990:131).

THE MOON—*TAQQIQ*

There is fear in
Feeling the cold
Come to the great world
And seeing the moon
—Now new moon, now full moon—
Follow its own footprints
In the winter night.

(Tatilgak, *in* Rasmussen 1927)

In contrast to the remote and virtually inaccessible Sun, the Moon, in both its secular and spiritual roles, appears close, familiar, and accessible, its influence on human affairs immediate and palpable.[42] The Moon's features, unlike the Sun's, are discernible to the naked eye, permitting at least some knowledge of its qualities. These attributes, together with the Moon's characteristic swiftness and changeability, provide rich material indeed for fertile imaginations. It is no wonder then that the Moon holds a preeminent place in Inuit astronomy.

At the secular level the Moon provides much needed illumination during the dark months of winter, a role periodically enhanced by its tendency, in some years, to remain completely above the horizon for extended periods of time. This phenomenon, known as "the circumpolar moon," is winter's spectacular equivalent of summer's midnight sun.[43] The Moon's influence on weather conditions, on ocean tides and currents, and on the movement of land and sea animals were well understood and used by Inuit; his predictable phases and intervals provided them a basic measure of time.

The phases of the Moon were usually explained with reference to the appropriate passages in the Sister-Sun/Brother-Moon myth (see page 274). A typical example comes from the Bering Sea area, paraphrased by Edward Nelson: "The moon, being without food, wanes slowly away from starvation until it is quite lost from sight; then the sun reaches out and feeds it from the dish in which the girl had placed her breast. After the moon is fed and gradually brought to the full, it is then permitted to starve again, so producing the waxing and waning every month" (Nelson 1899:482).

Interestingly, a non-mythological explanation of the Moon's phases based on perspective was given to Bishop Archibald Fleming during his ministry in the Eastern Arctic: "The moon is a thin round disk of ice which follows the sun and turns about of itself, so that it sometimes looks big and sometimes thin" (Fleming 1928:58).

The Moon's special associations with winter, cold, and snow were also embodied in myth. Nansen, referring particularly to Greenland, writes: "The moon is supposed to be the cause of cold weather.[44] He produces snow by whittling walrus tusks, and strewing the shavings upon earth. . . . It is quite natural that such associations should attach to the moon, since it is in the ascendant during the night and in the winter" (Nansen 1893:278).

Traditionally, the Moon, through the workings of its spirit, was the focus of a large part of Inuit ritualistic and spiritual life. Feared in some areas, particularly in Greenland and the Western Arctic, the Moon-spirit among the Iglulingmiut was generally considered benevolent; Rasmussen, in fact, refers to it as "the only good and well-intentioned spirit known" (Rasmussen 1929:74). Crucial matters, such as the enforcement of taboos, the assurance of human fertility, and above all, the provision of animals for food, fell within the Moon-man's purview. In Igloolik, the Moon's role as provider was symbolized by the attitude of each month's waxing crescent moon: "There is a saying that if the moon appears to be leaning towards its back while growing, Inuit weren't happy about it because it's not carrying animals. But if it appears to be leaning forward, people were happier because they believed it is carrying wildlife" (Akatsiaq 1989:28).

Abused and childless women, as well as the plight of orphan boys, were a particular concern of the Moon-man and a number of legends revolve around these themes. About the Moon-man as a "maintainer of fertility," Rasmussen gives the following account:

When a woman is barren . . . it is the moon that helps her. Sometimes this is done simply by letting the full moon shine on her bare lap, but for the most part, the Moon Man himself goes down to earth driving across the

Land of the Sky with his team of dogs. . . . Thus driving, he comes to the village where the barren woman lives; sometimes he will lie with her there. . . . [But he may carry] her off to the Land of Heaven . . . until she is with child. Any human being who visits the Moon Man must never make a secret of the fact; to keep it secret would mean death. [Rasmussen 1929:75]

The phases of the Moon, in particular those associated with strong tidal activity, were linked to the menstrual cycle in women. George Kappianaq remembers hearing from his parents that "at the times of the full and new Moons the tidal currents are much faster and so it is at these times that woman have their menstrual periods" (Kappianaq 1991, IE-174).

In East Greenland the Moon-spirit could also bestow fertility but usually through the intercession of shamans who frequently visited its realm on a wide range of altruistic errands calculated to benefit their people in one way or another: "Under the category of sickness come also cases in which a man is incapable of hunting seals, or a wife is unable to bear children. In the latter case, the angakut [shaman], supposing he has the power, must make a journey to the moon; whence a child is thrown down to the wife, who afterwards becomes pregnant. After having performed this toilsome journey, the angakuk has the right of sleeping with the wife" (Holm 1914, *in* Thalbitzer 1914, part 1:97).

Among the Iglulingmiut, the Moon-spirit's regulation of animal life, particularly the movement of sea mammals, required the observance of a number of specific rituals to ensure that young or infant boys would become prolific hunters:

At every new moon [the boys] run out to a spot where the snow is clean and free from footmarks. From here they take up a lump of snow, and call up to the moon: "Give me luck in hunting." Then they run into the house and put the snow in a water vessel. The reason for this is that the seals, who live in salt water, are always thirsty.[45] And the snow water thus offered is given by the moon to the seals that are to be captured in the future. On the same principle, their mother must sprinkle water out in the direction of the moon, the first time the baby boy in her amaut sees the moon. [Rasmussen 1929:75–76]

Woman Who Went to the Moon.
Stonecut/Stencil. By Tikitu Qinnuayuak. Cape Dorset, 1989.
Reproduced with the permission of the West Baffin Co-operative Ltd.

★ ★

"Her tattoos stood out clearly."

See page 221.

Woman showing Tattoos. Green stone sculpture. By Dominique Tungilik.
Netsilik Inuit, Gjoa Haven, King William Island, NWT, c. 1980.
Royal Ontario Museum. Gift of Richard C. Martin.

★ ★

*"One will hear a splashing sound . . . made by
the release of all the sea mammals and animals
which Uinigumasuittuq had withheld."*

See page 31.

**Mother of the Sea. Soapstone sculpture. Possibly Aivilingmiut from Repulse Bay,
Melville Peninsula, NWT. c. 1957. Royal Ontario Museum.
Gift of Frances Westman.**

★ ★

"He sends down a snowstorm upon them unawares
when they are out on their sledges, or on the ice at the blowholes,
or in their kayaks, and then he can be heard laughing
through the storm."

See page 180.

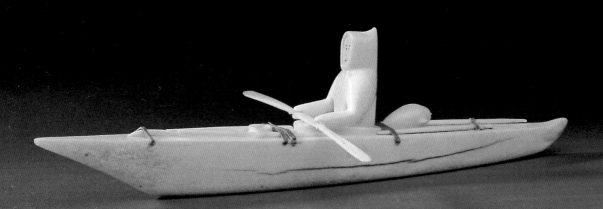

**Kayak. Sculpted ivory and depilated skin. Pangnirtung area,
Baffin Island, NWT, 1933–1942. Royal Ontario Museum.
Dr. Jon A. and Mrs. Muriel Bildfell Collection.
Purchased through the generosity of Mr. Donald Ross.**

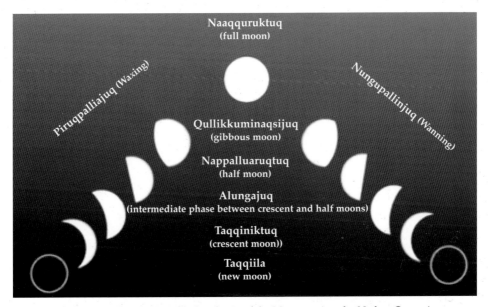

Iglulingmiut designations for the phases of the Moon as given by Nathan Qamaniq (pers. comm., 1998). *"Qullikkuminaqsiq,"* the gibbous phase, likens the shape of the Moon to that of the *qulliq*—a soapstone lamp.

François Quassa of Igloolik remembers practicing this observance as a boy: "When there was a new moon we used to be asked to bring in a small piece of snow. The reason was connected to the fact that one day we would have to hunt, so bringing in snow would help us to catch animals" (Quassa 1990, IE-156).

For the Umingmakturmiut, observances on the new moon had similar overtones: "When boys see the new moon for the first time, they must run in for a scoop of musk-ox horn, put a little water in it, and then throw the water at the moon, at the same time praying for beasts to hunt" (Rasmussen 1932:43).

Among the Inuit of East Greenland, the Moon-man was especially feared where his principal function was the enforcement of taboos and the punishment of those who broke them. More examples of the Moon-spirit's influences, particularly those of a malevolent nature, are included in the following section dealing with eclipses.

★ ★ ★

ECLIPSES

Eclipses of the Sun and Moon, though relatively uncommon, are well known to Igloolik elders. A number have recalled observing them, particularly those of the Sun. The term *pulamajuq* is applied to all eclipses and carries the connotation of being "obscured" or being "covered with a blanket."

Whatever fears, terrors, or catastrophic consequences Inuit traditionally associated with eclipses in earlier times have now, at least for the Iglulingmiut, all but vanished. Niviattian Aqatsiaq had no recollection of people being afraid of eclipses, adding that only recently she had heard warnings on the community radio that eye damage could result from watching one in progress without the proper shades!

Mark Ijjangiaq, however, remembers being terrified as a boy when he witnessed an eclipse of the Sun:

> One afternoon when I was inland with my family for the summer there was an eclipse of Sun. I was nine years old at the time and indeed I was horrified by the experience. It had the same effect as when one is wearing sunglasses. The Sun had the same characteristics as the Moon when it is just coming into its first or last quarter. My mother was still alive at the time. We had a place we drew water from—a small stream, very close to our tent. After the eclipse was over my mother asked me to go and fetch water with a small pail. But I did not want to go for I was afraid that once I went a little distance [from the tent] there might be another eclipse while I was all alone. [Ijjangiaq 1991, IE-184]

Childhood memories of a solar eclipse were also recalled by Michel Kupaaq who once mistook the Sun's darkened disk for the Moon: "That summer I saw the Moon but it turned out to be the Sun in partial eclipse!" Kupaaq goes on to relate how his aged aunt, Ulluriaq, reacted fearfully to an eclipse of the Sun. During the eclipse Ulluriaq is said to have cried out, *"Siqini qiaguuq nunamun irnijattulippuq!"* ("The Sun must be going to Earth to bear her child!") (Kupaaq 1990, IE-166).

Much of the fear and mystery inspired by eclipses was dispelled by visiting explorers, surveyors, or missionaries possessing the means to forecast such phenomena.[46] Noah Piugaattuk vividly recalls witnessing an eclipse of the Sun at Pond Inlet in the company of a geologist who had predicted the event:

> When the eclipse was about to happen he at once got his equipment ready and told us what time the event was going to occur. He was accurate in every way about the eclipse. When he peeked through his telescope it looked as if he was looking at the horizon. . . . He certainly did not aim it at the Sun.[47] As he looked through the telescope he said that the Sun was getting covered, but with our eyes we could detect no difference at all. Soon the Sun started to lose its brightness so we could see that it was getting partially covered. Inuit that were there with him would peek through his telescope which certainly was not aimed at the Sun. My curiosity got the better of me so I peeked through the telescope and there, to my amazement, was the Sun! My curiosity was satisfied. For certain this experience was a turning point. People now realized that an eclipse of the Sun was not something to be feared but a natural phenomenon. [Piugaattuk 1991, IE-181]

Piugaattuk nevertheless allowed that some Inuit who had not seen an eclipse before might be wary of the effects it could have on *Sila* [the weather or atmosphere]. He points out that during a summer eclipse of the Sun, the temperature drops so much "that you can see your breath" and that "afterwards the air temperature seems to get unusually warm"[48] (Piugaattuk 1990, IE-147).

Eclipses, according to Michel Kupaaq, were natural phenomena and had no ill effects on *Sila* except that, following an eclipse, the Moon's remaining phases were said to speed up and so deprive travellers of their full quota of moonlight: "When an eclipse of the Moon occurred they knew that the Moon was going to complete its cycle sooner than normal. In those days, when snow machines were not used, moonlight was important to travellers. After an eclipse they used to say that . . . the Moon would immediately move into its last quarter" (Kupaaq 1990, IE-166).

In earlier times eclipses were not looked upon so rationally. Lyon's account of an eclipse of the Sun at Winter Island on 21 February 1822, "during which the diminution of light was very considerable,"[49] shows that Inuit of that period regarded the phenomenon with alarm if not terror:

An eclipse of the sun took place in the afternoon, while a number of Eskimaux were on board. They appeared much alarmed, and with one accord hurried out of the ship. Before they were all on the ice a brisk squall came on, and added not a little to their terrors. Okotook ran wildly about under the stern, gesticulating and screaming at the sun, while others gazed on it in silence and dread. The corporal of the marines found two of the natives lying prostrate with their faces to the ice quite panicstruck. We learned that the eclipse was called *shiek-e-nek* (the sun) *toonilik-pa.* [Lyon 1824:151–52].

In the evening of the day of the eclipse, Lyon was given a "long story" about the event by Ayokitt, one of the Inuit visiting his ship. Ayokitt was sure that Okotook's actions had frightened away the eclipse and that all the Inuit were terrified except Ayokitt himself "[who] seeing we were not frightened . . . was very brave, and laughed, disdaining to fall on his face, and say *ya-whooi*" (Lyon 1824:153).

In Greenland, beliefs and rituals attached to both solar and lunar eclipses were unusually elaborate: "At an eclipse of the sun the women pinch the dogs by the ears; if they cry, 'tis a sure sign that the end of the world is not yet come; for as the dogs existed before men, therefore according to Greenland logic, they must have a quicker sensation of future things. But should they not cry (which however the poor dogs always do) then the dissolution of all things is at hand" (Cranz 1767, I:233).

Lunar eclipses, it seems, were particularly feared: "An eclipse of the moon is called 'pudlasson' ('glide in,' 'visit'); . . . and the moon is said to have gone to defecate. An eclipse is considered bad, and feared, though for no definite reason" (Cranz 1767, I:259).

For East Greenland, Graah adds the following: "When an eclipse of the Moon takes place, they attribute it to the Moon's going into their houses, and peeping into every nook and corner in search of skins and eatables, and on such occasions accordingly, they conceal all they can, and make as much noise as possible, in order to frighten away their unbidden guest" (Graah 1837:124).

In order to avert or reduce the phenomenon's expected ill effects, eclipses of both Sun and Moon often required specific actions to be taken, or taboos to be observed, on the part of those experiencing them: "He [the Moon] rejoices when the women die, and the sun in her revenge has her joy in the death of men; therefore the men keep within doors at the eclipse of the sun, and the women at the eclipse of the moon" (Cranz 1767, I:232).

In East Greenland an eclipse of the Sun required that "all drinking water . . . be covered up" (Ostermann 1938:195), while during an eclipse of the Moon "women who are with child should creep under the platform skin in order that the children may be healthy"[50] (Holm 1914, *in* Thalbitzer 1914, part 1:105).

The notion that eclipses were one of the main causes of epidemic disease (as well as a presage of war) seems to have been well developed among the Inuit of the Bering Sea area. The rationale of the practice of shielding one's person or covering up utensils against the effects of the eclipse, mentioned in a number of the foregoing passages, is made clearer in the following statement from Nelson:

> An eclipse of the moon is said to foretell an epidemic, and the shamans immediately proceed to learn the cause in order to appease the being living there and, by diverting his anger, save the people. Among the inhabitants of the lower Yukon it is believed that a subtle essence or unclean influence descends to the earth during an eclipse, and if any of it is caught in utensils of any kind it will produce sickness. As a result, immediately on the commencement of an eclipse, every woman turns bottom side up all her pots, wooden buckets, and dishes. . . . The length of duration of an eclipse is said to indicate the severity of the visitation to follow. [Nelson 1899:431]

Nelson also gives a specific and enlightening account of an epidemic directly attributed to an eclipse of the Moon and of the efforts of two shamans to halt the ensuing sickness:

> One winter on the lower Yukon, about the middle of February, there was an eclipse of the moon, and soon after throat disease caused the death of about a dozen people. Two shamans, father and son, started to visit the man in the moon to find out why the disease had been sent and to learn how to stop it. . . . [On returning they] reported that when they had climbed nearly to the moon the old man became tired and stopped for a while, but the young man went on. When he was near the moon the man came down to meet him and was very angry, asking what he wanted there; the young man was very much frightened, but told the reason for his approach. He was then told that the disease would kill several other people before it would stop. [Nelson 1899:430]

Inuit of Coronation Gulf also held beliefs about the dangers of eclipses and similarly relied on the services of their shamans to stave off the phenomenon's ill effects. When the Sun's face "is covered with black at eclipses, *siriapaluk*, . . . the Eskimos know it is trying to kill people and the shamans have to wipe away the black" (Jenness 1922:179).

A few explanations are offered to account for eclipses, all deriving from the manner in which the Sun and the Moon are personified in Inuit mythology. One, as we have seen, explains that the Moon has "gone to defecate" (Cranz 1767, I:259), another that the Sun has "died and come to life again" (Nelson 1899:431), or that she has come to Earth to bear a child (Kupaaq 1990, IE-166). Among the Nunamiut of Alaska an eclipse of the Moon indicates that the *"tatqimiñua"*—the moon spirit –is ashamed (presumably because of his treatment of his sister, the Sun) and wants to visit the Earth (Gubser 1965:194). Lastly, a more poetic explanation has the brother and sister continuing their pursuit of each other across the sky: "The boy has pursued her ever since, becoming the sun, and sometimes overtakes and embraces her, thus causing an eclipse of the moon"[51] (Nelson 1899:281).

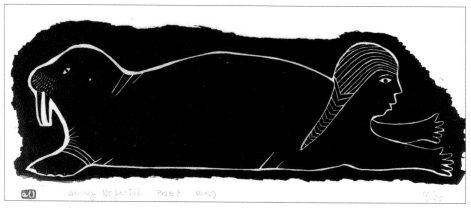

Untitled print. Stonecut. By Henry Napartuk. Itivimiut. Kuujjuaraapik, Quebec, 1963.
Royal Ontario Museum.

★ 140 ★

CHAPTER 5
The Atmosphere

For us true Inuit it was like this.
We were told always to observe the atmosphere
and be alert.

(Eli Amaaq, 1989)

★ ★ ★

METEORS AND SHOOTING-STARS

A meteor is the flash or streak of light emitted by a meteoroid (usually a particle of rocky material) from outer space as it enters the Earth's atmosphere. Fragments of meteoroids which survive the fiery passage through our atmosphere and reach the surface of the Earth are termed meteorites.

Numerous meteors can be observed from virtually any geographic location, given a clear, dark night. Parry (1824:386) mentions an especially bright meteor seen by one of his officers in Igloolik on 19 December 1822 which "in size and brilliancy . . . resembled the planet Jupiter." Meteors large and small are well known to Inuit all across the Arctic and have a place in their folklore and mythology.

In Igloolik, as in many other Inuit areas, the term most used to designate meteors or "shooting-stars" is *ulluriat anangit*, "star feces." Some of the Igloolik elders maintained that this is a child's name for the phenomenon and that the proper term is *ingnirujait*, "bearing fire or sparks."[1] Others thought *ulluriat anangit* described ordinary "shooting-stars" while *ingnirujait*[2] was reserved for unusually large, bright meteors of the kind referred to in English as "fireballs." In the following passage, George Kappianaq explains these various phenomena, interestingly including his beliefs about meteorites:

> It is called *ingnirujaq* because it is brighter than fire, brighter than the flame of a *qulliq* [a soapstone lamp]. It is said that the *ignirujaq* falls from the heavens with such tremendous speed that it is ignited. As children we used to say *ulluriaq ana&appuq* ("a star has defecated") but adults would say *ingnirujaq*. Big ones are capable of lighting up the surrounding ground. Sometimes they will actually fall to the ground where one can recognize them by the characteristics of the stone. They are called *tuqituralaattut*. They contain shiny gold-coloured particles similar to that found in soapstone. These particles will not themselves break even when the stone is broken. So that is why they are called *tuqitut* as they can last for a long time. [Kappianaq 1990, IE-155]

Hubert Amarualik adds:

> I have seen meteors from the time of my childhood. . . . I know that Inuit used to call them star droppings, so one would say that "a star had defecated." Once they get close to the ground they will disappear. But sometimes they will make contact with the earth and you can see them on the ground with the surrounding areas covered with mud or dirt. I have seen a few of these at Maluksittan. . . . When they make contact [with the ground] some will splatter into small pieces and dust will form. You can hear them when they hit the ground. Sparks will fly around. When you get to [the place of impact] you will notice the surrounding area looks like mud. I have seen them hitting the snow in the winter time. [Amarualik 1992, IE-212]

The distinction between "shooting-stars" and meteors appears to have been made in other areas as well. For the Inuit of Coronation Gulf, according to Jenness and later confirmed by Rasmussen (1932:24), "falling stars are *annak* (feces) of the larger ones, but bright meteors are called fire, *ignik*" (Jenness 1922:179). Around Point Barrow, Ray has recorded that the term for meteor is *"u.glu.ri.a a.nuk.tu.a"* (star feces) but elsewhere mentions that the Inuit "believe that the pyrites [which they use to start fires] come down from heaven in the form of meteors and they call it fire-stone for that reason" (Ray 1885:46, 55). Although Ray does not record the Inuit term for "fire-stone" it is clear that a distinction is being made between meteors on the basis of their relative brightness.

In the Bering Strait region meteors are again referred to as "star feces," *agyam anaa,* a Yup'ik term also used for the puffball mushroom (*Lycoperdon* sp.), which meteors are said to turn into when they land on Earth (Jacobson 1984:48). Nelson merely mentions that "shooting-stars are termed star dung" (Nelson 1899:449), while Simpson, from the same region, records that they are "portions thrown off by the fixed [stars]" (Simpson 1875:271).

From the area around Repulse Bay, NWT, the explorer John Rae links stars, meteors, and the aurora to Inuit conceptions about the afterlife: "The stars are supposed to be spirits of the dead Esquimaux that have fixed themselves in the heavens, and falling stars or meteors, and the aurora borealis, are those spirits moving from one place to another whilst visiting their friends"[3] (Rae 1850:80).

This view, however, is not representative of the attributes usually given to meteors and shooting-stars in Canada's Eastern Arctic. Rae may well have incorporated here a Greenlandic tradition about shooting-stars noted by Cranz: "They have discovered the shooting-stars to be souls, that have a mind to take a tour once from heaven to hell on a visit" (Cranz 1767, I:230). Another Greenlandic tradition about shooting-stars is mentioned for the Egedesminde area by Birket-Smith. On seeing a shooting star a woman should call out: "*Pilagagsara* (those, whom I am going to flense). This is in order to get a seal soon" (Birket-Smith 1924:437).

The wider and more accepted tradition which considers shooting-stars to be "star feces" is explained in a version of the *Ululijarnaat* legend given by Zipporah Innuksuk (see pages 223–25). At one point in the story, the Moon-man, *Taqqiq,* removes a scapula from the floor of his house which has been covering up a small peephole. Through this hole the Earth and its people can be seen: "Then *Taqqiq* said, 'listen to this.' He spat down upon the Earth, and the people below became excited and began to shout, '*Ulluriaq anarpuuq! Ulluriaq anarpuuq!*'—'The stars are shitting! The stars are shitting!'" (Z. Innuksuk 1990, IE-088).

Large meteors could bestow remarkable powers and abilities on the humans with whom they came in contact. Indeed, to be "struck" by a meteor seems the absolute metaphor for the mediating relationship between the shaman and the cosmos. An *ingnirujaq,* a meteor of "fire-ball" proportions, is the subject of a story from the Igloolik area collected by Rasmussen around 1923. Here, a woman named Uvavnuk, mother of the shaman Niviatsian, was physically entered by a meteor and thereafter became a shaman with considerable powers "when the spirit of the meteor lit up the spirit light within her." Niviatsian, we are told, was able to inherit from his mother some of her exceptional shamanistic prowess (Rasmussen 1929:122–23).

Coincidentally, other visitations from the sky could bestow similar powers. Among the Umingakturmiut of the Bathurst Inlet area, a legendary "sky-lemming" fell on the back of the shaman Ilatsiaq, thus making him "a very great shaman" (Rasmussen 1932:23). Apparently shamans were virtual lightning conductors for all manifest spirits of the air. These spirits, according to Rasmussen

> saw the shamans in the form of shining bodies that attracted and drew them and made them wish to go and live in them and give them their own strength, sight and knowledge. When such a spirit beset a shaman, it went in by the navel and found a place in the breast cavity, whence it inspired him. Compared with the shining shamans ordinary people are like houses with extinguished lamps: they are dark inside and do not attract the attention of the spirits. [Rasmussen 1932:28]

George Kappianaq believes that the legendary *Arnaktatuq* was conceived by an *ingnirujaq* and thus was given the power to be repeatedly reincarnated over time as a different kind of animal each time, and so learned the secrets and taboo requirements of each species (Kappianaq 1990, IE-155).

In Alaska, the ability of shamans to transform themselves into balls of fire and fly about the sky was especially feared. These flights were usually observed "in autumn, during the first dark nights, and one could see fire-ball after fire-ball rushing through the sky; 'now that we are Christians, we never see them'" (Ostermann 1952:131).

The well-known iron meteorites at Savissivik, near Cape York in Northwest Greenland, have naturally found their way into local traditions. The celestial origin of these meteorites was explained to the explorer Robert Peary. According to his account, they were "originally an Innuit woman and her dog and tent hurled from the sky by Tornarsuk [the Evil Spirit]" (Peary 1898, II:559). The meteorite known as the "woman" was an important source (Peary says the only source) of blade iron for the Polar Eskimos prior to the time of European contact. Supernatural powers were attributed to this "woman" after Inuit tried to transport a portion of her (the head) back to their camps north of Cape York. In the failed attempt, the Inuit involved were dramatically reminded of their society's strict sanctions against greed and the excessive accumulation of property: "The sea ice suddenly broke up with a loud noise, and the head disappeared beneath the water, dragging down with it the sledge and the dogs. The Eskimos themselves narrowly escaped with their lives, and since that time no attempt has been made to carry away any but the smallest fragments of the heavenly woman" (Peary 1898, II:561).

That is until 1895 when Peary, without incident, carried away the "woman" and the "dog." But the removal of the largest "iron," the "tent" meteorite, in 1897 proved a challenge which Peary barely met. The meteorite's seeming intransigence gave rise to superstitious dejection among Peary's crew:

> Under the circumstances I could certainly almost forgive their associating supernatural agencies with the meteorite, and it was a strange but actual and unexaggerated fact that, as the great mass crept slowly over the bridge and across the ship's rail, patches of blue sky appeared overhead; and when at last it rested safely over the main hatch, the last tie which bound it to the land completely severed, the horizontal rays of the low mid-night sun burst past the cliffs of Signal Mountain, fell upon the meteorite, changing it into molten bronze. . . . It was as if the demon of the "Saviksoah" ["great iron"] had fought a losing fight, accepted the result, and yielded gracefully. [Peary 1898, II:586–87]

In fact, the "demon" meteorite had more in store for Peary. On his voyage south the mass of meteoric iron played havoc with the ship's compasses, forcing Peary to make a longer and more dangerous voyage along the coast. His ship eventually reached Sydney, Nova Scotia, "burning her last ton of coal." (Peary 1898, II:594).

Unusual powers are similarly attributed to a large black rock in the Point Barrow area, thought by Inuit to be of meteoric origin. Rochfort Maguire's journal (Bockstoce 1988:541) gives the following account:

> Among the few remarkable features of this dreary coast is a large stone, about four sleeps from Point Barrow, near Point Tangent. . . . The natives assert it is a "fire stone," and fell from the sky within the memory of people now living. No one saw it fall; but one woman, about sixty years of age, said she travelled that way yearly as a girl, when there was no such stone there, and that in returning one summer, her people were much surprised to see it, and believed it had fallen from the sky. . . . It is said to enlarge and present a full rounded appearance at times, where deer are plentiful in the neighbourhood, as it feeds upon them, killing and devouring a great many at a time.

★ ★ ★

Aurora Borealis—*Aqsarniit*

Conventional physics explains that the aurora is caused by the glow of molecular gases in the atmosphere which have become "excited" by proton and electron particles from the Sun carried into the ionosphere by solar wind. The interaction of these charged particles with different gases causes the emission of a variety of coloured light: greenish-white or red light coming from atomic oxygen, crimson or purple light from molecular nitrogen.

The aurora borealis occurs most frequently in a broad belt known as the "auroral oval" some 500 to 1000 km wide centred approximately on the magnetic North Pole. The mid-section of the auroral belt in the Canadian north runs approximately along the sixtieth parallel. Atmospheric scientists have found a link between the intensity of auroral displays and "sun spots," and so, at times of intense solar activity, the northern lights can be seen well beyond their normal range.

More than any other atmospheric phenomenon the aurora borealis seems to have captured the rapturous attention of early European and American visitors to the Arctic regions. Their most extravagant literary efforts were frequently directed towards attempts to depict the aurora and, as a result, their journals are strewn with gems attesting to this effort. The following passages, extracted from some of these journals, convey useful descriptions of the variety of auroral display typically observed in the Igloolik region and, as such, put the discussion of the phenomenon in some context.

The first excerpt is from Winter Island, slightly below the Arctic Circle and just within the auroral oval; the second is from Igloolik itself situated on the northern edge of the oval, where typically, auroral displays are less frequent and lack some of the intensity and colourfulness of those slightly more to the south:

During the most splendid part of [the aurora's] continuance, it is, I believe, almost impossible to convey to the minds of others an adequate conception of the truth. It is with much diffidence, therefore, that I offer the following description. . . . Innumerable streams [or] bands of white or yellowish light appeared to occupy the greater part of the heavens to the southward of the zenith, being much the brightest in the S.E. and E.S.E., from whence it had indeed often the appearance of emanating. Some of these streams of light were in right lines like rays, others crooked and waving in all sorts of irregular figures and moving with inconceivable rapidity in various directions. Among these might frequently be observed those shorter collections or bundles of rays, which, moving with even greater velocity than the rest, have acquired the name of the "merry dancers," which, if I understand aright the descriptions given them by others, I do not think I ever saw before. . . . The colour of the light was most frequently yellowish-white, sometimes greenish, and once or twice a lilac tinge was remarked, when several strata, as it were, appeared to overlay each other, by very rapidly meeting, in which case the light was always increased in intensity. . . . The intensity of the light was something greater than that of the moon in her quarters. Of its dimming the stars there cannot, I think, be a doubt. [Parry 1824:143]

The "white light" referred to in the next passage is typical of auroral coloration at the latitude of Igloolik. It is also at times tinged with light greenish hues:

The appearances of the Aurora Borealis were neither frequent or brilliant during this month [November, 1822]. On the 7th near midnight this phenomenon appeared from the E.S.E. to S.W., forming an irregular arch of white light—about eight degrees high in the centre. From the upper margin of this arch, coruscations now and then shot upwards from the zenith. On the morning of the 21st, Mr. Ross remarked a bright arch of Aurora passing through the zenith from east to west, and meeting the horizon at each end. An arch of the same kind appeared at night in the south-west quarter of the heavens. [Parry 1824:381]

An observation by John Rae clearly draws the distinction in quality between auroral displays that occur within the "auroral oval" and those at its margins:

As the aurora was seldom noticed after this date [3 April 1847], I may here make a few remarks on this subject. It was often visible during the winter, and usually made its appearance first to the southward in the form of a faint yellow or straw-coloured arch, which gradually rose up towards the zenith. During our stay at Fort Hope [Repulse Bay, NWT] I never witnessed a finer display of this strange phenomenon than I had done at York Factory, nor did it on any occasion affect the horizontal needle as I had seen it do during the previous winter there. [Rae 1850:96]

One final, particularly inspired, passage comes from a journal of Charles Francis Hall and describes an experience in the Repluse Bay area. Of special interest here is the novel method Hall uses to satisfy himself about the auroral display's proximity to the ground:

At length patches of aurora burst forth here and there. Gradually the main arch reached the zenith, and then was the grand part of the scene. Much of what was before in perpendicular rays shot athwart and across the heavens swiftly like a river of molten gold, here and there forming vast whirlpools, here and there an eddy, here and there a cataract of stupendous fall. When above my head, it seemed less than a pistol-shot distant. Indeed it was near by. When I moved quickly, running up to the top of the hill by the igloo, making a distance of less than 50 fathoms, the arch of the aurora, that seemed stationary while I was by the igloo and in transit, was now several degrees to the southwest of me. I returned as quickly to the igloo, and the auroral belt was directly overhead. So small a base, with so palpable a change in the bearing of the aurora, proved that it must have been quite close to the earth. A ball of fire fell during the display, and burst just before it reached the earth, throwing out prismatic scintillations in every direction. [Nourse 1879:83]

Across the Arctic, from the Bering Strait to East Greenland, Inuit tradition relating to the aurora borealis is remarkably consistent, the phenomenon being usually characterized as spirits of the dead playing a game of football, usually with a walrus skull for a ball.[4] Other characteristics more or less universally attributed to them by Inuit are that the aurora make audible sounds when active and that they can be made to approach closer by whistling.

The aurora are known to Inuit throughout the Eastern Arctic as *aqsarniit*— "football players." In their interviews, a number of Igloolik elders spoke about the phenomenon. A fairly typical description is given by Mark Ijjangiaq:

In the past the *aqsarniit* seemed to be more frequent than they are now, probably because there was less outside lighting then. I have heard that they used a walrus head for a football, and one can see the football players moving around. I have not heard what the *aqsarniit* are made of but you can hear the swishing sound they make. If they get too close you can chase them away by twisting your tongue to the upright position. We used to do this when the *aqsarniit* got too close and it always had an effect. When one was watching them you could see them getting closer and closer until one could hear the swishing sound. At the same time they would be moving sideways also making this sound. [Ijjangiaq 1990, IE-081]

Catherine Arnatsiaq recalls the terror she felt about the aurora as a youngster:

When we were children . . . I used to see different coloured *aqsarniit*— some were bright pink in colour. I had heard it said that the *aqsarniit* cut

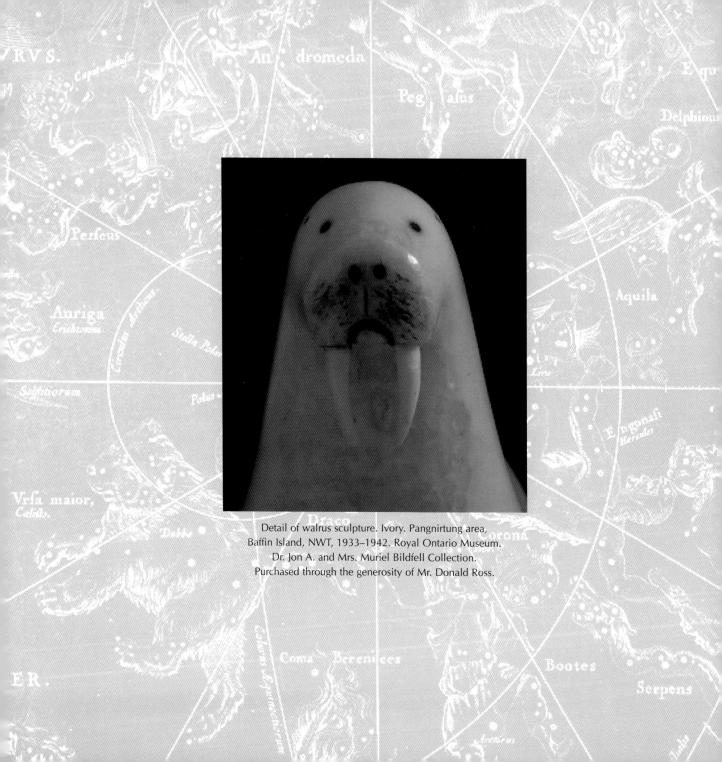

Detail of walrus sculpture. Ivory. Pangnirtung area,
Baffin Island, NWT, 1933–1942. Royal Ontario Museum.
Dr. Jon A. and Mrs. Muriel Bildfell Collection.
Purchased through the generosity of Mr. Donald Ross.

peoples' heads off. I tended to believe this because I was also aware of the saying that the *aqsarniit* used walrus heads for footballs, and so I was scared of them! I think it has something to do with the speed they go at: if they touch your head then it will be cut off. Although I never heard of anyone losing their head because of the *aqsarniit*, they still feel frightening. The other thing was that when we whistled at them they would make swishing sounds and would pick up speed. Seeing this made me really terrified thinking that they would indeed cut off my head. Of course that was a child's way of thinking about them.

It was at Avvajjaq, when we used to play outside a lot, dressed in our caribou-skin clothing. We would play the game *amaruujaq*[5] for hours. When the *aqsarniit* appeared we would whistle at them and they would increase in speed and colour. [Arnatsiaq 1990, IE-077]

Niviattian Aqatsiaq talks about the aurora's relationship to the spirit world and the manner in which the spirits played football with a walrus head.

I have heard something about northern lights. My natural mother had a father-in-law who survived a murder attempt against him; they were trying to kill him but he escaped. His wife bore many children but died giving birth by loss of blood. On account of this at her death she was covered with blood. She was then buried without breeches but was clothed in brand new *atigi* [a caribou-skin parka]. As the years passed he would perform a shamanistic ritual in order to visit his wife amongst the dwellers of *aqsarniit*.

Here, in the *aqsarniit*, they play football with a walrus skull. The way they play is this: they kick a head of a walrus in such a manner that when it falls the head will always turn to face the kicker and sink its tusks into the ground. The *aqsarniit* are in the area below the heavens. The woman who died through loss of blood was amongst these. She had been placed amongst the northern lights because she had died without having been sick or because the cause of death was not through illness; she died only from a loss of blood. One must also bear in mind that when walruses are hunted they are bled.[6] The woman had died from the loss of blood so that is also why she had been placed with them. She never had her breeches on even though she was a woman, but she had on a new parka when her

husband visited her among the *aqsarniit*. He afterwards told his descen-
dants (as women will continue to bear children) that should one of them
happen to die from the loss of blood during childbirth they should
always make sure to put breeches on the deceased, as women look pitiful
without their breeches.

When we would play outdoors we would whistle at the northern
lights to make them come closer. They would make a swishing sound. I
don't know what they may be; perhaps they once were alive amongst the
living. [Aqatsiaq 1990, IE-079]

Intensive and active auroral displays can be truly awe-inspiring and it is little wonder that the fear of them was universal across the Arctic. As we have seen
from the accounts of the Igloolik elders, it was believed that the *aqsarniit* could be
extremely dangerous if enticed close to the ground by whistling. Children, with
their talent for daring, were often cautioned about the consequences of teasing the
aqsarniit. George Kappianaq recalls:

We were forbidden to make fun of the *aqsarniit*. We were told that we
should never whistle at them to make them closer because there was a
possibility that they might take us up to the skies, which they are capable
of when they get too close to the ground. When they came close we
would [drive them off] with sounds made by rubbing our finger nails
together. By doing so the *aqsarniit* would go higher up in the sky. I per-
sonally took on this habit and found it effective. [Kappianaq 1990, IE-267]

Joe Tasiuq, whose younger years were spent in the Pelly Bay area of the
Northwest Territories, used a more dramatic method of warding off the *aqsarniit* but
again relying on the generation of a particular sound. Returning to their camp from
a midwinter trading visit to Igloolik, Tasiuq and his wife found themselves in the
midst of a particularly dynamic auroral display: "[The *aqsarniit*] came closer and
closer and at the same time they started to make a whistling sound. As they moved
. . . they came very close to the ground. I had heard that if you lash a whip the *aqsarniit* will back off, but you have to be sure to use the whip in such a way that it makes
a whizzing sound. . . . So I used the whip accordingly and the *aqsarniit* returned to
the location where they first made their appearance" (Tasiuq 1990, IE-267).

For the inhabitants of Point Barrow, Alaska, where the aurora was similarly feared, wielding a knife served much the same purpose as Tasiuq's whip: "They dislike to go out on a dark night, but if obliged to, they generally carry a bone or ivory snow-knife or a long-bladed steel knife, to keep off Tuna [a powerful spirit] and Kiolya (aurora),[7] which they believe to be equally evil" (Ray 1885:42).

Rasmussen's account of Iglulingmiut traditions about the aurora places the *aqsarniit* among the "Udlormiut"—"the Land of the People of the Day"—to which those "dying by violence or by their own hand" go after death. This "Land of the Day," according to Rasmussen, is the preferred dwelling place of the dead "where the pleasures appear to be without limit." Rasmussen's account also includes a traditional explanation of auroral sound:

> Here, they are constantly playing ball, the Eskimos' favourite game, laughing and singing, and the ball they play with is the skull of a walrus. The object is to kick the skull in such a manner that it always falls with the tusks downwards, and thus sticks fast in the ground. It is this ball game of the departed souls that appears as the aurora borealis, and is heard as a whistling, rustling, cracking sound. The noise is made by the souls as they run across the frost-hardened snow of heavens.[8] If one happens to be out alone at night when the aurora borealis is visible, and hears the whistling sound, one only has to whistle in return and the lights will come nearer. [Rasmussen 1929:94–95]

One explanation of the cause of auroral illumination as well as another one for the origin of auroral sound is reported from Labrador by Ernest Hawkes, whose account of the aurora's connection with the spirit world closely matches that of the Iglulingmiut:

> Only the spirits of those who have died a voluntary or violent death, and the raven, have been over this pathway. The spirits who live there light torches to guide the feet of new arrivals. This is the light of the aurora. They can be seen there feasting and playing football with a walrus skull.
> The whistling, cracking noise which sometimes accompanies the aurora is the voices of these spirits trying to communicate with the people of the earth. They should always be answered in a whispering voice.

Youths and small boys dance to the aurora. The heavenly spirits are called *selamiut*, "sky-dwellers," those who live in the sky. [Hawkes 1916:153]

Nelson accounts for the aurora in much the same way for the Bering Strait area but, more typically, has the auroral curtain represent the football players: "The aurora is believed to be a group of boys playing football, sometimes using a walrus skull as a ball. The swaying movement of the lights back and forth represents the struggles of the players. When the light fades away the Eskimo utter a low whistle, which they say will call the boys back" (Nelson 1899:449).

In West Greenland we find similar traditions about the aurora. They are, on Cranz's account, "the souls of the dead striking at a dance or a foot-ball" (Cranz 1767, I:233). Rink, who offers a less favourable view of the auroral spirit land than does Rasmussen, has this to add: "Those who go to the upper world will suffer from cold and famine; and these are called the *arssartut*, or ball-players, on account of their playing at ball with a walrus-head, which gives rise to the aurora borealis, or Northern lights" (Rink 1875:37).

In East Greenland, however, the region of the northern lights appears to be exclusively reserved for deceased children. Football is still played, but with a walrus placenta rather than a walrus skull. In the following account from Holm, the typical movements of the auroral display are explained in terms of children actively playing games:

Children who are put to death and still-born children "go to heaven, where they cause the northern lights." The children take each other by the hand and dance round and round and swing in mazes; now they wind around each other at one end of the ring until they form a spiral, and now untwine again. They play ball with their after-births, and when they see orphans they run towards them and knock them down. They accompany the games with a shrill whistling sound.

The native narrator accompanied this description with lively gestures, giving a vivid picture of the northern lights as the games of children. The first game is seen when the northern lights appear as broad streamers or draperies, in which the single rays point to the zenith and are continually in wavy or maze-like motion. The ball game is seen when single rays from the streamers shoot out at a great speed towards the zenith. The children may be seen running towards the orphans and knocking them over, when single rays swiftly dart out in a horizontal direction, and, as it were, chase away the rays already present. The northern lights are called according to the children, *Alugsukat*. [Holm 1911, *in* Thabitzer 1914, part 1:82]

Drum Dancers' Dream. Stonecut print. By Gyta Eeseemailee.
Pangnirtung, Baffin Island, NWT, 1976. Royal Ontario Museum.
Gift of Richard C. Martin.

For Inuit everywhere the two basic physical properties of the aurora, in addition to its luminosity and movement, are the sounds it makes when active, and the fact that its display can occur close to the ground, if not actually at ground level. While most atmospheric scientists reject these opinions, typically dismissing anecdotal reports of auroral sound as "ice cracking on lakes," and low-level occurrences of aurorae as optical illusions, it is noteworthy to find that a number of European and American explorers, on the basis of their experience with the aurora, shared the Inuit view on these points.[9] The following passages from various expedition journals vividly illustrate, if nothing else, the sense of acute physical proximity to the aurora felt by these observers:

> While Lieutenants Sherer and Ross, and myself, were admiring the extreme beauty of this phenomenon from the observatory, we all simultaneously uttered an exclamation of surprise at seeing a bright ray of the Aurora shoot suddenly downward from the general mass of light, and *between us and the land* [Parry's emphasis], which was there distant only three thousand yards. Had I witnessed this phenomenon by myself, I should have been disposed to receive with caution the evidence even of my own senses, as to this last fact; but the appearance conveying precisely the same idea to three individuals at once, all intently engaged in looking towards the spot, I have no doubt that the ray of light actually passed within that distance of us. [Parry 1835, III:172–73]

> Captain Back (N. Am., 1820) observed an aurora moving within 2 feet of the ground and parallel to it, attended with a rustling noise continuing for five minutes. No other Arctic observer has been satisfied that any sound proceeded from the Aurora. [Collinson 1889:366]

> Hall found himself unable to decide whether any noise actually proceeded from the aurora. On questioning the Innuits as to whether they were accustomed to hear noises during its display they answered "Yes"; one of them endeavoring to imitate the sound by a puffing noise from his mouth, which noise, Hall says, did remarkably accord with that which he thought he had heard himself during the time of the most active displays. [Nourse 1879:84]

Lieutenant Hooper, R.N. . . . spent the winter of 1849–50 near Fort Franklin, on Bear Lake. He wrote in his journal: "I have heard the aurora, not once, but many times; not faintly and indistinctly, but loudly and unmistakably. . . . At first it seemed to resemble the sound of field-ice, then it was like the sound of a water-mill, and, at last, like the whirring of a cannon-shot heard from a short distance.[10] [Nourse 1879:84n.]

It might also be pointed out that inhabitants of other northern regions, including John Rae's countrymen, commonly attributed sound to the aurora: "The Esquimaux, like the Indians, assert that the aurora produces a distinctly audible sound, and the generality of Orkneymen and Zetlanders maintain the same opinion, although for my own part I cannot say that I ever heard any sound from it" (Rae 1850:96).

For some Inuit the relative intensity and activity of auroral display was indicative of the kind of weather to follow. In West Greenland, for instance, when the aurora "seem still and motionless, mild weather follows, and when they look red and the streams move vehemently, stormy weather out of the south ensues" (Cranz 1767, I:49). Isapee Qanguq, of Pond Inlet, NWT, who remembers his elders telling him that foul weather is to be expected after auroral displays, would doubtless agree with these ancient forecasts of his Greenlandic cousins (Qanguq 1990, IE-266). It is interesting that atmospheric scientists are now beginning to accept as "reasonable" the notion "that auroral phenomena might have some triggering effect on storm development" (Davis 1994:180).

* * *

HALO PHENOMENA

A variety of atmospheric phenomena caused by the refraction of light through airborne ice-crystals are common in Arctic regions. Known collectively as "halo phenomena," the most frequently observed of these are the Sun's parhelia. Parhelia, popularly called "mock suns" or "sundogs," appear as two bright spots, or bars, seen on opposite sides of the Sun, each on the perimeter of the solar halo, level with the Sun's altitude. Prismatically coloured, parhelia typically occur at an angular distance of approximately 22° from the Sun.[11] Similar phenomena involving the Moon are called paraselenae.

Haloes, along with mock suns and moons, are, of course, well known to Inuit who have incorporated them into their mythology and weather lore. All manifestations of these phenomena are usually said to be harbingers of stormy weather.

In Igloolik, there are two Inuktitut names for the full halo. The first, *avaluarutaq,* means "framed" or "surrounded," and is a matter-of-fact reference to the halo-encircled Sun (Emil Imaruittuq, pers. comm., 1990). The second term, *niaqusiqtuq,* probably of Nattilingmiut origin and meaning "wearing a headband" (Tasiuq 1990, IE-137), seems more in keeping with traditions about the personifications of the Sun and Moon. Similarly the Sun's parhelia are called *tuglirutit,* the so-called "hair sticks" traditionally used by Iglulingmiut women (and occasionally men) to adorn their hair. Peary (1898, I:243) records that the Inuit of Etah, Greenland, also used the term *tugli* to designate parhelia.[12]

Among the Umingmakturmiut of Bathurst Inlet, Rasmussen was given the following explanation of halo phenomena:

> Sometimes a ring forms around the sun; it is called *qilauta:* the drum of the sun; for it forms a figure round about the sun just like the drum we used in the festival house. We do not quite know what this means; some believe that, simply because it resembles the drum we dance to, the sun drum is an omen of something pleasant that will happen. . . . If it is not a ring, but only an arc that forms around the sun it is called *natainiq,* which is thought to mean a part of the wooden rim of the drum. This, then, means someone has died. [Rasmussen 1932:23]

For Inuit around Point Barrow, Alaska, a mock sun—particularly the "vertical bar in a parhelion"—was called the "Sun's walking stick" (Nelson 1899:449), an image evidently linked to the stormy weather said to be predicted by the phenomenon. In this vein, Jenness (1922:179n) explains that at Barrow "two mock suns, one on each side of the real sun, are said to be its walking sticks, *aiyopiak* (*ajauppiak,* 'crutches'). The sun holds them out to steady itself when a gale is imminent." He also records that parhelia, for the Inuit of Coronation Gulf, could invoke premonitions of death: "The appearance of two mock suns . . . is ominous to travellers and hunters, who will be cut off by sudden death and never reach their homes again" (Jenness 1922:179).

The Pallirmiut, to the west of Hudson's Bay, referred to parhelia as "the sun's drum." Lunar haloes were said to be "the white skin tucks on the trousers of the man in the moon" (Birket-Smith 1929:157). Unfortunately, Birket-Smith does not provide the equivalent Inuktitut terms.

Another phenomenon, closely related to the halo, is the vertical prismatic column, or pillar, which, given the proper atmospheric conditions, is typically seen above the Sun at sunrise or sunset. The Alaskan Yup'ik Eskimo call these columns *akertem ayarua*—"the sun's walking-stick" (Jacobson 1984:50). This is the same designation given specifically to parhelia at Point Barrow, just slightly to the northeast of the Yup'ik region, suggesting, perhaps, that in this area all such vertical, or nearly vertical, prismatic phenomena were termed the Sun's "walking-sticks."

★ ★ ★

RAINBOWS

Inuit in Igloolik have two names for the rainbow depending on whether it is full or partial. A rainbow with a complete arc, having each end touching the horizon or sky line, is called *kataujak*—literally the "entrance to an igloo."

Ajagutaq, on the other hand, is a partial rainbow, especially one with the upper part of the arc missing and only the end segments visible (Emil Imaruittuq, pers. comm., 1990). The term in Igloolik means "pillar"[13] or "support" (J. Kopak, pers. comm., 1994) and, etymologically, has close associations with the Yup'ik word for "walking-stick"—*ayaruaq* (Jacobson 1984:98).

The significance of rainbows for the Umingmakturmiut was apparently based on the rainbow's height and the steepness of its sides. A high rainbow with steep sides "means happiness for all; but if it is not high, and its arc is flat, it means disaster and someone will die" (Rasmussen 1932:23).

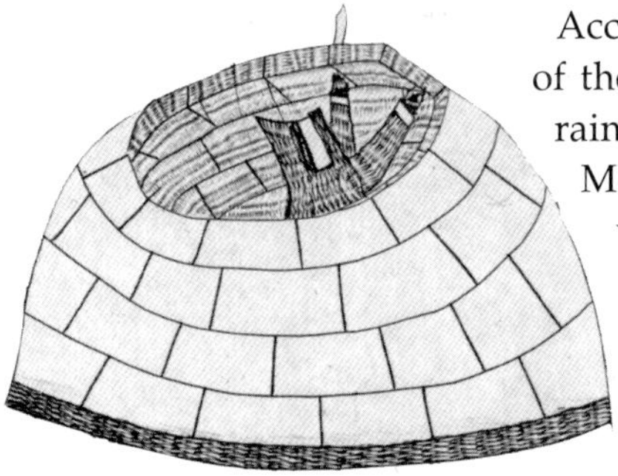

According to Robert Spencer (1959:258), in "the older cosmology" of the North Alaskan Eskimo, the Sun and the Moon "rest on the rainbow," a view linked to a version of the Sister-Sun/Brother-Moon myth. In Spencer's paraphrased version of this tale, in which the protagonists are man and wife, rather than brother and sister, the woman who becomes the Sun "went up into the sky by the rainbow."

CHAPTER 6
Navigation

*Have you followed the Fox Star[1] across the sea ice
Or travelled the barrens by moonlight
with fresh dogs?
Have you watched the snowdrifts rise from the snow
and map the way to far places?*

(Duncan Pryde)

INTRODUCTION

Reliable wayfinding is an essential element of Inuit culture. Simply put, survival depends as much on locating and killing animals as it does on returning safely home with the product of the hunt. Understandably, Inuit place an exceptionally high value on the skills that enable them to move efficiently around their territory. Stories recounting feats of wayfinding under extreme conditions are legion across the Arctic. A good navigator is quietly revered, a poor one gently ridiculed.

The impressive, almost uncanny, ability of most Inuit hunters to find their way accurately over vast areas of frozen, seemingly featureless, terrain in virtually any weather, has long amazed and puzzled European visitors to the Arctic.[2] Captain George Francis Lyon, himself an accomplished navigator, who spent the winter of 1822–1823 at Igloolik with Parry's expedition, was no exception:

> I was for some time incredulous as to their knowledge of the position of the cardinal points of the compass, conceiving that a people who, for weeks or months (according to the part of the coast they are living on), do not see the sun, and again for the same time have it continually above the horizon, could have no idea of east or west, which we Europeans misname the points of the sun's rising or setting. I was ultimately convinced of my error, and from many concurring circumstances was led to suppose that the stars, and particularly the constellation Ursa Major, were their guides in this respect. [Lyon 1824:160]

Some months later, however, Lyon is less sure about the role of stars, and, instead, tends to think that familiar landmarks are the more significant factor: "In travelling the Eskimaux are entirely guided by well-known points or objects on the shore; and therefore, though they know the cardinal points of the compass, and are also acquainted with particular stars, they have, as far as I can learn, but little occasion to depend on the clearness of the heavens, or the presence of the sun" (Lyon 1824:342).

Lyon's divided opinion on the basis of Inuit wayfinding unwittingly exposes the truth of the matter, namely, that no single method consistently predominates. When navigating, Inuit bring all their knowledge, experience, and senses to bear on every available environmental sign and circumstance, including wind direction, the set of snowdrifts, landmarks, vegetation, sea currents, clouds, and various astronomical bodies; clues are even derived from the behaviour of sled-dogs and other animals. Birket-Smith understood this approach very well: "Eskimos, who from childhood move about here and there, gradually acquire an astonishing knowledge of the country in all conditions and, what is more, an outstanding ability to orientate themselves by means of a number of quick and scarcely conscious decisions as to the position of celestial bodies, the meteorological state and so on" (Birket-Smith 1929:154).

This broad, innate-like, approach to wayfinding, developed over generations and based on close and constant observation of the natural environment, does not constitute a rigorous "system" or "method" in the sense usually applied to European or even Polynesian navigation.[3] Unlike such systems, Inuit navigational skills are learned experientially rather than formally and it is perhaps for this reason that Inuit elders, invited by the uninitiated to talk about their wayfinding practices, never quite give a fully satisfactory account. Snowdrifts, wind direction, and stars are all mentioned but how these and other external markers translate into that comprehensive ability that enables Inuit to excel as wayfinders, seems to elude complete description.

Doubtless, part of the answer lies in the way Inuit perceive and classify the world around them. The elaboration of Inuit spatial perception, as demonstrated through their language's use of certain word categories, termed "localizers" by linguists, attests to the high priority accorded accurate orientation. As Raymond Gagné (1968:38) points out, Inuit are able "to specify, with more precision than is found in most languages, where things and places are located, how to reach them, [and] their attributes in relation to their settings." Such linguistic precision, Gagné stresses, is the "underpinning" of what he calls the "cognitive maps" used by Inuit to represent their spatial environment.

The role of language is also important in Inuit place-naming. In striking contrast to the European approach—particularly that of explorers who tended to fill out their maps in memory of monarchs, mentors, and friends—Inuit place-naming sought to portray the physical, biological, or ecological significance of the land. Inuit rarely named places in honour of persons, and only occasionally to commemorate events.[4] A glance through the *Gazetteer of Inuit Place Names in Nunavik*, particularly the section listing non-Inuit place-names alongside their Inuktitut equivalents, convincingly illustrates this point (Müller-Wille 1987:353–63).

A recent trend in Inuit place-naming, driven by the needs of officialdom, is the coining of terms to designate areas such as Baffin Island, Melville Peninsula, or Northern Quebec—to mention only a few. From the Inuit point of view, names for such features would have been geographically and navigationally irrelevant.[5] Yet each of these areas was intimately known and defined through a wide network of local place-name sets. Again, remarkable proof of this is furnished in Müller-Wille's *Gazetteer,* where more than 7000 Inuit place-names are listed for Northern Quebec alone.

Regrettably, across the Arctic acculturation is also taking its toll on the corpus of traditional Inuit place-names. In Igloolik, older Inuit consider the demise of this knowledge a major factor in the increasing tendency of young, inexperienced hunters to get lost on the "land."

An incident in Igloolik illustrates this point and underlines the crucial importance of local place-names as an aspect of Inuit wayfinding. A few years ago a number of young Inuit left Igloolik on snowmobiles to hunt caribou. The day after their departure they ran into an unusually severe blizzard which lasted two full days. In an attempt to find their way back to the community they became hopelessly lost and ran out of gasoline. They sensibly camped on the sea ice and waited out the storm. The third day dawned calm and clear. On their short-wave radio they called to Igloolik, explained their predicament, and asked that a snowmobile be sent out carrying sufficient gasoline to get them all back to the community.

It was at this point that a problem became apparent. Whereas from their camp they could see familiar distant islands and points of land, under questioning by elders over the short-wave radio they were unable to name any of the observed features. Nor could they tell their would-be rescuers the name of the land last seen before the blizzard struck. After some difficulty the young hunters were eventually located and, needless to say, given a lecture on the necessity of knowing the place-names which could have pinpointed their exact position and spared the search-and-rescue party much concern and effort.

The increasing loss of local place-name knowledge is also accompanied by a general weakening of all the skills required for effective wayfinding. Noah Piugaattuk remembers being appalled at the lack of navigational ability recently displayed by two young men who left Pond Inlet for Igloolik and ended up first in Arctic Bay and then in Agu Bay before eventually reaching their intended destination: "I lectured them saying that they were ignorant because they could see the sun and the ground. . . . They were old enough but they were not trying to know these things" (Piugaattuk 1988, IE-040).

The Sun

In high Arctic latitudes, the Sun's rising and setting positions during the course of the year range virtually over the entire compass rose, rendering useless the convention so fondly held in more southerly regions that the "sun rises east and sets west." In Igloolik, excepting the midsummer and midwinter periods, when the Sun is either continuously above or below the horizon, or during the equinoxes, when it does indeed conform to our "east/west" expectations, its risings and settings occur, respectively, along the eastern and western horizons at various points spanning approximately 165°—almost an entire semi-circle. By way of contrast, the Sun's rising and setting positions on the horizons of Ottawa (latitude 45.5°N) span only 70°.

The diagram below illustrates sunrise and sunset positions at Igloolik on selected dates. With the exception of December, when the Sun never rises, or June, when it never sets, the approximate rising and setting positions for the remainder of the year can be readily interpolated.

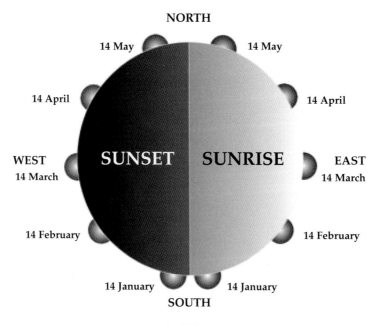

Igloolik hunters are acutely aware of the Sun's complex itinerary in their region, so much so, in fact, that knowledge of its approximate bearing at any given time is more or less taken for granted. When mentioned in a navigational context, reference to its absence, rather than its presence, was more frequently inferred, meaning that when the Sun could not be seen, some other means of orientation had to be used. This was especially true on the open sea, out of sight of land, where the Sun would be the only reliable reference point whereby the traveller could check his course or confirm changes in wind direction. On moving ice, with no land-based references, the Sun, like the stars, served the same purpose.

In overland travel, awareness of the Sun's bearing relative to one's course provided a point of reference which could be used in conjunction with available landmarks. But, with the exceptions noted for open-sea voyaging and hunting on moving ice, the Sun for Iglulingmiut was hardly a primary navigational tool, perhaps because, when visible, the generally clearer atmospheric conditions allowed travellers to use familiar landmarks.

As a time-keeper, in the days before clocks and watches were introduced to the Inuit, the Sun's role was undisputed: its daily rounds and constantly changing positions of rising and setting marked the passage of both seasonal and diurnal time.

The Moon, while mentioned infrequently in a navigational context, was doubtless incorporated into the collection of celestial and terrestrial markers used by Inuit for orientation. But its phases, monthly disappearances, speed through the sky, and relatively complex patterns of rising and setting seem to have made it less convenient to use than either the Sun or the stars.

The Moon's effect on sea currents and tides, as we will note later, did, for some Iglulingmiut, have occasional navigational significance and for this reason, as well as for time-keeping, its phases were carefully noted.

★ ★ ★

THE STARS

The role played by stars in Inuit navigation appears equivocal. The anthropological record, if it mentions the matter at all, usually sides with the view that stars were of minor importance for Inuit in wayfinding. Lyon, as we have seen, was convinced that Inuit had little need to depend on "the clearness of the heavens." Of the more recent observers, Edmund Carpenter's comments are typical: "Stars are sometimes used as guides, but rarely, and stories were told . . . of men who had been misled when they used them" (Carpenter 1973:22). Similarly, the Nunamiut of Northern Alaska made little use of stars in navigation, preferring to be guided by the wind and "occasional glimpses of terrain" (Gubser 1965:195).[6] George Simeon, in his study of Inuit orientation on King William Island, found that "the sun and moon never played a crucial role in . . . wayfinding, and the stars also play a minor role because most travel is during the daylight hours." He does, however, allow that "a few unnamed stars . . . may be used if necessity arises" (Simeon 1983:42).

With some notable exceptions, these observations essentially agree with the information offered by most Igloolik elders interviewed on the subject. Not surprisingly, the degree of importance attached to stars tended to reflect the context of the interviews. Thus when elders were asked to talk about wayfinding skills in general, the stars, when mentioned, were usually accorded only secondary importance. On the other hand, when asked specifically about the role of stars, the resulting responses were much more affirmative, one or two of them indeed being eloquent testimonials to the stars' primacy in navigation. Clearly, asking about stars and navigation in the same breath generated responses that tended to embellish the stars' significance.

Stars in Inuit navigation were used in two basic ways. The first, and more straightforward, method involved using them to maintain a heading once an actual course had been determined by other means. Any bright star of convenient bearing and altitude would be followed, making periodic adjustments for the star's apparent movement. This method requires no particular knowledge of the arrangement of stars on the celestial sphere and, as Emil Imaruittuq points out, "you don't even have to know the name of the star you're following" (1993, pers. comm.). In this case the star is being used as a convenient celestial landmark, hardly essential to orientation, but easing the task of maintaining a course on a dark night when, for instance, the snowdrifts are difficult to see.[7]

The second method uses stars alone to determine the course of travel. More complex than the first, this method involves a thorough knowledge of star and constellation positions in relation to their seasonal and nocturnal rounds as well as their bearings relative to the observer. Stars in this role become the primary and under some circumstances the only instrument of orientation, particularly when travelling at night on moving sea ice.

Noah Piugaattuk makes the strongest case for the use of stars in wayfinding, declaring them "essential for navigation" when travelling by dog-team (Piugaattuk 1988, IE-040). He goes on to explain that, on long trips, "using one star for direction we would travel for some time . . . then we would start to move to the left of the star." This technique of keeping on course, which was also used for the Sun and Moon, demonstrates an acute sense of the relationship between one's speed over ground, the passage of time, the movement of the star, and its bearing relative to the target destination. Cain Iqqaqsaq explains: "When I am depending on a star to take me home I must not actually follow that star. I must follow behind the star, to the left. This is more so when you are walking. In walking you are slow and you have to stop to rest so the stars will appear to move faster. You would then have to change your course to the left in order to head away from that particular star. When you do that you can get close to your destination" (Iqqaqsaq 1993, IE-257).

A similar technique was apparently used by Inuit dog-team drivers in the Coronation Gulf area:

The usual routine is to follow the star as it rises obliquely (or sets for that matter, if you are following a setting star) on the horizon. The rapid displacement of the star means you can only use the star for a short time, then you discard it and pick up a new star roughly where the original one rose. Once the travelling-star has been displaced about 25° (roughly a handsbreadth at arms length) from its original spot it is far enough away to start looking for another star to follow. The star has to be very low on the horizon since your eyes are focussed ahead of the dogs to look out for rough ice or any other problems in your path, and if you have to keep looking away and then back it can eventually become bothersome. You can be certain that if you have to raise your head to see the star then it is too high, and if you have to turn your head to see the star then it is too far to the side. Only low stars in sequence are any good for dog travel.[8] [Pryde 1995:30–31).

Piugaattuk's views on the importance of stars are accentuated by his belief that the true purpose of celestial mythology is to teach Inuit how to recognize and remember the stars so that they can be properly used for navigation. "Stars," he says, "have legends behind them to pin-point their exact location" (Piugaattuk 1988, IE-040). Hubert Amarualik agrees: "Stars were well known and they were named so they could be easily identified whenever it was clear. They were used for directional purposes as well as to tell time. . . . Stars could be remembered by the legends associated with them. The people before us had no writing system so they had legends in order to remember" (Amarualik 1993, IE-252).

The choice of stars used in wayfinding depended, of course, on a number of natural factors including the season, time of night, direction of travel, and extent of cloud cover. Beyond this, the actual stars or constellations used by Inuit in their travels tended to be a matter of individual, almost idiosyncratic, preference. Some elders, in fact, were keen to point out that the stars *they* used were not necessarily the same as those used by others.

Nevertheless, a casual survey of some dozen interviews on star navigation reveals a clear pattern of preference. *Tukturjuit* (Ursa Major) ranked first with *Quturjuuk* (Capella and Menkalinan, and Castor and Pollux) a close second. *Ullaktut* (Orion's belt), *Nuutuittuq* (Polaris), and *Sakiattiak* (the Pleiades) all shared third place. There were, in addition, a few references to *Sivulliik* (Arcturus and Muphrid) and *Akuttujuuk* (Betelgeuse and Bellatrix). Appropriately, the only mention made of *Singuuriq* (Sirius), in a positive navigational context, was by an elder who had lived most of his life around Repulse Bay where this star is a more familiar feature of the sky than it is in the Igloolik area.

With the obvious exception of Polaris, the particular stars and constellations chosen by Inuit for navigation were normally the same ones they used to gauge the passage of time—hardly surprising, given the link between a star's position and the time of night—a crucial link for effective wayfinding.

At its most rudimentary level the successful use of stars in navigation depends on a thorough knowledge of the structure of at least one constellation and its changing orientation in accordance with the passage of time. The emphasis on these basic principles is apparent when Cain Iqqaqsaq tells us how his father first taught him about stars:

Our parents had different ways of teaching their children. My father used to get me to use the group of stars [called] *Tukturjuit* [Ursa Major]. This constellation is one of those that are higher in the sky than the others. . . . If the lower sky is overcast so that you cannot see other stars, my father used to tell me that *Tukturjuit* are useful to tell time and direction. Even if I did not have a watch, the movement of these stars can tell me the time. The *Tukturjuit* are easily recognized because they have the form of a caribou. When [the caribou] appears to stand on its hind legs and its head starts to get higher this is an indication that midnight is approaching. It was mainly *Tukturjuit* that I was taught to observe. [Iqqaqsaq 1993, IE-257]

In South Baffin Island the stars of *Tukturjuit* were also used for orientation: "When you are a long distance out on the sea ice and the shore of Baffin is obscured—raise your left hand and when your fingers and thumb match the constellation's stars [with the thumb covering Phecda, the forefinger Megrez, and the remaining fingers Alioth, Mizar, and Alkaid] your arm points towards the mainland."[9]

★ ★ ★

POLARIS

The role of *Nuutuittuq*[10] (Polaris) in Iglulingmiut navigation calls for separate consideration. This ultimate "guiding star" of the northern hemisphere's middle latitudes, this European metaphor for constancy and reliability—Shakespeare's star of "true fix'd and resting quality"—takes on a questionable reputation in the high Arctic. The problem with Polaris is that its height above the horizon corresponds almost exactly to the latitude of the observer: the farther north the observer, the higher the star. This quality of Polaris, a boon to navigators in lower northerly latitudes,[11] is useless in the higher Arctic regions where its altitude is simply too great to yield an accurate directional bearing.

At the latitude of Igloolik, Polaris approaches the extreme northerly limit of its usefulness. Though hardly ignored to the extent that it is in Northwest Greenland, where, apparently, the Inuit there have no name for it (Peary 1898, I:494), Polaris among the Iglulingmiut is by no means universally regarded as an essential star. Elders' opinions on the usefulness of Polaris in wayfinding varied from one extreme to the other, some claiming it was *the* most important star, others, seemingly well-informed about the sky, admitting little or no knowledge of it: "It was pointed out to me once, but now I am unable to show anyone where it rests. I have no knowledge of that star" (Amaaq 1989, IE-074).

But Polaris did have its loyal adherents, significantly most of them having in common an upbringing in areas well to the south of Igloolik proper where the lower altitude of the star would increase its usefulness for navigation. In this context we also recall that in Kangiqsujuaq, Northern Quebec, Inuit referred to Polaris as *Turaagaq*—"something to aim at."[12] A few more comments offered by Igloolik elders illustrate how this star was regarded and used. Hubert Amarualik begins:

> Another important star was *Nuutuittuq* because it was stationary while the rest of the stars moved along. This star was also called *Ulluriajjuaq*. It was important to determine the direction of the west-northwest wind *Uangnaq*. If you are lost this star can tell you which direction to go because it is always stationary and can lead you on the right track home. The star is also useful when there is no wind to guide you. I have used this star for navigating. . . . You can find *Nuutuittuq* easily as it is the largest in the location where it is situated. You can also locate this star even when there is a slight overcast. [Amarualik 1992, IE-212]

Of those interviewed, only Amarualik mentioned an alternate name for *Nuutuittuq: Ulluriajjuaq*. This term, meaning "great star," is usually reserved for the planets (see page 92) but presumably his use of the superlative in this case extols the importance of Polaris, rather than its size. On moving ice the primacy of *Nuutuittuq*, and indeed of all stars used by Inuit for wayfinding, is beyond question: "When I hunted [with my father] on the moving ice there would be no sign of land and we would be surrounded by frost smoke. . . . It was difficult to see anywhere. On a clear night he would point to the star *Nuutuittuq* and then point in the direction of the land and the land-fast ice. Yes, I have on more than one occasion used that star to determine the direction of the land" (Amarualik 1993, IE-252).

Panikpakuttuk's first awareness of Polaris is interesting in that it did not derive from his own traditions but from Graham Rowley, an archaeologist, who worked in the Foxe Basin area between 1936 and 1939:

> The only time I learned about that star was from Makuttunnaaq [Rowley],[13] when I was but a boy. As we travelled he would constantly keep track of *Nuutuittuq*. He would use his compass and the star for navigating. We would have a definite destination, so he would get his bear-

An Arctic landmark, the *inuksugaq* is a navigational icon.
Photo: John MacDonald.

ings with the star and his compass. At night when we made camp he would poke a stick into the ground pointing to *Nuutuittuq.* When we woke up in the morning, he would use that stick to get his bearings before we moved on. Before Makuttunnaaq I had never heard of *Nuutuittuq.* [Panikpakuttuk 1991, IE-201]

Abraham Ulaajuruluk used a similar method to satisfy himself that Polaris indeed did not move like the other stars:

After we had returned from our *mauliq* (seal hunting at breathing holes in the ice) I got curious about this star which was pointed out to me and called *Nuutuittuq.* So on the lee side of a snow wind-break *(uquutaq)* I positioned a harpoon shaft pointing directly to this star to see if it would in fact move. In the morning I checked it and discovered that while *Tukturjuit* (Ursa Major) had changed its position completely from the preceding night the harpoon was still pointing at this star. It was then that I discovered the stationary star, *Nuutuittuq!* [Ulayuruluk 1992, IE-211]

For both Panikpakuttuk and Ulaajuruluk, the unmoving Polaris seems to have been more of a passing curiosity than a star essential for their navigation. Not so for Philip Qipanniq who spent most of his life in the Repulse Bay area some 350 km south of Igloolik: "The star I used most was known as the one that does not move—*Nuutuittuq.* I first would determine the general direction of my home and compare it with that star so as I travelled I would keep to that direction using this star to determine my destination" (Qipanniq 1991, IE-197).

We leave the final comment on Polaris to Noah Piugaattuk, one of Igloolik's most renowned dog-team travellers. When asked about his own use of *Nuutuittuq* in navigation his response was politely circumspect, perhaps not wishing to disappoint: "One thing we can honestly say is that the people before us would have used this star for navigation. But for myself I did not use it to the extent that I would use other stars. No doubt they would have used that star especially when they had to spend the night out in the open on moving ice where there are no materials to build a shelter. As for myself I did not use that star as much as it was used by others" (Piugaattuk 1991, IE-181).

If there is consensus at all on the use of stars in Iglulingmiut wayfinding, it is that they were usually of secondary importance except, of course, when navigating on moving sea ice at night. Along with the Sun and, to a lesser extent, the Moon, stars provided a convenient but hardly essential guide, once the direction of travel had been established by other means, typically by landmark or prevailing snowdrifts. In addition, stars were not always available, being frequently obscured by cloud, fog, or blowing snow and, for almost five months a year, lost in the daylight of spring and summer. Aipilik Innuksuk stresses this point while advocating that the "ground"—here meaning snowdrifts—provides the more reliable tool for navigation:

> Some people would get lost when they used only the skies for navigation and did not pay attention to the ground. They would get lost because the stars are continually moving. Of course you can get a bearing from the skies but, for myself, I have never really looked at the stars . . . [although] I don't totally ignore them. I try to be aware of how they are but I do not use them for navigation. If I used the stars and it became cloudy or if the wind died down I would probably get lost. That is why I have to be aware of the ground. [A. Innuksuk 1988, IE-039]

★ ★ ★

SNOWDRIFTS

In the Igloolik area, "the ground," including the sea ice, can be snow-covered for up to eight months of the year, usually from early October to late May. By definition, this is also the period in which the most extensive travel by dog-team occurred and, consequently, the period having the greatest need for reliable land-based navigational skills.

Snow, that indispensable element of Inuit material culture—which in its various forms quenches thirst, provides shelter, and gives swift access to distant hunting grounds—is also the basis of the Iglulingmiut's most used and most trusted navigational key. In concert with the winds, snow is formed into drifts—technically "sastrugi"—of various shapes, sizes, and densities, each leaving a visible and tangible record of the particular wind that formed it. Most drifts are of limited duration, lasting only as long as the next strong blow, but those set down or acted on by *Uangnaq* (the prevailing west-northwest wind) can endure throughout the winter. Such drifts are termed *uqalurait* (singular *uqaluraq*[14])—a reference to the elevated tongue-shaped form found at their west-northwest extremity.

The processes by which *uqalurait* are formed are well known to Igloolik elders. First, in early winter, a snow-laden blizzard, often from the southeast, deposits large, soft, mound-like drifts called *uluangnait* ("resembling cheeks"), on the land and sea ice. These more or less amorphous drifts are then acted on persistently by the prevailing wind and gradually, through erosion and impaction, transformed into the hard, elongated *uqalurait* with the distinctive tongue-like formation at their windward end. Another form of drift known as *qimugjuk* ("ridged"; plural *qimugjuit*) is also created by the prevailing wind. This is usually found on the lee side of some obstacle, such as a boulder, a protrusion of old or rafted sea ice, or even the "tongue" of a previously formed *uqaluraq*. *Qimugjuit* are long, ridge-like drifts tapered towards their east-southeast ends. They, too, are useful in navigation but are not so common on surfaces lacking protrusions, particularly flat expanses of sea or lake ice. Abraham Ulayuruluk gives a detailed explanation of drift-forming processes:

> During a blizzard the snowfall is usually soft. A type of snow mound, *uluangnaq*, is formed. The [prevailing wind] then erodes this mound, thereby forming an *uqaluraq*—a drift with a tip that resembles a tongue (*uqaq*)—which is pointed and elevated from the ground. From this formation another kind of drift we called *qimugjuk* is going to build up. *Uqalurait* are formed by the *Uangnaq* [the west-northwest wind]. There is a very minimal formation of *uqalurait* made by *Nigiq* [the east-southeast wind] and these are usually very small. I believe the *Uangnaq* is the strongest of all the winds, at least in our homeland. There are hardly any other winds that cause *uqalurait* except for *Nigiq* which can also cause *qimugjuit* on the lee side of rocks. On a smooth surface, without rocks or pressure ridges, *qimugjuit* can only be formed by the west-northwest wind. Some of these drifts remain *qimugjuit* while others will be transformed into *uqalurait*. [Ulayuruluk 1993, IE-256]

Other elders also mentioned the possibility of tongue-like drifts deriving from winds other than *Uangnaq* but pointed out that these are easily distinguishable from the "proper" *uqalurait:* the former are much smaller and less compacted, whereas well-established *uqalurait* (and *qimugjuit*) are often difficult to penetrate with the point of a snow-knife. The lasting qualities of *uqalurait*, their ability to become old, established drifts, *aputituqait* (Iqqaqsaq 1993, IE-257), contributes significantly to their usefulness in Inuit navigation. On occasion, following contrary winds or a snowfall, when the *uqalurait* become buried under a fresh layer of snow, all one has to do to check a bearing is to "kick away the fresh snow and reveal the form [of the *uqaluraq*] below" (A. Innuksuk 1990, IE-165).[15]

Iglulingmiut attribute the distinguishing qualities of *uqalurait* drifts—dense, hard, sculpted, and persistent—to unique characteristics of the west-northwest wind, *Uangnaq*. This wind, the prevailing wind of the region, is also the coldest. But unlike the other winds, particularly *Nigiq,* which tends to be milder, of shorter duration, and blows at a steady pace, *Uangnaq*'s force is variable. These attributes are said to give the *uqalurait* their unique form: "*Nigiq* [the east-southeast wind] covers the ground nicely and evenly, without drifts; it repairs the snow and smooths the ground. When *Nigiq* blows it is usually constant without much gusting even when it is blowing hard. *Uangnaq,* on the other hand, is never stable and gusts a great deal, thereby making the ground very rough and uneven" (Kappianaq 1993, IE-265).

George Kappianaq's views on the complementary qualities of *Uangnaq* and *Nigiq* are echoed by Theo Ikummaq: "The west-northwest wind, once it starts blowing, doesn't blow at an even pace. It dies and then it blows, dies and blows, and that is why it forms *[uqalurait].* By contrast the east-southeast wind is steady— it doesn't fluctuate much—so it evens out the snow" (Ikummaq 1993, IE-236).

This apparent fickleness of *Uangnaq* earns it a feminine personification in Igloolik.[16] *Nigiq,* on the other hand, is characterized as male: "When it blows it is usually constant because this wind is a man." The west-northwest and east-southeast winds are also seen to be in a perpetual state of tension and opposition: "If *Uangnaq* blows hard, *Nigiq* will always retaliate with his own wind. This is the reason why after a strong blow from *Uangnaq* the wind will shift to *Nigiq* most of the time" (Kappianaq 1993, IE-273). Resorting to mythology, George Kappianaq offers additional explanation:

> *Nigiq* has a man *inua* while *Uangnaq* has a woman *inua*. When the woman with her words intimidates him, he does not get agitated as a woman would under the circumstances. He is able to cope with this intimidation

for a length of time. That is why he is able to smooth things over, where-as, as always, a woman will make things rough. . . . It is said that when *Uangnaq*'s igloo gets holes in it (as a result of the seams between the snow blocks melting), she will move outdoors and remain there until the holes have been repaired. . . . In the winter when *Uangnaq* is prevailing without any sign of easing, a shaman would try to ascertain the cause. He would find the woman standing outdoors, miserable because her igloo is full of holes. Once the holes are properly plugged by the shaman, the woman would go back into her igloo and the *Uangnaq* wind would abate. [Kappianaq 1993, IE-265; IE-273]

Michel Kupaaq substantially agrees with George Kappianaq on the respective female/male personification of the northwest and southeast winds but attributes the supposed characteristics of these winds to particular aspects of male and female nocturnal behaviour:

The northwest wind's person is said to be a woman, while the man is the southeast wind. In the past . . . women settled down for the night by removing their footwear and getting up on to the sleeping platform in a squatting position. If the north wind, being a woman, has been raging throughout the day it will [often] die down at nightfall, indicating that the woman has removed her footwear [and is ready to retire]. As for the southeast wind, in the manner that men are active in the middle of the night going from household to household, so too will this wind become active and stronger during the night. [Kupaaq 1991, IE-182]

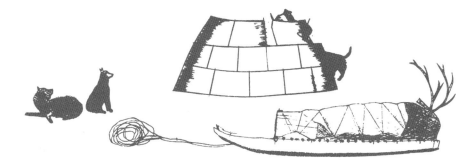

The importance of drifts formed by the *Uangnaq* wind as a reliable indicator of direction was mentioned frequently by elders, even by those who tended to favour stars. Emil Imaruittuq has this to say on the matter:

> *Qimugjuit* and *uqalurait* can be used for wayfinding when the stars are not visible. Many natural phenomena can be used to determine direction but some of them may not be reliable. One that is not reliable, and may mislead a person, is the wind. It has a tendency of shifting direction so gradually that it can fool you. . . . This happened to me once. But snow formations that have stabilized [*qimugjuit* and *uqalurait*] will not take on different characteristics easily, thereby making them the most reliable source for establishing bearings. [Imaruittuq 1990, IE-101]

Abraham Ulayuruluk confirms this assessment:

> The *qimugjuit* all face *Uangnaq* [the west-northwest wind], therefore the *uqalurait* also face *Uangnaq*. If you know the direction of your destination but have lost sight of it, or when you no longer know the general direction of your destination, you can use the *qimugjuit* and the *uqalurait* to guide you. These are the snow formations that you observed during the daylight hours and that you noticed were facing towards the *Uangnaq*. When the visibility is obscured, either through darkness or bad weather, these drifts will be your only available aid. [Ulayuruluk 1993, IE-256]

Over the course of a winter, particularly on flat land and ice surfaces, the *uqalurait* can grow to sizes large enough to hinder travel. Such surfaces, gouged and tortured by the wind, resemble rough seas in which the waves have simply frozen in place. In these conditions, the drifts, as a number of elders mused, are a mixed blessing: "They are not what we want. . . . They are nothing but a hindrance on our journey, but they have a use that we surely cannot do without when the visibility is poor" (Ulayuruluk 1993, IE-256).

For the Igloolik area the prevailing west-northwest wind and its resulting snowdrifts provide Inuit with a "cardinal axis": west-northwest/east-southeast. Throughout the year *Uangnaq* blows frequently from its familiar quarter, and in winter, the *uqalurait* and *qimugjuit* drifts are everywhere, subtly—at times forcefully—impressing on the observant traveller their distinctive orientation.[17] A hunter, if asked, can, without a moment's hesitation, transect an *uqaluraq* with his snow-knife to indicate precisely the angle at which the drift must be crossed to reach a specified destination anywhere in the local region. But if asked to do this on a drift set along any other axis, the demonstration may not be as fluent or as accurate.[18]

Drifts made by winds other than *Uangnaq* are also useful for orientation, but they "are difficult to tell if you are not experienced" (Kappianaq 1993, IE-265). Elders also stressed the necessity to be especially observant of the winds and to remember from which direction the last storm came so that, if need be, its drifts could be used for navigation.[19]

Sea ice early in the winter often lacks sufficient snow to allow the formation of proper directional drifts but even in these conditions the experienced hunter can derive clues from the ice surface:

> When I am travelling on flat sea ice without proper snowdrifts there are usually some small formations called *kanngutikuluit;* those too are readable and are very useful, although they might break when touched. But if they haven't been tampered with they are as useful as the larger drifts for navigation. When there is a new sheet of snow and there are no drifts then you're liable to get lost. But you can blow away the snow cover to find the underlying *ipakjugait* [surface striations[20]] which, although small, are very good for navigation as well. [A. Innuksuk 1988, IE-039]

Given the widespread use Inuit make of snowdrifts in navigation it is remarkable how infrequently the topic is treated in Arctic literature. An early mention is made by Boas (1888:643), noting that after a gale Inuit "feel their way by observing the direction of the snowdrifts." Stefánsson's *Arctic Manual* (1944)—a work prepared for the United States Army—describes snowdrift morphology and its role in orientation doubtless deriving from, but without any direct reference to, Inuit techniques. Incidental references to "sastrugi" are made by George Simeon in a paragraph explaining the "paramount importance" of wind direction "for many of the Gjoa Haven [NWT] Eskimo" (Simeon 1983:33). And, again, Edmund Carpenter, in *Eskimo Realities,* mentions snowdrifts merely as a method of establishing wind direction: "[The hunter] quickly senses any change in the wind's direction and confirms it by checking wind cuts in snowdrifts and ridges" (Carpenter 1973:22).[21] More helpful is Richard Nelson's fairly detailed account of the phenomenon in *Hunters of the Northern Ice* which allows an interesting comparison of snowdrift formation and use around Wainwright, Alaska, with that of the Igloolik area. Note that in Wainwright the prevailing winter winds are from the northeast:

> Realizing in which direction the drifts trend, the problem is knowing from which direction the wind blew that formed them. The solution is not difficult. First, the wind deposits snow on the lee side of any obstruction, whether it is a marble-sized lump of snow or a mountainous ice pile. In flat areas the surface of the snow is usually studded everywhere with small lumps of snow less than two inches high, behind which there is a small "tail" of snow that tapers to a point several inches behind the lump. This little tail was left there because it was on the lee side, the tail pointing downwind and the flat end forming the upwind side. The tail usually points southwest or west in this area. Snow accumulates on the lee flank of hummocks, often in deep soft drifts called *mauya*. The windward side is always blown free of all loose snow, leaving bare ice or hard packed snow *(sillek)*. . . . Large snowdrifts formed without any obstruction are shaped exactly the opposite way, tending to have a long tapered windward end, both in cross section and top view, and a more steep and abrupt leeward end. This type of drift is called *kaiuhulak*. [Nelson 1969: 104–5]

We conclude this segment, fittingly, with Ivaluardjuk's account of the "Spirit of the Snowdrift—*Oqaloraq [uqaluraq]*." Ivaluardjuk's evident loathing of this spirit is in sharp contrast to the generally useful qualities attributed to the *uqaluraq* proper by the Iglulingmiut:

> Oqaloraq is the name given to the firm, sharp edges of a snowdrift. They have a spirit, the Snowdrift Spirit. He lives in the sharp declivities of the snowdrifts, where the wind whines and blows most fiercely. When a blizzard is raging over the country, and the driving snow makes it impossible to see, then this spirit is filled with delight, and if you listen you can hear him laughing in the storm. The wilder the gale, the happier he is and the louder he laughs. He knows that men hate him, and for that reason

he persecutes them. He sends down a snowstorm upon them unawares when they are out on their sledges, or on the ice at the blowholes, or in their kayaks, and then he can be heard laughing through the storm when harm comes to the human beings that hate him. He wears close-fitting clothes, made of caribou skin, and does nothing but laugh and chuckle through the blizzard whenever men suffer harm. Such is the Spirit of the Snowdrift. [Rasmussen 1929:73]

★ ★ ★

WIND

Wind is the principal arbiter of Iglulingmiut hunting activity, and the most close-ly observed and frequently discussed of all environmental phenomena. Awareness of atmospheric conditions, particularly the winds, was encouraged early in life and most elders have vivid childhood memories of being sent out-doors each morning to check the weather. Their reports, once confirmed and con-sidered, would launch the day's activities. Moderate northwesterlies, for instance, meant the prospect of successful seal hunting at a clean floe-edge, while easterly winds, packing the floe against the land-fast ice, might give hunters access to wal-rus out on the moving ice.

A cogent illustration of the crucial link between wind direction and Iglulingmiut hunting activity comes from Pingiqqalik, an ancient, now aban-doned, settlement near Igloolik, once famed for its walrus hunters. Here, a north-east wind—the wind most favoured for walrus hunting—was given its own local name and referred to with unusual metaphorical flourish as *Qukturaaqtuq*—"the broken thigh." Noah Piugaattuk explains:

Near the sod houses at Pingiqqalik there is a small pond lying in a north-westerly direction. They call this pond *Qukturak* (because it is shaped like a human thigh). As was our custom, the first person who went outdoors in the morning would check the weather and inform the rest. If the wind was seen to be coming from the direction of the moving ice, in other words blowing across the pond, it was said that the thigh was broken. The person who observed this, especially if an elder, would then go back indoors and announce that "the thigh is broken!" ("*Qukturaaqtuq!*"). At this, the men immediately became lively with anticipation, knowing that the conditions were just right for walrus hunting on the moving ice. That's the way they did things at Pingiqqalik! [Piugaattuk 1986, IE-054]

The more commonly used Inuktitut terms to denote wind direction around Igloolik, however, do not quite share the esoteric qualities of Pingiqqalik's *Qukturaaqtuq*.

★ IGLULINGMIUT WIND TERMINOLOGY ★

Iglulingmiut designate four "primary" winds—*Uangnaq, Kanangnaq, Nigiq*, and *Akinnaq*—from which all other local wind directions can be specified. When related to the divisions of a European compass rose these four primary winds have the following approximate values:[22] *Uangnaq*, WNW (296°); *Kanangnaq*, NNE (019°); *Nigiq*, ESE (119°); and *Akinnaq*, SSW (202°).[23] It will be noted that there are two sets of roughly opposing, or counterbalancing, winds, one on the *Uangnaq-Nigiq* axis, the other on the *Kanangnaq-Akinnaq* axis. To the Iglulingmiut this arrangement of "opposites" is symbolically important, especially in the pairing of *Uangnaq* and *Nigiq* which, as we have seen, are personified respectively as female and male and are said to "retaliate" against each other. It is, in fact, not uncommon to have a west-northwest gale followed by a contrary blow from the east-southeast.

The term *akurruttijuq*, used in conjunction with any two adjacent primary names, indicates a "midpoint" wind, hence *uangnamillu kanangnamillu akurruttijuq* signifies a wind bearing approximately NNW (338°). Winds occurring in the sector between a given cardinal point and the *akurruttijuq* "midpoint" line take the nearest primary name to which is added the suffix *-passik*. Thus *uangnaqpassik* is a wind bearing approximately 317° (NW), while *kanangnaqpasik* bears almost true north. In this way, variation in wind direction down to gradations of 23° can be readily specified.

Iglulingmiut use a number of terms to indicate wind force or condition. Expressed in increments roughly corresponding to the Beaufort Wind Scale the common terms for wind force are as follows: *ikulliaktuq*—"calm" (*uqsuarqtuq* is used for calm seas); *anurajaaqtuq*—"a light breeze"; *anurikittuq*—"a gentle breeze"; *anuraaqtuq*—"a moderate breeze"; *anuraariktuq*—"a strong breeze"; and *anuraaktualuk*—"a gale." *Saqijuq* describes a veering or shifting wind, hence *"uangnarmit kanangnarmut saqijuq"* means that the wind is shifting from *Uangnaq* to *Kanangnaq*. Other words denote wind conditions specifically involving snow: *natiruviaqtuq*—"ground-drift" and *pirsiqtuq*—"blizzard," for example. The term *qakiijauniq* is reserved for a storm-force winter wind which, acting with airborne snow particles, is capable of eroding snow-houses to the point of destruction: "An igloo can be eaten away by this wind. . . . When it appears that this is going to happen, the best way to treat the igloo is to coat it with water. . . . *Qakiijauniq* can be very dangerous and, for this reason, during a blizzard we always try to build a storage extension on the windward side of the igloo. This offers some protection" (Imaruittuq 1990, IE-101).

★ WIND IN NAVIGATION ★

The crucial importance of wind in so many facets of Iglulingmiut life does not extend, at least directly, to their navigational practices. Changeability is seen as the wind's defining characteristic and for this reason its use as a primary aid in wayfinding is avoided. Many elders warned about the dangers of relying exclusively on the winds for orientation and some told of how they had been led astray by them. Nevertheless, the winds are frequently used for maintaining a given direction but only after a reliable course has been established by other means such as landmarks, snowdrifts, or stars.

Thus for the Iglulingmiut the essential value of the wind in Inuit wayfinding is not from the way it happens to set during a journey but rather, as is made clear in our discussion of snowdrifts, from its persistent and reliable working of the snowy landscape into sculpted pointers as directionally true as any compass needle.

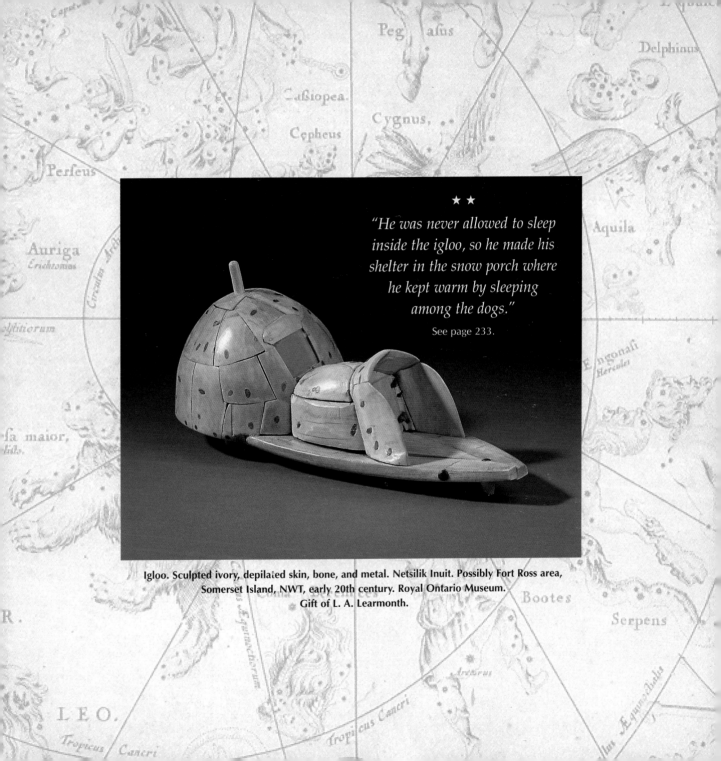

★ ★

"He was never allowed to sleep inside the igloo, so he made his shelter in the snow porch where he kept warm by sleeping among the dogs."

See page 233.

Igloo. Sculpted ivory, depilated skin, bone, and metal. Netsilik Inuit. Possibly Fort Ross area, Somerset Island, NWT, early 20th century. Royal Ontario Museum. Gift of L. A. Learmonth.

"Nikurrautiit *are . . .*
two stars side-by-side and
one star up front.
We have pot-holders like
that for our qulliq."

See page 63.

Rachel Uyarsuk of Igloolik
tending her *qulliq* (soapstone lamp)
during festivities welcoming
the return of the Sun
after winter's dark period.
Photo: John MacDonald.

*"She should simply place her cooking pot over
her lamp . . . and her cooking pot
would thus be replenished."*

See page 222.

Woman Tending Fire. **Silkscreen print. By Ulayu. Sikosuilarmiut.
Cape Dorset, Baffin Island, NWT, 1964. Royal Ontario Museum.
Gift of Mr. and Mrs. E. W. Vanstone.**

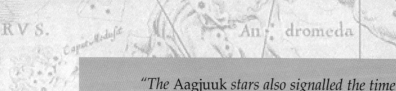

"The Aagjuuk stars also signalled the time for the midwinter celebration. This festival was usually held in a qaggiq—a large igloo specially built for the purpose."

See page 88.

Building a *qaggiq*—festive igloo—to celebrate the signing of the Nunavut Land Claim Agreement-in-Principle, Igloolik, NWT, 30 April 1990.
Photo: John MacDonald.

★

(Left) Snow knife. Ivory and wood sculpture. *(Right)* Flensing knife. Ivory sculpture. Pangnirtung area, Baffin Island, NWT, 1933–1942. Royal Ontario Museum.
Dr. Jon A. and Mrs. Muriel Bildfell Collection.
Purchased through the generosity of Mr. Donald Ross.

OTHER POINTERS

★ CURRENTS ★

Less frequently, Iglulingmiut, and doubtless other Inuit groups as well, turned to a number of other environmental indicators to give them clues about their orientation. Among these, sea currents were mentioned most often: "When you are in the open sea and there is no means of getting your bearings you can use the floating seaweed (*qiqquaq*, 'kelp') for this purpose. The root of the kelp is floating on the surface and its frond is submerged, positioned by the tidal current. From this you will be able to tell what course to take.[24] This is a good method of finding your way, especially when you cannot see the sun" (Piugaattuk 1992, IE-246).

Obviously, the ability to use sea currents confidently and accurately for orientation purposes requires an intimate knowledge of the area's coastal topography and tidal characteristics. Theo Ikummaq, perusing a map of the Igloolik region, makes this point clearly:

> The currents vary a lot. For example, in the Igloolik area, there's a current going down here, and another one goes in this direction. In this area the seaweed would be pointing in a southerly direction. But should you travel a little closer [to the shore] the current would now be flowing to the northwest. So you have to take into consideration where the currents are coming from. And then with all those islands out farther in the Foxe Basin the currents vary a lot depending on how shallow the water is. [Ikummaq 1992, IE-263]

Aipilik Innuksuk tells a remarkable tale of two men lost on the moving sea ice who eventually reached safety because one of them had knowledge of the workings of tidal currents:

> On the main ice we use the snowdrifts for guidance but when on moving ice we have to use the currents when there is nothing else to help you find your way. . . . Long ago people were lost on the moving ice. One of the men tried to find his way, using, I suppose, the daylight, wind, and stars

for direction. But his companion used instead a harpoon and float to determine the direction of the tidal currents. He would let his float drift on the water to see which way the current was going. He kept an eye on the current. . . . He knew that with the current setting outwards, the loose ice would be moving away from the land-fast ice. And he knew that as the outward current started to slow down an inward current would soon take over. So he kept an eye on currents and in this way he knew which direction he was facing. . . .

His companion [who was using the daylight and the wind to guide him] started to walk home in a southerly direction, but the one [who had observed the currents] would not follow, saying he cared about himself and he was going to walk towards the north. So one man went towards the south and the other, who had paid attention to the setting of the currents, . . . went to the north where he knew he would reach the land-fast ice. . . . The one who went southwards, after walking a fair distance, turned around and started to follow the person who was going north. They both made it to the land-fast ice; but one of them, perhaps not paying attention to the currents, had almost walked south to danger. His companion, it is said, always paid attention to the tidal currents. Indeed, these currents are very important, not just on the moving ice, but also when you are hunting at the floe edge. That is how it is. [A. Innuksuk 1988, IE-035]

⋆ THE WATER-SKY—*TUNGUNIQ* ⋆

The "water-sky" is a marker often used for orientation around the Igloolik area during the winter and spring months.[25] Known in Inuktitut as *tunguniq*—for its bluish colour—the phenomenon results from the skyward mirroring of the sharply contrasting, contiguous surfaces at the floe-edge: the bright, snow-covered land-fast ice and the darker open water. With increasing light levels, the contrasting effect is greatly enhanced, making the *tunguniq* much more noticeable as winter gives way to spring.

The *tunguniq* which, on a clear day, can be seen from a distance of thirty to forty km, is a reliable directional reference for those travelling on the flat coastal terrain of the northeastern Melville Peninsula, particularly the stretch between the communities of Hall Beach and Igloolik (Piugaattuk 1988, IE-040).

★ Aurora Borealis—*Aqsarniit* ★

Igloolik elders are well aware that, throughout their area, displays of the aurora borealis tend to occur most frequently in the southern sector of the sky. There was no indication that the phenomenon was ever used by them as a navigational aid, perhaps because of its relatively infrequent occurrence in the skies above Igloolik. Interestingly, in Alaska, the northern lights were used for orientation by the Inuit of Wainwright:

> Several Eskimos mentioned, when asked, that the northern lights are sometimes used for navigation, because they are always oriented in bands running from east to west across the sky. Throughout the entire winter notes were kept of auroral orientation, usually observed around midnight. The results . . . show a monotonous regularity at this hour; the east-west orientation occurred in nearly 100 per cent of the observations, whenever there were long cohesive bands. . . . It is worth noting, also, that the more spectacular displays of aurora produce enough light to aid the traveller in picking out landmarks if there is no moon light. [Nelson 1969:138]

★ Mirage—*Puikkaqtuq* ★

A spectacular mirage-like phenomenon known as "looming" is common in Arctic regions during the late spring and early summer. Caused by the refraction of light through layers of air of differing temperature, "looming" is generally seen over open water or sea ice. Typically the phenomenon appears as an inverted, distorted image reflected in the sky a few degrees above the horizon. Such images are usually of distant land or floating ice, often situated below the observer's horizon.

Inuit call this phenomenon *puikkaqtuq,* meaning, roughly, to "pop-up" above the level of the sea. The effect has been used by Inuit boating in the Foxe Basin to make accurate landfalls at destinations not otherwise observable from their departure point. And during the open-water season, particularly in relatively ice-free areas of the sea, *puikkaqtuq* mirages are used to locate drifting pans of ice likely to be associated with walrus. In well-defined mirages even the herds of basking walrus can, to the experienced observer, be made out in the "looming" ice (Emil Imaruittuq, pers. comm., 1993).

★ Animal Indicators ★

Occasionally the behaviour of animals would yield clues about orientation. In particular, the seaward feeding sorties of nesting loons and Arctic terns were mentioned. But, in the absence of other markers, close observation of these birds was required before any reliable decision, based on their line of flight, could be made. Zachrias Panikpakuttuk recalls a time when loons were used to guide a hunting party back to land: "Arnajjuaq once used loons to show him the way—this was in the days before motorized boats. They [Arnajjuaq and his companions] were hunting bearded seals when the sky became overcast, completely obscuring the sun. They were paddling a canoe. Arnajjuaq noticed that the loons were going back and forth and when he figured out which loons were heading towards the land he just followed that direction and soon landed" (Panikpakuttuk 1992, IE-219).

Walrus, too, with their apparent sensitivity to changes in wind direction, could be used in a similar way:

> Walrus can be used as indicators. They tend to act before the wind starts—my stepfather told me this—he and I used to be alone on hunting trips. On one particular trip we were returning back to land with a good load [of walrus], so our boat was low in the water. The walruses were moving in the direction of the land, so he said the wind was soon going to change to a northerly direction. Walrus tend to move closer to the land when northerly winds prevail. [Panikpakuttuk 1992, IE-219]

★ Dreams ★

The intuitive side of Inuit navigation is perhaps given its ultimate expression in Aipilik Innuksuk's dream experiences. On more than one occasion, when lost in a blizzard or in fog, Aipilik was guided out of his predicament by voices coming to him in his sleep or dreams. He recalls one of these instances:

> Once while travelling to Nirliviktuuq we made camp between Manittuuq and Angmaarajjuk. Taqaugaq told me to go and get some cached meat to use as dog food on our journey. I think I must have had some difficulty

in getting the meat out, for by the time I had completed my task a storm was starting to blow. We were camped right in the middle of the sea ice in an area devoid of landmarks. I was lost and could not find our camp. I knew that if I continued onwards I would bypass it—so I stopped and made a windbreak. [Here I spent the night.] I would fall asleep and then, waking, would get up on my feet to warm myself before going back to sleep again. Each time I got up I would check the dogs to see that they were still in their harnesses.

I heard someone say to me [in my sleep], *"Iglusi takanna uqussinniiti-appuq! uqummuttiaq ingiraguvit iglusinnut angirarunnapputit!"* ("The direction of your camp is right on your lee side; if you just go downwind you can get home!") I could not see the person who told me this nor did I know who or what it was. . . . When I awoke it was dark. I thought about the words that had been spoken to me but I did not act on them immediately because of my doubts. I went back to sleep. It was getting light when I woke up again. Standing up I saw that the weather had cleared . . . and there, not very far away, was our camp, downwind from where I stood! . . . This was not the only time I was given directions in my sleep. Should other people have similar experiences I would advise them to do as they are told. [A. Innuksuk 1990, IE-164]

ROUTES AND LANDMARKS

No sketch of Inuit wayfinding—even one centred on celestial and atmospheric factors—would be complete without some mention of routes and landmarks. These, after all, are the very arteries and nodes, the topographical anatomy, through which Inuit comprehend the totality of their land and access its life-giving resources.

Inuit everywhere acquired a detailed knowledge of their home area's topography. They knew the land intimately, from its obtrusive mountains and jutting promontories down to its subtle variations in vegetative cover and rock formation. Moreover, they knew it in all conditions of weather, both summer and winter, rarely being confounded by the garb of snow, or the lack of it. This minute attention to topographical detail, this preoccupation with the land's physical and ecological features is reflected in Inuit place-naming practices.

Major journeys usually involved a series of stages marked by predictable, named landmarks: hills, lakes, islands, river bends, raised beaches, erratic boulders, and the like. Occasionally, a stone cairn—*inuksugaq*[26] (plural *inuksugait*)—might signal a turnoff point or the beginning of a land crossing, particularly in areas lacking distinctive natural landmarks of their own. In this way, the traveller always knew his position relative to a number of familiar locations.

There is a vital dimension to established Inuit routes that outsiders can never fully appreciate: their antiquity. What might to the casual observer appear as rather haphazard wandering or purposeless deviations from course is, to the Inuit, an orderly progression along paths travelled by their ancestors over countless generations. Theo Ikummaq points out that routes were chosen with one overriding consideration in mind—that they allow the most advantageous use of dog-team and ice-shod sled:

> All these trails that we follow now, for example *Itillikuluk,* the trail at the end of *Avvajja,* . . . you don't hit rocks on these trails. . . . They are easy on the snowmobile and sled runners and are used year after year. The same thing applies to trails between here and Pond Inlet. . . . You know the trail is where there is the least amount of rocks. [When people from Igloolik] travel to Pond Inlet they use the same trail at all times and once they make camp [they call in] on a short-wave radio, [and] say the name of the

place where they are. . . . Automatically people from either here or Pond Inlet will know exactly where they are because of the constant use of that trail. So trails and place names, you know, they've been used since time immemorial. [Ikummaq 1992, IE-263]

Inuit today travel in the knowledge that their traditional routes have stood the test of time, are safe and efficient, avoid the hazards of thin ice and boulder fields, and make optimal use of local topography and prevailing snow conditions. These ancient routes, in spite of modern snowmobile technology, remain, in general, the most practical way of gaining access to the land and its resources.

For longer journeys, however, the increasing use of large-scale topographic maps is beginning to impinge on the traditional wayfinding practices of Iglulingmiut. In this context Mark Ijjangiaq's comments are revealing:

The time Kupaaq and I took Atata Lursuu [Father Larsen, a Roman Catholic priest] over to Mittimatalik [Pond Inlet] I did not believe in maps. There was a good trail that we could have followed easily, but Atata Lursuu insisted that we follow the trail that was marked on the map. . . . So we ended up following what was shown on the map and sure enough it was the right trail to follow. From that moment on I started to believe in maps. I started to take maps seriously and was able to read them consistently. When one is travelling by dog-team we usually travel at a steady pace, so I am now able to determine how long it will take us to reach our destination following the map. I would be able to determine how long it would take to reach a certain point on the map . . . even if I have never been to that place before. I am now convinced that maps are as accurate as they can be, but there was a time when I did not believe in them. [Ijjangiaq 1990, IE-138]

Ijjangiaq's new-found faith in the topographical map seems to have had a profound effect on his journeying preferences, even to the point of his abandonment of some of the long-established routes: "When I first started reading maps I would travel to places by routes that were not frequented. I started to take routes that looked good on the map, which I found to be much better. [For instance] the route passing through Qukiutitalik, that used to be taken by my father and others, is no longer the route I would take. I had found a better one" (Ijjangiaq 1990, IE-138)

But for Noah Piugaattuk the descriptive power of Inuktitut remains sufficient to convey, indelibly, all the directional information one needs when journeying to an unfamiliar destination. Responding to a question about Inuit and mapping, Piugaattuk mentions that oral instructions were sometimes supplemented by drawings in the snow but emphatically adds: "No, they didn't make maps. When [directions] are explained clearly, without scolding, it is very hard to forget what is said; it makes you listen carefully. Using the winds as references, the *Uangnaq* wind for example, they would explain how the land looks. It was very hard to forget what they said" (Piugaattuk 1988, IE-040).

Stone cairns, *inuksugait*, built by Inuit hunters for a variety of purposes—caribou drives, memorials, or simply to pass the time—became useful landmarks long after their original purpose had been served or forgotten. *Inuksugait* were also used to help hunters locate their meat caches, particularly in areas where deep snow could be expected:

> I do know that *inuksugait* were used for markers especially if they thought that their caribou meat cache might get buried in snow. This usually was the case when the cache was made in a gorge—often the only place where there would be stones enough to cover the meat. An *inuksugaq* would usually be erected on a rise not far from the cache. A pointer would be set on top of the *inuksugaq* pointing in the direction of the cache. In this way it would be known exactly where the cache was situated should it be buried under the snow when they returned to retrieve it in the winter time. [Piugaattuk 1990, IE-147]

A new genre of man-made landmark, born of the establishment of government-sponsored settlements and defence radar stations, is pervading the North American Arctic. Illuminated radio masts, community lights, radar towers, and huge oil storage tanks are now incorporated into the network of landmarks that

define each local area. These structures are becoming indispensable guides, particularly for younger Inuit hunters, who increasingly come to rely on them at the expense of the more traditional wayfinding methods. As early as the mid-1960s Richard Nelson was attributing the demise of traditional wayfinding on the North Alaskan coast to the introduction of these artificial landmarks: "This helps to explain the loss of native skills in navigation by heavenly bodies. It would be difficult for today's Eskimos to do without these landmarks, especially the high towers and beacons of the Dew Line stations" (Nelson 1969:138).

The extent to which DEW Line structures in the Igloolik–Hall Beach area have supplanted traditional methods of navigation became evident when the Department of National Defence proposed, in 1990, to dismantle the radar screens at Hall Beach: "To the surprise of DND officials, the hamlet asked that the huge screens be left standing. The explanation given was that most of today's hunters had grown up using them as landmarks, since they are visible across the flat landscape 40 miles from the town. . . . The irony of this was not lost on many older Inuit residents of Hall Beach who before 1955 did not need a radar tower as an *inukshuk*" (Picco 1993:252).

The far-reaching consequences of the erosion of Inuit navigational skills in the face of cultural change is aptly, if poignantly, contemplated by George Simeon:

> Beyond the range of a purely physical orientation to their environment . . . was their cosmology which never really was construed as functionally separate from the environment. Thus, no artificial boundary existed between the land, its flora and fauna, and the Eskimo world view, but rather, environment, cosmology, and the survival and health of the individual and the group were inextricably woven. When one strand of this weave is lost or broken the physical shell may survive but the inner fabric may be lost to be replaced by anomie. What this implies is not a diminution of affective attachment to the land but rather an erosion of the cognitive and physical skills necessary to live as a free people within its confines. Cognitive mapping ability strictly speaking can, and indeed does, exist without the buttress of a traditional way of life, but it is then merely a skill rather than part of an indigenous holistic orientation to man and nature. [Simeon 1983:26–27]

CHAPTER 7
Time

They used the Sun to tell the time,
they did not have calendars to follow;
they knew nothing of Easter.

(Noah Piugaattuk, 1989)

A generation ago in the Arctic Quebec community of Kangiqsualujjuaq a government development officer was explaining the virtues of hard work and efficiency to a rather polite Inuit audience. During his talk the enthusiastic official used the expression "time is money" and his interpreter, confused but compliant, translated this gem of capitalistic wisdom as "a watch costs a lot!" Inuktitut indeed has no word for time, not, at least, in the abstract, regimented sense commonly understood in Western industrial society.[1] This does not mean of course that Inuit somehow lacked any comprehension of the links between time and so-called economic activity, a view all too often perpetrated on cultures whose perceptions of time do not coincide with those of the Western world. All cultures have constructed time to their particular social, economic, spiritual, and technical needs, and in this, Inuit are no exception.

Traditional Inuit society extolled the productive use of time and there were consequences, beneficial or otherwise, depending on how time was used. Oversleeping, for instance, was said to result in poor hunting, for it was "necessary to show the souls of the animals that one is eager to capture them," while long life (and for pregnant women an easy childbirth) was assured to those who rose early in the morning, went outside, and walked "three times round the house in the direction of the sun" (Rasmussen 1929:181). The habit of early rising was a social value instilled in all Inuit children. Many Igloolik elders have childhood memories of being sent outside early in the morning to observe the weather and begin the day's activities. Hubert Amarualik's recollections are typical: "We had to *anijaaq* [go outdoors[2]] immediately after dressing in the morning. We would observe the sky conditions, note the types of clouds, and the position of the stars" (Amarualik 1994, IE-314).

A useful summary of the factors on which Inuit traditional perceptions of time were based, prior to European contact, is offered by Finn Gad, a Danish historian:

> Formally [they] had been quite content with the changing of the seasons and the known migratory habits of the animals [they] hunted. Wind and weather might upset everything, but on the whole there was a predictable series of changes in a relatively rigid sequence, which applied also to the rising and setting of the sun, its height over the horizon, the period of darkness, the midnight sun in the north and finally the phases of the moon and tide. Besides that there was a rough system for reckoning longer periods of time, but this was more an individual measure, in relation to important events in one's own life or the life of the settlement. . . . The individual and his immediate family had their private calendar based on landmarks on the growing-up of their children, especially the boys. [Gad 1973:265]

Here Gad touches on three measures of Inuit time: the migrations of animals; the cycle of the Sun and the Moon; and "landmark" events in the life of an individual, his family, or community.[3] The first two can be reduced to a single category incorporating the annual solar cycle and nature's response to it. Termed "ecological" or "eco-time" by the astronomer Anthony Aveni, it "connects people with the environment through changes in nature to which they react" (Aveni 1990:169). Gad's third category, which Aveni refers to as social or structural time, "connects people with one another" and was reckoned, more or less linearly (though not numerically), over much longer periods—in the case of Iglulingmiut to about four or five generations. A final category, "mythic time"—a misnomer, perhaps, given the "timelessness" implied—might also be added. Apparently much a part of Inuit consciousness, mythic time linked people to their very beginnings in that distant, uncertain epoch when all was darkness and disorder. Only through the creation of the Sun, Moon, and stars, as we have seen, did order, light, and the predictable succession of seasons prevail.

In the past, and indeed well into the "modern" era, the ecological calendar, represented by up to thirteen named lunations—"moons"—was the dominant regulator of virtually all Inuit life. For Iglulingmiut, as for most other Inuit groups, the changing seasons, determined not only their day-to-day activities but also their diet, dwelling locations, and communal groupings as they moved, predictably, about the local area in response to the seasonal migrations of the animals on which they depended.

The Inuit eco-calendar was relatively flexible and, being based on recurring events in the natural world—the return of the Sun, the nesting of birds, the break-up of the sea ice, and so forth—varied according to latitude. Moreover, the sequence of lunations did not always correspond precisely with the ecological events for which they were named. Thus, in Igloolik, the "moon month" *Manniit,* meaning "eggs"—a reference to the nesting of birds—could straddle the sixth or seventh lunation of the year, depending on an early or late arrival of the season.

On the astronomical front there was the problem of "harmonizing" the lunar and solar cycles (a major challenge for all moon-based calendars) to ensure that the sequence of lunations would, over time, keep in step with the recurring events in nature for which the moons are named.[4] Iglulingmiut appear to have circumvented this problem in much the same manner used by the early Romans—simply by not accounting for the time of the year when subsistence activity was at its lowest ebb (Aveni 1990:112). This approach is at least implicit in the explanation given to Rasmussen for the lack of Inuktitut names for the two midwinter months: "[Ava] called them simply: *ukiup tatqe,* i.e., winter's moons. These two moon periods, he said, resemble each other in that they are dark, cold, and hunting in them is difficult, so that they did not need any special designation" (Rasmussen 1930:63).

Among the Iglulingmiut an alternate designation, already noted, for the midwinter months is *Tauvikjuaq*, "the great darkness," which refers specifically to winter's sunless period—approximately 45 days at the latitude of Igloolik. This period necessarily involves portions of two lunations, one of which, at least for calendrical purposes, is ignored, thereby temporarily interrupting the practice of accounting for each new moon in an ordered, and named, sequence. Effectively time is put "on hold," as indeed nature herself seems to be during this sunless period and the eco-calendar can now be reset to begin afresh with the first new moon of the year—*Siqinnaarut*, the moon of the returning Sun.

A similar but somewhat more involved approach to keeping the Moon's months in tandem with the Sun's year—not substantiated by Igloolik elders—is reported by Franz Boas in a rather generalized passage on the Inuit calendar of the Eastern Canadian Arctic:

> They divide the year into thirteen months, the names of which vary a great deal, according to the tribes and according to the latitude of the place. The surplus is balanced by leaving out a month every few years, to wit, the month siringilang (without sun), which is of indefinite duration, the name covering the whole time of the year when the sun does not rise and there is scarcely any dawn. Thus every few years this month is totally omitted when the new moon and the winter solstice coincide. The name qaumartenga is applied only to the days without sun but with dawn, while the rest of the same moon is called siriniktenga. [Boas 1888:644]

The following table sets out the Iglulingmiut calendar in accordance with their thirteen named moon months. The table's columns present information on the seasons, of which Iglulingmiut reckon eight, and link each of the moon-months to various societal activities, animal migrations, and other observable seasonal markers.[5] Note that the European calendar months corresponding to the moon months are only approximations, particularly for the spring and summer seasons.

Moon Month	Season	Celestial Markers	Biological and Environmental Markers	Social Activities (Selected)
SIQINNAARUT "Sun is possible." (January/February)	UKIUQ "Winter."	Aagjuuk stars seen at dawn. mid January. Sun and Moon compete; ingiaqautijuuk. Sun leaves the horizon; kullutaniktuq.	Formation of uiguaq at the floe-edge. Mauliq[1] hunting for ring seals through the uiguaq.[2]	String games (ajaraaq) discontinued by taboo—replaced by ajagaq.
QANGATTAASAN "It (the Sun) gets higher." Also known as Akurlungnaq[3] (February/March)	UKIUQ "Winter."	Sun rising higher. "Pualutanikpuq"	Walrus migrate towards the land-fast ice. Bearded seal shunted through the uiguaq.	Winter camps established on the sea ice for seal-and walrus-hunting.
AVUNNIIT "Premature birth of (jar) seal pups." (March/April)	UPIRNGAKSAJAAQ "Towards early Spring."	Spring equinox. Days and nights of equal length.	Premature jar seals born. Snow conditions faster for dog sleds.	Longer journeys made by dog-team.
NATTIAN "Seal pups." (April/May)	UPIRNGAKSAAQ "Early spring."	Lengthing days, increasing twilight. Stars no longer visible.	Jar seal pups born. Increasing snowfall.	Seal-hunting by the Ajautaq method.[4] Playing anauligaaq (Inuit baseball).
TIRIGLUIT "Bearded seal pups." Also known as TUPIQTUUT, "tenting" month. (May/June)	UPIRNGAAQ "Spring."	Sun continuously above horizon: nipijuittuq ("does not set").	Bearded seal pups born. Snow too soft for igloo building. Arrival of migratory birds: snowy owls, buntings, snow geese.	Move from winter dwellings (igloos or sod-houses) to tents. Hunting basking seals.

[1] Mauliq hunting—hunting through seal breathing-holes in the ice.

[2] Uiguaq—formation of new ice along the floe-edge.

[3] Qangattaasan is also a reference to the development of the snow "cones" over the breathing holes of ring seals (George Kappianaq, pers. comm., 1997). Akurlungnaq is a reference to the formation of frost between the inner and outer layers of the back flaps (aku) of a caribou parka, in this coldest of months.

[4] A method using an indicator inserted into the seal hole.

Moon Month	Season	Celestial Markers	Biological and Environmental Markers	Social Activities (Selected)
NURRAIT "Caribou calves." (early June)	*UPIRNGAAQ* "Spring."	Sun continuously above horizon: *nipijuittuq*. Summer solstice. Snow melt begins.	Caribou calving. Arrival of migratory birds complete. Final spells of freezing weather prior to annual thaw.	The ball game *aullaujaq* played.
MANNIIT "Eggs." (late June/July)	*UPIRNGAAQ* "Spring."	Sun continuously above horizon: *nipijuittuq*	Migratory birds nest.	Egg gathering. Eider duck snaring. Hunting basking seals.
SAGGARUUT "Caribou hair sheds." (July/August)	*AUJAQ* "Summer."	Sun sets again: *nipittaliqtuq* (late July). Break-up of sea ice.	Caribou skin sheds. Old Squaw ducks and bumblebees molt.	Hunting seals in molt (skins used for making tents).
AKULLIRUT "Caribou hair thickens." (August/September)	*AUJAQ* "Summer."	Twilight returns, brighter stars visible again. Open-water season.	Seed styles of the plant *Malikkaan* (*Dryas*) uncoil. Caribou skins prime for winter clothing.	Inland caribou-hunting. Seal-, beluga-, and narwhal-hunting in open water.
AMIRAIJAUT "Velvet peels from caribou antlers." (September/October)	*UKIAKSAJAAQ* "Towards early autumn."	Autumnal equinox —days and nights of equal length.	Shedding of "velvet" from caribou antlers. Spines of the "four horned" sculpin peel. Heavy morning dew. Ice forms in small ponds. Accumulation of snow.	Inland caribou-hunting, particularly for bulls, continues. Caribou skins ideal for bedding.

Moon Month	Season	Celestial Markers	Biological and Environmental Markers	Social Activities (Selected)
UKIULIRUT "Winter starts." (October/November)	*UKIAKSAAQ* "Autumn."	Days shorten.	Winter starts. Caribou mate. Fish (Arctic Char) spawn. Sea ice starts to form.	Move to winter quarters. Fishing through thin lake ice.
TUSARTUUT "Hearing" (news from neighbouring camps). (November/ December)	*UKIAQ* "Early winter."	Sunlight restricted to a few hours around noon.	Sea freezes over.	Travel (by dog-team) resumed on land and sea. Seal-hunting. Blubber stored for winter fuel. Fox-trapping starts. Sewing of new caribou-skin clothing; this task had to be completed prior to the onset of the dark period.
TAUVIKJUAQ "Great darkness." (December/January)	*UKIUQ* "Winter."	Sunless period begins early December. Pre-dawn appearance of *Aagjuuk* stars in the northeast and *Akuttujuuk* stars seen westerly in the evening. Winter solstice. Circumpolar Moon in some years.		*Tivajuut*, a festival of renewalheld after the appearance of the *Aagjuuk* stars. Seal hunting.

Star Time

While the succession of the seasons and their constituent moon months were marked, as we have seen, by the coincidence of various celestial and terrestrial events, the progressions of day and night were reckoned by the stars and Sun alone—reckonings at which Inuit were particularly adept. An example of this adeptness is given by Elisha Kent Kane, an American explorer journeying in Northwest Greenland. Late one night a number of Inuit visited his expedition's hut seeking a place to sleep. However, one of Kane's companions, a man named Petersen, apparently not given to hospitality, tried to persuade the visitors that it would soon be daylight and that they should move on: "No," [said one of the Inuit visitors] "when that star gets round to that point," indicating the quarter of the heavens, "and is no higher than this star," naming it, "will be the time to harness up my dogs." Petersen was astounded; but he went out the next morning and verified the sidereal fact (Kane 1856, I:426).

In common with other Inuit groups living in the higher northern latitudes, where winter daylight is sparse, the Iglulingmiut shared the problem of timing their hunting activities to coincide with whatever light the day offered. In this, as was the case with Petersen's visitors, stars were their only guide. Many Igloolik elders still recall the days, not so long ago, when the position of various stars, collectively termed *qausiut*—"indicators of daylight"—signalled the start of each winter morning:

> In those days . . . everyone lived in igloos. The hunters usually had a peek hole in the igloo to observe the stars that were used to determine the time of the morning. . . . Everyone went to sleep early in comparison to what we do today. They would spend the early mornings getting prepared for the day's . . . activities. Dogs had to be fed, traces prepared; fuel had to be readied for the *qulliq* [soapstone lamp]; and snow or ice melted for water. On waking up there were plenty of things to be done. [Nasook 1990, IE-159]

Iglulingmiut use of stars for telling time is based on two principles: the revolving of the constellation *Tukturjuit* (Ursa Major) around *Nutuittuq* (Polaris), and the easterly rising and westerly setting of the non-circumpolar stars. Of this latter variety the two stars of the constellation *Aagjuuk* (Altair and Tarazed) were the most commonly used, not only in Igloolik but across many other regions of the Arctic. The *Aagjuuk* stars, as we have seen (pages 44–51), were also used to mark the winter solstice and to predict the Sun's return after the annual "dark period." Peter Tatigat Arnattiaq of Igloolik nicely sums up the dual uses of *Aagjuuk* as a keeper of both diurnal and seasonal time: "*Aagjuuk* is the morning [constellation]. The Inuit used to say "*Aagjulirpuq*," meaning that the dawn is not far off. . . . There is another saying—"*Aagjuuk agujjalirpuq*." This means that the *Aagjuuk* stars are starting to catch up with the daylight. Earlier [in the season] *Aagjuuk* would appear when it was still dark but as [the season] progressed *Aagjuuk* and the daylight would coincide"(Arnattiaq 1991, IE-186).

The four stars comprising the "collar bone" constellation, *Quturjuuk* (Pollux and Castor, and Capella and Menkalinan), barely circumpolar at the latitude of Igloolik, were also used to foretell daybreak: "Using *Quturjuuk* as a timepiece, in the evening its stars will be tilted to the left; later they will be aligned [with the horizon], looking as if they have straightened out. Then the stars will tilt in the other direction [to the right] when the daylight is about to come" (Amaaq 1989, IE-073).

Cain Iqqaqsaq explains how the *Tukturjuit* constellation could be used for telling time: "*Tukturjuit* is useful to tell the time and direction. . . . [The constellation] is easily identifiable for it has the form of a caribou. . . . As midnight approaches it appears as if [the caribou] gets up on its hind legs and its head starts to get higher" (Iqqaqsaq 1993, IE-257).

Whereas Iqqaqsaq relies solely on the apparent attitude of Ursa Major—the rising of the "caribou"—to tell the time, Peter Arnattiaq's method involves the constellation's changing relationship to Polaris with the progression of time: "I know the star *Nuusuittuq* (Polaris). The *Tukturjuk* (Ursa Major) stars go round it. As the night progresses *Tukturjuk* would face this star in a position different from that of the early night" (Arnattiaq 1991, IE-186).

From the Mackenzie Delta, through the Coronation Gulf to Boothia Peninsula in the Central Arctic, the constellation *Sivulliik* (comprising the stars Arcturus and Muphrid) seems to have been the preferred sign of morning. In the manner already described for *Quturjuuk*, the *Sivulliik* stars appear tilted to the right in the late evening, almost horizontal during the "wee" hours, and tilted slightly to the left around dawn. Throughout the night the progressively altering attitude of the stars Arcturus and Muphrid gives the appearance that the constellation is turning "over" or "upside down." Duncan Pryde, a trader and linguist who lived in the Coronation Gulf area, has vivid memories of lying in his sleeping bag listening to his travelling companion announce, while widening the ventilation hole in the snowhouse roof to see the stars, *"Taquaq, tupangnaqsijuq. Sivulliik kuujjangajuk."* ("Duncan, it's time to wake up. The *Sivulliik* stars are hanging head-down.") (Duncan Pryde, pers. comm., 1995).

Accurately estimating time in the dark mornings of winter was clearly a priority for many Inuit groups across the Arctic. But the stars, as Michel Kupaaq explains, were also used to signal the end of the waking day: "The *Ullaktut* [Orion's belt] stars when they first appear [in the evening] are slanted; when they straighten up it's time for bed" (Kupaaq 1996, IE-370). And for the people of the Kobuk River, Alaska, the appearance of the Pleiades in a certain position would also indicate bedtime (Giddings 1961:43).

★ ★ ★

SUN TIME

Iglulingmiut divide each day-night cycle into ten named segments of somewhat unequal length as shown in the idealized diagram on the next page (arbitrarily set around the equinoxes). Five of the segments derive their names from the word *ulluq* (day), the other five from *unnuk* (night). With the exception of *Ullulluaq* (the midday segment) and *Unnuaq* (the midnight segment) the divisions are not directly dependent on the Sun's position at any given time. For example, *Ullaaq* (that part of the morning when daily activities are normally underway) maintains the same relationship to the divisions on either side of it (*Ullaaraarjuk* and *Ullaaqpasik*) independently of the region's widely variable light levels—from darkness to full sunlight—prevailing during the course of the year.

Depending on the season, times of day or night within any given division can be specified with some precision by referring, for instance, to the position of the Sun—particularly around noon (*qitiraqtuq*), sunrise (*siqinniliqtuq*), or sunset (*nipiliqtuq*); or to changing light levels—the first signs of dawn (*akisuliqtuq*), the morning transition between twilight and full daylight (*ijunajuq*), or the evening transition between full daylight and twilight (*ijulirtuq*); or, in the spring and summer months, to the time of day when the Sun is warming up (*kiakpallaktuq*), at its warmest (*kijjiqtuq*), or cooling off (*niglaliqtuq*).

★ 201 ★

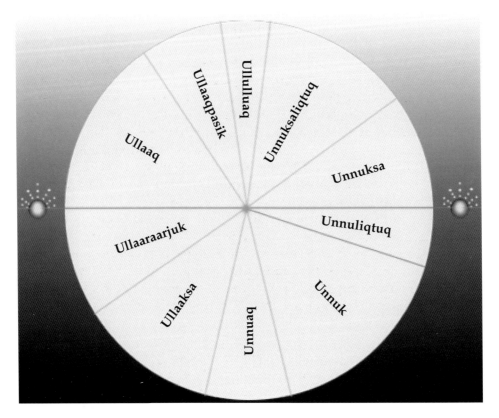

The "midnight sun" period—in Igloolik from May to July—is called *nipisuiq-tuq* (literally "[the Sun] never sets"). During this period "night-time" is referred to as *unnuattak* in contrast to *unnuk,* the term used for "night" when actual darkness occurs.

Progressive seasonal measurements of the Sun's altitude taken variously by harpoon *(unaqtaniktuq),* thumb *(kullutaniktuq),* and mitt *(pualutaniktuq)* during the first three months of the year were important to Iglulingmiut as well as to other Inuit groups in the Eastern Canadian Arctic. These stages of the Sun's gain in altitude and their significance to Inuit are discussed in detail in Chapter 4.

THE NEW TIME

In 1822, Inuit in the Igloolik area were treated to their first lesson in the strict regimes of European time when Captain Parry attempted—unsuccessfully as it turned out—to regulate the Sunday visits of Inuit to his ships and, naively, to introduce them to that rather arbitrary division of time, the week: "A number of Esquimaux coming before the church service we gave them to understand by the sun that none could be admitted before noon, when they quietly remained outside the ships till divine service had been performed. We then endeavoured to explain . . . that every seventh day they must not come to the ships, for without any intention of offending, they had become rather an annoyance in this way" (Parry 1824:172).

Early in the next century Vilhjalmur Stefánsson, on his second visit to the Western Canadian Arctic, thought himself similarly inconvenienced by the effects of Inuit behaviour on his schedule, but for quite the opposite reason. By then, many of his Inuit guides had embraced Christianity and were reluctant to travel on Sundays, thereby impeding the progress of his expedition. Stefánsson with customary ridicule also deplored the effects of Sunday observance on Inuit whale-hunting activities:

> There is no regularity about the migration of the animals, and often at the height of the whaling season the crews may be encamped for a week at a time without seeing any; and then, all in one day, scores of whales may come along. . . . This day of opportunity is . . . as likely as not to be a Sunday. When the Eskimo had learned that God had forbidden work upon the Sabbath they took the point of view that it does not profit a man that he gain the whole world if he lose his own soul, and although the catching of whales was the one thing in the world which all of them most desired, nevertheless they agreed that the loss of one's soul was too great a price to pay even for a bow-head whale. Accordingly they would commence on Saturday afternoon to pull back their boats from the edge of the ice and get everything ready for the Sabbath observance. . . . It usually took them half of Monday to get everything ready for work again. In this manner they lost two days out of every seven from a harvest season of only six weeks in the year. [Stefánsson 1922:91]

CALENDARS

Spreading north from Cumberland Sound, one of Christianity's major hubs in the Canadian Eastern Arctic, news of the Christians' day of rest reached Igloolik well ahead of the missionaries' arrival:

> Christianity . . . started out from the Pangnirtung area. The concept of keeping one day a week to observe Sundays was passed from person to person, reaching great distances throughout the region. The people knew in advance that there would be a number of days without restrictions or taboos followed by one day that should be observed—a day of abstention to be fully respected, vital to the Christian belief.[6] [The Iglulingmiut] heard about this requirement well before they started converting to Christianity. [Piugaattuk 1991, IE-181]

Conversion to Christianity, and with it the practice of Sunday observance, apparently relieved Inuit from many of the obligations required by their own taboos. The frequent and unpredictable abstentions required by these were now exchanged for a single, predictable day: "They found that it was much easier for them to observe [this] one day. So on that account they fully respected Sunday" (Piugaattuk 1991, IE-181). Christianity, however, introduced to the Igloolik area in the 1920s, was soon to change the manner in which the Inuit of the region reckoned and used time. Gradually time's references began to include the liturgical demands of the new religion. Noah Piugaattuk mentions some of the practical difficulties in adjusting to the time-keeping requirements of Christianity:

> It was hard when we started to live by the new religion. We had to make sure that we did not bypass the day on which no work was to be done. It was hard as there were no such things as calendars at that time. [Piugaattuk 1991, IE-170]

> The women of the camp would consult each other [to determine Sunday] and, after that, they made sure to keep track of the days, making a mark

on [a piece of wood] for each day that passed. Whoever was recording the days would make sure not to lose their record. [Piugaattuk 1991, IE-177]

Certainly there were times when two people, from different camps, met on the trail and exchanged stories and so forth, and wondered which day it was. During periods of intense hunting no attention was paid to the days (or nights). [The hunters] would not keep track of time. This responsibility usually fell to the ones who were not engaged in doing other things. . . . One must realize that, at times, the hunters would not sleep for days on end when hunting conditions were favourable. Under these circumstances they would, no doubt, lose count of the days. But there were always elders that kept track of time for the rest of the camp. [Piugaattuk 1991, IE-181]

Later, with increasing missionary activity in the area, the task of keeping the days in proper order was made easier: calendars became standard issue. In his travels with "Mikinnirsaq" (the Anglican missionary, John Turner), Piugaattuk recalls that they gave the people "Bibles as well as calendars" and "informed them about the daily lessons following the calendar" (Piugaattuk 1989, IE-044).[7]

The first calendar introduced to Igloolik by the Roman Catholic mission in the 1930s interestingly included the dates of solar eclipses along with, presumably, those of important religious festivals. This demonstration of predictive astronomy was not lost on the Inuit parishioners:

After [the Roman Catholic priest] started to live among us he made a calendar with a small typewriter he had brought with him. This was not much of a calendar [by today's standards]. He made the letter "I" for each weekday; for Sundays he marked an "X." That was the first time I had seen a calendar. . . . Each of the days were marked off with a pencil.[8] Our priest knew that on certain days there would be an eclipse of the sun and he would mark these days on the calendar. . . . As the day of the eclipse approached we would keep a close watch on the sun, and, sure enough, the sun would start to darken.

Even when people started to use calendars there were times when they would lose track of the days. When this happened they would pick a certain day that might have some significance to them and [declaring it Sunday] would resume counting the days after that until the correct [order of the days] could be determined. [Ijjangiaq 1991, IE-184]

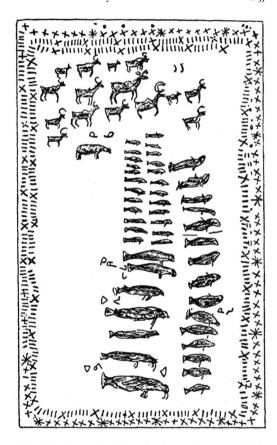

The calendar of Kroonook, a hunter who kept this interesting record of his year's work. The border represents the days, straight strokes for week days, crosses for Sundays. The pictures show deer of various sorts, a polar bear, a walrus—readily distinguished by the tusks, and several varieties of seal and fish. (Revillon Frères: 1923:21)

For the Greenlanders the introduction of Christianity, though occurring much earlier than in the Canadian Arctic, brought with it the same requirement to divide the year into weeks. As Finn Gad writes: "In this matter they were obliged to rely on the missionary's authority. Some, however, made their own 'weekly calendar' consisting simply of a piece of wood with seven holes in it, into which [they] fitted a little wooden peg for each day of the week 'so that they shall not mistake Sunday'" (Gad 1973:265).

Clocks

The missionaries' calendars were soon followed by the traders' clocks—a popular trade item—arbitrarily dividing the days into hours, the hours into minutes, and the minutes into audible seconds. Time's passage in ever-decreasing divisions could now be seen, measured, and even heard, in a context quite removed from the tempo of the natural world. Curiosities at first, clocks, like the calendars before them, had a hesitant introduction to Inuit society:

> Before clocks were widely used the only way to determine time was by the stars. I suppose they found clocks more convenient than having to go outdoors to tell the time. When the clock stopped—usually when they forgot to wind it—they would say outright that it was "dead." It would then be reset, mainly by guess-work, according to the time of day. [In these days] they had no use for the clock's long hand at all. If, for example, the short hand was at seven and the long hand at three they would say "it is seven o'clock." [Imaruittuq 1990, IE-161]

Inuit from the Keewatin region apparently used a method of telling the clock's time not directly involving the numerical value of the numbers on the dial. Instead, they named the hours with reference to the perceived shape of the numerals, to the orientation of the hour hand, or to some regular activity associated with the hour:

> They did not use the numbers on the face of the clock. They would give the hours names such as *ulamautinguaq* ["it looks like an ax"—7 o'clock], *igganguaq* ["it looks like spectacles"—8 o'clock], *qulilluanga* ["it's at the top"—12 o'clock], *saniralluanga* ["it's at the side"—3 o'clock], and *atilluanga* ["it's at the bottom"—6 o'clock]. Then there was *ullurummitavik* ["time for the midday meal"—12 o'clock]. . . . When the clock struck nine, they use to say *sukatirvik* ["winding time"], so at that hour the clocks would be wound. [Nasook 1990, IE-159]

The introduction of alarm clocks and, more recently, radio clocks brought predictability and precision to the waking hours. Formerly the problem of timely waking in the morning was tackled in various ways. In addition to an early to bed, early to rise routine, bladder function was mentioned by a number of hunters who would begin the day's activities after rising for their second urination of the night. Infants, as Martha Nasook explains, could also ensure that no one overslept in the morning (or stayed up too late at night):

> Once when Apak [her infant son] was not yet a year old, we were over on the mainland, caribou hunting. . . . We did not have a clock at all except for Uyarak [who was away at the time]. We had to depend on our children to determine the time in the morning. When the morning came the children would be wide awake and it would still be dark outside. At night when they fell asleep, it was an indication that it was time [for all of us] to sleep. Indeed the children in those days were instrumental in keeping time. Apak was our timepiece. [Nasook 1990, IE-159]

With the possible exception of Christianity—itself profoundly calendar-regulated—no other element of European culture has had a greater effect on present-day Inuit society. Western time—Aveni aptly terms it the "imposition of order"—is both a symbol and purveyor of cultural change in Inuit communities across the Arctic. The work-day, the school-day, the weekend, religious and civic holidays, scheduled airline flights, store hours, birthdays, and anniversaries—all ordered by calendar and clock—immeasurably affect the way in which Inuit now relate to each other and to their environment.

But for all that some of the old perceptions of time tenaciously persist alongside the new. In many Arctic communities the arrival of spring triggers an irresistible urge to partake of nature's bounty, to renew the social bonds engendered by the proper coincidence of time, place, and activity. A mass exodus to traditional fishing and hunting grounds ensues. Employers' clock-driven schedules fall apart as the new time temporarily gives way to the old. And recently, a young man in Igloolik when asked for a definition of time, tellingly, and without hesitation, replied, "Time is nine to five."

CHAPTER 8
Igloolik Legends

Our tales are narratives of human experience,
and therefore they do not always tell of beautiful things.
But one cannot both embellish a tale to please
the hearer and at the same time keep to the truth.
The tongue should be the echo of that
which must be told,
and it cannot be adapted according to
the moods and the tastes of man.
The word of the new-born is not to be trusted,
but the experiences of the ancients contain truth.

(Osarqaq, *in* Rasmussen 1921)

INTRODUCTION

In free English translation, this chapter offers a selection of myths and legends told by Igloolik Inuit elders between 1986 and 1992.

Each legend is prefaced by a short introduction touching mainly on the astronomical significance of the narrative. Chapter 9 contains a representative selection of these same legends rendered in Inuktitut transcription. The transcriptions were made verbatim by Leah Otak, of Igloolik, from the original audio-taped recordings.

By way of contrast, Chapter 10 is a selection of Inuit legends, on the same broad theme, gleaned from previously published sources, more or less representative of the entire Arctic region. While none of these chapters makes any claim to completeness, taken together, their contents demonstrate the role of myth in developing and sustaining Inuit views of the universe and clearly reveal the underlying unity of these views across the length and breadth of their vast territory.

Knud Rasmussen pointed out long ago that Inuit tales were never intended to be read. In print they are completely out of context, like notes on a musical score. Here they lack the essential vitality bestowed by the narrator who "stamped them all with the force of his own personality" and made each telling a creation, a unique event. In the free translations that follow, they are, of course, even further removed from their original source—from the poetic qualities of the language that gave them birth. The Inuktitut transcriptions partially make up for this deficiency.

These myths also have been removed from their true temporal and spiritual contexts, their meanings challenged and diluted by other world views suffusing the Arctic over the past century. In offering their myths, some of the Igloolik elders, rather self-consciously, took pains to point out that these tales were not true, but "simply stories," having no basis in fact. For others there was the uncomfortable sense that their myths, like other defining elements of pre-contact Inuit culture—among them shamanism and drum dancing—were anathema to their Christian beliefs. And so we might keep in mind something else that Rasmussen has said about Inuit myths: "If in them there are things which seem to be contrary to common sense, it is merely because the later generations are unable to grasp everything which, to their forebears, were obvious truths" (Ostermann 1939:3).

THE SUN AND THE MOON
TOLD BY GEORGE KAPPIANAQ

Most versions of this tale told in the Canadian Arctic omit any explanation of the boy's blindness. Rink, however, in a Greenlandic legend, explains that a dispute over the use of the skin of a bearded seal (Phoca barbata), *that the boy had killed led directly to his blindness. The mother had wanted to use the skin for a platform covering whereas the boy insisted that the skin be made into harpoon line. Then his mother, as she was removing the hair from the skin in preparation for line-making, grew angry and cast a spell on the skin, saying: "When he cuts thee into thongs, when he cuts thee asunder, then thou shalt snap and smite his face." And so it happened that while the boy was scraping the tightly stretched thong it snapped "and hitting both eyes, blinded him" (Rink 1875:99–100). This explanation, combined with the central events in the following version of the Sun/Moon legend told by George Kappianaq, furnishes from the Inuit point of view all the necessary preconditions for the transformation of human beings into celestial personalities: dispute, violence, and the breaking of taboos.*

George Kappianaq's telling of the Sun/Moon legend differs from most modern versions of the tale in that his narrative incorporates episodes usually offered elsewhere as complete legends in themselves: for example, the creation of the narwhal (Spalding 1979) and the story of the blind boy (Rink 1875). The result is a tale of almost epic proportions.

I have heard stories how the moon and the sun came to be.

Two orphans, a brother and a sister, were staying with their grandmother, their only living relative. The boy, who was blind, was known as Aningaat. One day all the other people in their camp left, leaving these three behind.

They lived in a *qarmmaq* [a semi-permanent winter house made from stone, bone, and sod] which, although insulated, was not much of a dwelling, but at least it was a shelter. They had one dog with them.

One day a polar bear came upon their camp. Their dog was able to alert them to the presence of the bear, which had now come to the window of their dwelling. The blind boy had bow and arrow, so when the bear broke the window open, the old woman handed the bow to the young man and aimed it at the bear for him. When she gave the command to shoot, the boy let fly an arrow.

"You shot the window frame, you shot the window frame," exclaimed the old woman.

To this the blind boy replied: "I was sure I heard the sound of a wounded animal." He had indeed heard the arrow strike the bear, followed by the sound of the wounded animal falling to the ground.

The old woman now instructed her granddaughter to go out and check to see if the bear was dead. To do this she told her granddaughter to first throw a small snowball at the bear. When she went out she could see the bear lying near the entrance of their house, where it had slid down backwards at the edge of the porch. She knew that the animal had been wounded and although afraid, she threw a small snowball at the bear's rump as her grandmother had told her to do. The bear did not budge. So she went back inside and told her grandmother. The old woman now instructed her to go out again and, this time, to kick the bear in the rump. So she went out and approached the bear again and kicked the animal in the rump. Again the bear did not budge. On hearing this the grandmother said: "Yes, the bear is dead."

The old woman then took her *ulu* [a woman's knife], which was probably dull, sharpened it, and they went outside. She skinned and butchered the bear. Meanwhile she told her granddaughter to strangle the dog, their only dog and the very one which had just alerted them to the approach of the polar bear. The dog was also butchered.

The boy who had shot the bear was now confined to living in the porch area of their dwelling and was made to eat cooked dog meat, while his grandmother and sister secretly lived on bear meat.

The girl was filled with sympathy towards her brother for he was being fed only dog meat. Being forbidden by her grandmother to give the boy any bear meat, she nevertheless took it upon herself to sneak some of this meat to him whenever she could. Thus when the old woman and her granddaughter were eating, the girl would take a portion of her meat and hide it in her sleeve. Each time the girl asked her grandmother for more, the old woman would say: "You seem to be eating so quickly; perhaps you are giving some of the meat to your brother?"

But the girl denied this, saying that her hunger makes her eat so quickly. And so she would take a few more pieces of meat and hide them in her sleeve. Thus she fed her brother cooked polar bear meat.

One day Aningaat asked his sister, "Are the lakes still without red-throated loons?"

She kept saying no to this question. The snow was now melting, exposing the earth. Once again he asked: "Are the lakes still without loons?"

"No, the lakes now have loons in them," she finally replied.

The blind boy then asked his sister to take him to a lake, and told her, before she left him there, that she should mark the way back to the *qarmmaq* with stone markers. He asked her to make the markers close to each other so he would be able to feel his way home.

So she took Aningaat to a lake on which were two loons and she left him there. On her way home she made stone landmarks all the way from the lake to the *qarmmaq* as instructed by her brother.

Aningaat could hear the loons on the lake. Then he heard what seemed to be the sound of a *qajaq* [kayak] right in front of him, accompanied by the noises of loons. He heard someone summoning him to climb on to the *qajaq*. Guided by the voice he felt his way to the shore. When he got to the *qajaq* he was told to lie down on his belly on the *qajaq*'s aft section. He did as he was instructed.

He could hear that he was being paddled towards the middle of the lake. At that moment he was taken for a dive. They were submerged for a time until he started to feel the need for air, so they surfaced. After he took in some air and his breathing was normal again they started to paddle further out into the lake and again he was taken for a dive. This time they were submerged for a longer period and the need for air was greater when he was finally taken to the surface.

He was asked: "Can you not see a little bit?"

"No, I cannot see, but I'm starting to see the brightness in my eyes," he answered.

So they went for another dive which lasted even longer than before and his want of air was much greater. When they at last surfaced the voice asked: "Can you not see a little bit more?"

"I am starting to see the land," he replied.

The stranger then licked the eyes of the blind boy. The boy noticed that the stranger's tongue was very coarse, so coarse, in fact, that he felt it would cut him through.

Again Aningaat was taken for a dive. And when he was thoroughly in need of air he was taken to the surface.

"Can you still not see," asked the voice.

"No, I can see the land beyond," the boy replied.

The stranger again licked Aningaat's eyes and then they dived again into the waters of the lake. On surfacing once more the stranger asked: "Can you still not see the grass on top of the hill?"

"No," replied Aningaat, "I can see a little of the grass, but it seems hazy."

So once again they dived, this time for much longer than before until he was desperately out of breath. When they finally surfaced he was getting worried that they had stayed too long under the water. Aningaat's eyes were again licked, and he was taken for a final dive. Once back on the surface of the lake, the stranger again asked: "Can you still not see the grass on top of those hills?"

Aningaat replied that he could now see the grass. In fact he could even see it being moved by the wind on top of the hill. Indeed he was able to see a long way off. Aningaat was now ready to be taken to the shore.

When they reached the shore, the stranger told Aningaat not to look back at him until he had paddled well out onto the lake. But when Aningaat could hear the stranger paddling farther and farther from the shore, he quickly peeked under his arm, and he saw that the stranger's back was without skin. As soon as he saw this he became frightened and immediately looked away.

Aningaat now started for home using the stone markers that his sister had piled up for him. He felt sorry for his sister for having done all this work. Cutting a portion of skin from the upper part of his boots he made a sling and, while following the stone markers in the direction of his home, he used the sling to fire stones at the Arctic terns.

When he reached home he walked in to the *qarmmaq* and asked his grandmother: "Whose bear-skin is that outside? And whose dog-skin is that there?"

"The people that came by *umiaq* [skin boat] left them here for me," his grandmother replied falsely.

After his eyesight was restored to normal Aningaat made himself a harpoon. About this time the white whales were passing along the shores. He was able to catch young whales using the harpoon. Aningaat and his sister now began to provide food only for themselves, leaving little for their grandmother but ensuring that she would not starve.

One day when they went whale hunting, the grandmother decided that she would be the anchor for the harpoon line. Aningaat was hesitant at first but the grandmother kept insisting that the harpoon line be tied around her waist.

So they went down to the shore where the white whales would pass and she

Kayak. Ivory sculpture, depilated skin. Pangnirtung area,
Baffin Island, NWT, 1933–1942. Royal Ontario Museum.
Dr. Jon A. and Mrs. Muriel Bildfell Collection.
Purchased through the generosity of Mr. Donald Ross.

made ready to anchor the harpoon line by tying it around her middle. A pod of whales was passing and she started to cry out: "Harpoon the young one! Harpoon the young one!"

Aningaat took aim and pretended to strike the young white whale, but instead, and quite deliberately, harpooned a fully grown bull whale that was swimming behind the young one.

As the bull whale felt the harpoon strike it started to swim away and the old woman was pulled into the water. Indeed at first she was actually running on top of the water until she eventually submerged. But she would not suffocate, and soon she surfaced some distance from the shore. As she came up she was twisting her wet hair forward and again she was pulled under the water. She surfaced once more still twisting her hair which had now become long. Her hair then transformed into a spiraled tusk. And so from the old woman did the narwhals come into being.

After the loss of their grandmother Aningaat and his sister set out in search of other people. As they journeyed they made camp only to rest and continued to push onwards. They were able to keep themselves supplied with food as Aningaat was able to catch caribou from time to time.

So on they went and, one evening, they finally came upon a camp and here they decided to stay for the night. As it was by now winter, Aningaat started to build an igloo. But before he had completed putting the final snow-blocks in place he became thirsty and so asked his sister to fetch him some water to drink. She was afraid at first but, as her brother was very thirsty, she went to the entrance of one of the igloos and asked for some water. She was warmly welcomed. A person inside instructed her to enter the igloo backwards, carrying her water container, and to have the back flap of her parka pulled up. As she entered the igloo in this way the people inside jumped on her and started to scratch her back.

"Aningaat, over here!" she cried.

Aningaat, who was working close by, heard his sister's cries of alarm. He rushed over to the igloo his sister had entered and ripped open its window, which was made of animal intestines, using his long-handled harpoon. With this harpoon he now began to jab the people in the igloo and so caused them to release their victim. Some were killed when he struck them. An old man started for the bed and, licking his fingernails, said, "I kept telling you that her brother would come and strike you down."

He was not telling the truth but only trying to save himself.

After Aningaat had taken his sister back to his igloo, he urinated on her wounds in order to heal them. He now carried his sister on his back and would urinate on her wounds from time to time until she had healed completely.

Eventually they came upon more people in a camp where there were many igloos. This was towards evening, and in the windbreaks outside the igloos lay pieces of caribou back-fat, all neatly arranged. They looked so delicious! Unable to overcome her temptation Aningaat's sister took one of them. Just as she was about to take a bite, someone said: "Those are dung, those are dung."

No one was in sight but the voice had come from inside one of the igloos, so she put the piece of back-fat down. Aningaat now started to build an igloo and, as usual, became thirsty, and once again asked his sister to fetch him some water. This time she was afraid to go as harm might again befall her. But Aningaat assured her, saying: "If you cry out I will come to your aid, so go and get me some water to drink."

So she went to one of the igloos, and, on going into the entrance, announced: "My brother wishes to have water for he is thirsty."

Aningaat's sister was made welcome and told to help herself to the water in the container. She was also told to fetch her brother that he too might get water to drink. So Aningaat was brought into the igloo by his sister. Both of them were made welcome and, in fact, ended up staying the night there.

Aningaat and his sister now started to live with these people. Aningaat took a wife and his sister was given a husband.

The people they were living with, it seemed, were able to conceive children only by the man touching the woman's armpit with his elbow. So Aningaat's sister was baffled when asked by her husband to make her underarm available for his elbow. For his part, Aningaat, whose wife was seemingly normal in all respects, became confused and frustrated when all she could do was to urge him to touch her armpit with his elbow. He was completely frustrated.

Finally Aningaat's sister became pregnant. According to custom, as the time of birth neared, a small igloo to serve as a birthing place was added to the main igloo in which her in-laws dwelled. In due course she gave birth.

At this time they would regularly hold festivities in the *qaggiq* [a large, igloo-like snowhouse for communal activities]. While these celebrations were in progress, a person she did not recognize would sometimes come into her birthing place and extinguish the light of her *qulliq* [stone seal-oil lamp]. This person would then fight and fondle her, but she never knew who he was. Knowing she would be handled in this manner again, she devised a way to discover the identity of her visitor. So, during the next celebration, she blackened her nose with soot from her cooking pot and waited.

She was sewing or mending something when she suddenly heard a noise. All at once her lamp was extinguished and again she was fondled. Shortly afterwards the aggressor returned to the *qaggiq*. She could hear laughter coming from the *qaggiq:* the soot on her aggressor's nose had been noticed.

She put her boots on and, despite the taboo she was under, having recently given birth, went outside to see who the molester might be. It was her brother! Her own flesh and blood! She was devastated by this revelation. In despair she entered the *qaggiq* and exposing one of her breasts through the hood opening of her *amauti,* severed it and offered it to her brother, saying: *"Tamarmik mamaqtugalunga una niriguk."* ["I think all of me is tasty, so eat this too."]

After she had said these words she took some moss, dipped it in the oil of the *qulliq* and, having lit it, ran outside. Aningaat did the same and pursued his sister around the *qaggiq.* The flame on his moss soon went out but the sister's continued to burn brightly and so the chase around the *qaggiq* went on until eventually they both started to ascend into the heavens. She became the Sun and her brother, Aningaat, the Moon. It is said that Aningaat can be seen at night smouldering. [Kappianaq 1986, IE-071]

The Sun and the Moon
Told by Hervé Paniaq

The following version of the Sun/Moon legend is typical of contemporary renditions as well as of those found in many published accounts. It retells the final episode of the previous legend in which the Sun and the Moon are actually created. As we have seen, Inuit groups across the Arctic used key elements of these legends to explain a number of celestial and atmospheric phenomena. The sister's brightly burning torch compared with her brother's smouldering one, accounts for the difference in luminousity between the Sun and the Moon, and, coincidentally, recalls the brother's early blindness. The Moon's dark patches—its mountains—are the soot-smudged markings on the brother's face. Red sunsets and dark sunspots have their genesis in the gore resulting from the sister's severed breast. Solar eclipses result when the Moon, in his continuing pursuit of the Sun, periodically catches up with her and embraces her once again. A lunar eclipse, on the other hand, indicates that the Moon has temporarily returned to the Earth, by various accounts, either to hunt or defecate. There is even an explanation for the phases of the Moon. The sister, full of revulsion at her brother's incestuous acts, periodically leaves off feeding him. He gradually wastes away. Eventually his sister relents and begins again to nurture her brother, thereby restoring him to his former size, hence the recurring full Moon.

★ ★

The Sun and the Moon were siblings—a brother and a sister—without parents. *Siqiniq* (the Sun) was staying all alone in an igloo. The camp would hold festivities in the *qaggiq*. One day, as usual, they started to hold a *qaggiq* early in evening when it was dark. Someone rushed into *Siqiniq*'s igloo and blew out her *qulliq* at the same time. She was then pinned down and molested. This happened a number of times and *Siqiniq* was unable to find out who her attacker was.

Her cooking pot always hung over her *qulliq*. When her attacker came again, she reached out and tried to touch the pot but her lamp was out and it was completely dark. Finally she managed to touch the pot. She then wiped her sooty hands on the face of her aggressor. After she had been molested once again the aggressor left her igloo. She followed him to see where he would go, hoping to finally find out who he was. She saw him going to the *qaggiq* where the festivities were being held. As she neared it she could hear people laughing. Someone was saying: *"Taqqiq inutuarsiurasumut aasit naatavinaaluk."* ["*Taqqiq* (the Moon has been marked with soot as he has again been looking for someone who might have been alone.")]

So *Siqiniq* entered the *qaggiq* and saw that her brother's face was covered with soot. Embarrassed and angry, she took her breast, cut it off and offered it to her brother saying that, as he liked all of her so much, why not eat her breast as well.

Her brother refused the breast, but she continued to offer it. Then they both lit torches and ran out of the *qaggiq*. *Siqiniq* followed, breast in hand, still offering it to her brother. As she chased her brother around the *qaggiq*, *Taqqiq* fell down, extinguishing the flame on his torch, leaving only smouldering embers. *Siqiniq*'s torch continued to burn brightly. Soon they both went up to the sky where the sister became *Siqiniq*, the Sun, while her brother became *Taqqiq*, the Moon. [Paniaq 1990, IE-142]

★ ★ ★

ULULIJARNAAT
TOLD BY HERVÉ PANIAQ

This legend presents, among other things, Inuit beliefs about the celestial sphere. They see it as a world in itself, analogous in almost all respects to the Earth, its landscape similarly snowbound. Here, the Sun and Moon are neighbours, living in separate igloos. The narrative also establishes the Moon spirit as the protector of abused women, bestower of fertility, and provider of sustenance.

★ ★

There once was a man who was hot tempered and cruel to his wife. He would constantly beat her.

Finally his wife had had enough. One night, when the Moon was full she went out walking to a place where there were no trails or footprints. She knelt down, putting her elbows on her knees, and covered her head with her hood. In this position she started to call: *"Taqqi piksumaa aingaa, taqqi piksumaa aingaa."* ["You, Moon, up there, come and fetch me! You, Moon, up there, come and fetch me!"]

After she had said these words she heard a dog-team. The dog-team stopped by her side and she could hear the driver—the Moon-man—calling to his dogs:

"Woah Tiriattiaq, woah Pualukittuq, woah Arjjiq" [the names of the Moon-man's dogs].

The Moon-man asked her to get on the sled and soon after they started to move along the ground. He told the woman to close her eyes and not to open them again until he told her to. So the woman closed her eyes and they moved on.

At first she could hear the runners gliding along the snow. Then she heard a swishing sound. As they went along, other unfamiliar sounds were heard occasionally—these turned out to be the sounds caused by the dog-team passing through clouds as they journeyed upwards. At one point she opened an eye and almost fell off the sled, dropping one of her mitts. Startled, she immediately closed her eye again.

Soon she heard the sound of their sled runners gliding along the ground. The Moon-man now asked her to open her eyes and she saw immediately a dog-team trail so frequented that it glistened in the light of the full Moon.

As they journeyed onwards the Moon-man told her that she would soon be entering an igloo where she would see a woman beside the platform to the left of the entrance. She should not so much as glance at this woman or look her directly in the face. The igloo, she was told, will be visited by an old hag who will try to make her laugh. When that happens she should place her hands under her own *kinniq* [the front flap of a woman's parka] and shape them into the form of a *nanuujaq* [a model of a polar bear] and imitate the sounds of a bear. He told her these things as they travelled along.

When they finally reached their destination she entered the igloo that the Moon-man had pointed out to her. Without realizing it she took a quick glance at the person beside the side platform and immediately singed her eyelashes. As it turned out this person was the Sun.

She settled into her place on the bed platform. At the back of the platform were two people without entrails, their knees tucked into the cavities where their entrails should have been. They were still alive. While she made herself comfortable, a meat tray with a huge *ulu* on it was thrown into the igloo. Next came a huge old hag of a woman with *kammiks* that were *Timauttijut*.[1] She was extremely ugly and her tattoos stood out clearly. The old hag immediately started to dance and jest, saying,: *"Tunniqjuakka e he ay, kaujaqjuakka e he ay, paaparsu&arjuar-tuqe he he ay."*

The jester came right up to her, trying everything to make the woman laugh. Getting the urge to laugh, indeed having difficulty to hold back her laughter, the woman, remembering the Moon-man's instructions, put her hands under her *kin-*

niq, shaped them into the form of a polar bear and made bear-like sounds. The old hag, hearing these sounds, cried out: *"Ursuraliktalikjuit, ursuraliktalikjuit!"*[2], and, taking her meat tray, dashed out of the igloo.

The woman from Earth now lived with the Moon-man. One night, the Moon-man asked her to remove a caribou shoulder blade bone that was covering the igloo's *kangiq* [ventilation hole]. She did as she was told. He now asked her to look through the uncovered hole. Through the opening she could see the people down on Earth playing the wolf game *amaruujaq* [a game of tag]. Incredibly, the people she could see were those she had lived with before she was taken to the Moon. Among them she could see her husband, sitting down. The Moon-man now asked her to spit through the opening. Again she did as she was told and, as she spat, the people down on Earth immediately started to call out, "Ulluriaq ana&arpuuq, Ulluriaq ana&arpuq!" ["A star is shitting! A star is shitting!"]

The woman from Earth had now been living with the Moon-man for some time. He took her for a wife and soon she was with child. When her pregnancy was at an advanced stage the Moon-man decided to take the woman back to her home. But before returning her he asked that, after she had given birth, she should not feed the child anything from her husband's catch. Were she to ignore this request, both she and the child would surely die. The Moon-man also told her that, should she become hungry, she should simply place her cooking pot over her lamp as if to cook something, and her cooking pot would thus be replenished. Moreover, whenever her lamp ran short of oil she should just tilt it up and it too would be replenished.

Eventually she bore a little child. As instructed, she ate nothing of her husband's catch. For sustenance all she had to do was place her cooking pot over the lamp and, as the Moon-man had promised, meat was thereby provided. All her needs were provided for in this manner.

As the child grew bigger, the woman's husband became increasingly ill-tempered and angry at her refusal to eat any of the meat he provided. She explained that she had been instructed not to give the child any of his catch, at least not until the child had grown up. But her husband was persistent and vowed to make her eat of his catch.

Finally, the woman gave in. On the night after she had eaten of her husband's catch, she and her child fell asleep. Neither of them woke the following morning. [Paniaq 1990, IE-142]

Ululijarnaat
Told by Zipporah Innuksuk

*Identical in broad detail to the previous legend, this version interestingly includes a reference to the star Sirius. Here, Sirius—*Singuuriq *in Inuktitut—is personified as a woman tending her* qulliq—*a soapstone lamp. The lamp's flame, disturbed by the draft caused by people passing on their way to the Moon, explains the flickering colour changes characteristic of this star in Arctic regions.*

★ ★

There was once a woman who was beaten often by her husband. One day when her husband was out seal hunting, she heard a knock at the door. She did not answer right away thinking that she may be bothered by some other man. So, when there was another knock she went to see what was happening, and there in the doorway stood a man dressed completely in white caribou-skin clothing.

This man was *Taqqiq*, the Moon-man, who, in sympathy with the woman's plight had come to take her to the Moon.

In preparation for the journey he told her what she should do while travelling with him. In particular, she was not to open her eyes when they seemed to be passing through the air; if she did, she would fall down. The woman followed *Taqqiq*'s instructions carefully, but just once curiosity got the better of her and she opened one eye; immediately she dropped one of her mitts.

As they journeyed on, *Taqqiq* drove his dogs by saying, "*Uah Pualukittuq, Uah Tiriattiaq, Uah Tutiriattiaq.*" (These were the names of his dogs.)

Taqqiq told her again not to open her eyes until she could hear the sound of the sled's runners on the snow. When at last she heard this sound she knew that they were on the ground and so she opened her eyes. They were passing many houses with windows. In one of these sat a woman making a window for her igloo. A draft coming through the door was causing the flame of her *qulliq* to flicker and change colours. She looked up and muttered, "Passers by, passers by," expressing her annoyance at those who went by her house causing a draft. Her name was *Singuuriq*.[3]

When the Moon-man and the woman from Earth reached their destination, people came out to meet them. These people, who had very thin fur-trimming around their hoods, where whipped by *Taqqiq* and sent home.

Taqqiq and the woman prepared to go into his house, but before they entered he warned her not to look at the igloo on the right. Yet again, out of curiosity, the woman took a peek and this time immediately singed her eyelashes. *Taqqiq* now gave her more instructions: when entering the house she should be careful to look the occupants only straight in the eye.

Taqqiq also told her that a person named Ululijarnaat would come into the house to try to make her laugh. Should she get the urge to laugh she should put her hands under the front flap of her *amauti*, form them into the shape of a polar bear and, at the same time, pretend to make the sounds of an agitated bear.

When she was finally in the igloo and seated as instructed, a hare came in, hopped around the floor and sat down by the doorway; next came a meat tray, it too went around the floor and settled at the doorway. Finally came Ululijarnaat who, just as *Taqqiq* had said, was trying to make the woman laugh by singing like this: *"Pamayaya Pamaya, Tunnirjuakka ihihi ii, Qaujarjuakka ihihi ii."*

Feeling the urge to laugh, the woman put her hands under the front flap of her *amauti*, as instructed by *Taqqiq,* formed them into the shape of a polar bear and made the sounds of an agitated bear. Hearing this, Ululijarnaat rushed out of the igloo, shouting, *"Ursuqaliktalikjuit! ursuqaliktalikjuit"*!

All the other occupants followed Ululijarnaat. It was then that *Taqqiq*'s visitor, the woman from Earth, noticed that these people, who had been sitting in the igloo with their knees drawn up to their chests, where, in fact, without entrails. One of them was saying: "This is what I get for laughing at Ululijarnaat's jokes." So it was that those who laughed at Ululijarnaat's jokes would have their intestines torn out by her.

In the nearby igloo—the one the woman from Earth had been forbidden to look at—sat a woman wearing an *amauti*. Her leggings were off and revealed many scars and wounds, some healed, others still open. The woman from Earth was wondering how this had happened when, at last, the one with the scarred legs spoke up: "I have received these wounds through suffering."

This woman was actually the Sun. During her journeys around the Earth, she received her wounds as a result of people continuing to play string-figure games—*ajagaq*—after the Sun was back on the horizon.

One night after the woman from Earth had settled down in the Moon-man's house, *Taqqiq* lifted up a caribou shoulder-blade that was covering a hole in the igloo floor. Peering down through this hole, they could see igloos and people on the Earth below. A man was standing outside one of the igloos, and the woman asked who he might be. "He is your husband," *Taqqiq* replied.

Then *Taqqiq* said, "Listen to this."

He spat down upon the Earth, and the people below became excited and began to shout, *"Ulluriaq anarpuuq! Ulluriaq anarpuuq!"*—"A shooting-star! A shooting-star!"[4]

After living with *Taqqiq* for some time, the woman gave birth to a baby. Shortly afterwards, she was returned to her home on Earth. *Taqqiq* instructed her not to eat any of the animals caught by her husband until the baby was one year old. She was also not to use for her *qulliq* any oil rendered from her husband's catch. So every time her *qulliq* ran out of oil, she simply cleaned, put it right side up, and it would be replenished by *Taqqiq*. From time to time, when she heard noises outside the house, she would check and find that *Taqqiq* had left some meat for them.

All this time, the woman was strictly following *Taqqiq*'s wishes. But her husband finally became angry with her and started demanding that she eat the food he provided. Finally, giving in to these demands, she ate some of her husband's catch and so she soon died. [Z. Innuksuk 1990, IE-088]

ULLAKTUT OR ULLAKTUIT (THE RUNNERS)

Each of the following five versions of the legend Ullaktut *(the runners) offers some unique detail of its own. All relate to the three "belt stars" in the constellation Orion, one of the most obvious and elegant features of the midwinter Arctic sky. While none gives any explanation for the transformation of the three hunters into stars, a version from the Nattilik area, southwest of Igloolik, does. They became stars "because an unclean woman, a woman who had just had a child, came out and saw them" (Rasmussen 1931:211). This explanation is consistent with the notion that such transformations occur when taboos are breached. Only Niviattian Aqatsiaq's version mentions at the outset a fourth polar-bear hunter, who, going back for his dropped mitt, fell behind his companions and was transformed into either Rigel or Saiph, the two lower stars in Orion. In Piugaattuk's version, the fourth hunter is introduced at the end of the narrative; he does not become a star, however, but instead makes it safely back to Earth. The mitt-retrieval episode, an essential element in all the versions, probably suggests that the legend originally required a "fourth hunter" in order to explain the creation of Rigel or Saiph, or, alternatively, the return of one of the polar-bear hunters to Earth, a survivor, to tell the people what had happened. There is a widespread belief among the Inuit that in many disasters one person is saved so that a full account of the event can be made known and people can learn from it.*

★ ★ ★

ULLAKTUIT
TOLD BY NIVIATTIAN AQATSIAQ

Four men were playing football when they came upon a polar bear. Soon they started to feel that they were leaving the ground. One of the men dropped his mitt and started back for it so his companions left him trailing behind.

They rose higher into the heavens, the bear still ahead of them. While they ran they started to turn into stars. So now in the sky you will see the bear, *Nanurjuk* [the star Aldebaran], and ahead of the three runners, *Ullaktuit* [Orion's "belt stars"]. The fourth man is below the runners because he went back for his mitt and fell well behind the rest.[5] You can see them in the sky arranged in this manner. [Aqatsiaq 1990, IE-079]

★ ★ ★

ULLAKTUT
TOLD BY GEORGE KAPPIANAQ

Ullaktut is a group of three stars. The story has it that there were three brothers running after a polar bear when they rose up to the heavens. As they ran, they started to get higher and higher following the movement of *Sila*[6] and keeping up with its pace. One of the brothers, it might have been the youngest or the middle brother, dropped a mitt. As it fell towards the Earth he shouted: "I have dropped my mitt! I have dropped my mitt!" At that moment the eldest, who was in front, said: "There is a full moon and nothing to fear, go and fetch it." But he never did, so you will see them running, the *Ullaktut* trio. Once in a while, you can see the polar bear ahead of them. [Kappianaq 1986, IE-071]

★ ★ ★

ULLAKTUIT
TOLD BY FRANÇOIS QUASSA

I have heard the story about the three hunters who were hunting a polar bear at night. They started running after the bear. This, of course, was the way the polar bears were normally hunted. The brothers noticed that the bear appeared to cast a shadow as it ran away—that is, every time it lifted its paw they could see a dark area beneath it.

One of the brothers pursuing the bear dropped his mitt and said, *"Pualuapiga katakpara!"*—("I dropped my mitt!"). *"Taqiri&arami aliannajangilaq utiruk."*—("There's a full moon, no need to fear anything, . . . so go back and get it,") answered one of his brothers.

It happened that the brother who had dropped the mitt was *pinnailutaq*—that is, there was something about him which prevented him from getting into trouble, no matter what he did. So he returned for his mitt while his companions, still in pursuit of the polar bear, went up to the skies.

Apparently there were shadows on the bear as it started to go up to the skies. Now there are three stars together, one after the other, and ahead of them is the star, in line with these three, known as *Nanurjuk,*[7] the polar bear. [Quassa 1990, IE-156]

★ 227 ★

ULLAKTUT
TOLD BY NOAH PIUGAATTUK

In the legend they are known as *Ullaktut* (the runners). There are three stars, slanted upwards and evenly separated. They are most visible. Directly in front of these stars is a big star with many smaller stars around it. The big star is called *Nanurjuk* (the polar bear); . . . the smaller stars are known as the *Qimmiit* (the dogs).

The three runners—the *Ullaktut*—came across a polar bear at night and are known to have climbed up to the sky; that is the legend. They are quite visible. They are used for navigational purposes because they are easy to identify. The *Ullaktut* legend has it that there were three runners . . . actually there were four of them. They were out hunting and, during the night, they came upon a polar bear. As they were chasing the bear, one of the runners got really hot and took off his mitts. As he ran he dropped his mitts. After a while, this runner noticed he didn't have his mitts, so he went back for them and that is how he returned to Earth. He was the fourth person. Had he continued after the bear he would have been the fourth star. He was thus the only one of the runners that made it back to camp. That is the legend of the *Ullaktut* stars. [Piugaattuk 1988, IE-040]

★ ★ ★

ULLAKTUT
TOLD BY RACHEL UYARASUK

The creation of the Ullaktut *stars (the belt stars in Orion) are here accounted for using the Iliarjugaarjuk legend, more commonly associated, at least in the Igloolik area, with the stars Vega, Arcturus, and Muphrid. Rachel Uyarasuk spent her formative years in Clyde River, on the east coast of Baffin Island, a fact which may explain the different astral focus of her version.*

★ ★

There is a story about the three stars near the horizon that make a tilted straight line. They are called *Ullaktut*—"the runners."

This is how the story goes: There was an orphan boy living with his grandmother. They lived near other people including an old man named Uttuqaluapik.

Whenever the little boy visited Uttuqaluapik, the old man would chant: "You little orphan, go and eat your mother's tailbone and eat the scraps of meat, Paama!!"

For a long time, the boy never told his grandmother about Uttaqaluapik's chant and when he finally did, she spoke to him thus: "If the old man chants to you like that again, sing to him this song—'that he has murdered his brother-in-law in secret; that his brother-in-law is his secret and that at the further ice crack you did drown him'—and after you chant this, get out of his house quickly. If he should follow you I will come to your rescue."

So when the orphan boy again visited Uttuqaluapik the old man, as usual, chanted: "You little orphan, go and get your mother's tail bone and eat the scraps of the meat, Paama!!"

Then the boy, as his grandmother had instructed, sung out: "Old man, your brother-in-law is your secret; at the further ice you did drown your brother-in-law, Paama!!"

The boy then rushed out of the house.

Old Uttuqaluapik, mumbling that the boy had a loud mouth, got down onto the floor and took an antler hammer—that was used to pound the fat for the *qulliq*—and began to chase the orphan. The boy tried to hide behind the igloo but Uttuqaluapik followed and pursued him round and round the outside of the house. When the old woman saw what was happening she went out to defend her grandson, all three of them running round the igloo. Those inside the igloo could hear the sound of their running. Then suddenly there was silence. Someone went out to see what had happened. The runners had gone. They had apparently ascended into the sky where they can be seen to this day as three stars in a tilted line. They are called *Ullaktut*—"the runners." The old man's name was Uttuqaluapik ["the little old man"] and the boy was Iliarjugaarjuk ["the little orphan"]. I've never heard the name of the old woman. [Rachel Uyarasuk 1990, IE-076]

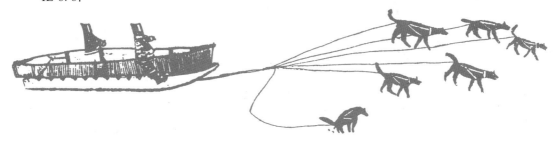

ILIARJUGAARJUK
TOLD BY HERVÉ PANIAQ

The theme of this legend is identical to the previous one, but involves a different set of stars. Here, the narrative's cast, Ningiuraaluk, *the old woman,* Uttuqalualuk, *the old man, and* Iliarjugaarjuk, *the little orphan boy, are transformed, respectively, into the stars Vega, Arcturus, and Muphrid. The choice of these three stars to illustrate this legend is particularly fitting; their spacing in the sky and relative size reflect the narrative precisely. Occasionally, the legendary names are used when referring to them, but, more commonly, as Paniaq points out, Vega is termed* Kingullialuk, *"the big one behind," while Arcturus and its companion star, Muphrid, are, together called* Sivulliik, *"the two in front."*

The three stars are known by other names. In the legend, Kingullialuk, *is known as* Ningiuq (*or* Ningiuraaluk) *"the old woman." Of the* Sivulliik *stars, the smaller one is known as* Iliarjugaarjuk (*"the little orphan"*) *and the bigger one as* Uttuqalualuk. *These names are given to the stars when telling the legend.*

Uttuqalualuk, when he was a young man, had murdered his brother-in-law and kept it a secret. He grew old with this secret. Iliarjugaarjuk, who had lost both parents, was now living with his grandmother. Whenever Iliarjugaarjuk visited Uttuqalualuk the old man would taunt him, chanting: *"Iliarjugaarjuup katuma arnavit pamiallua ailugu kikkaruk, pamaa!"*—"Orphan, go and get your mother's tailbone and eat the meat from it, pamaa!"

For some time Iliarjugaarjuk did not tell his grandmother about the old man's insults. When he eventually did, his grandmother told him to reply to Uttuqalualuk thus: *"Uttuqalualuup piksuma sakialli angialli qungnikut sallikut kivitipiuk, pamaa!"*—"Uttuqalualuk, your brother-in-law is your secret. On the crack at the further pressure ridge you did sink him, pamaa!"

Iliarjugaarjuk's grandmother taught him these lines.

For some time the orphan was anxious and uncertain and would not risk to say these words to the old man even though Uttuqalualuk continued to taunt him as before. His grandmother, however, kept asking if he had yet responded to Uttuqalualuk in the manner she had taught him, adding that if the old man became aggressive on hearing these words she would come to Iliarjugaarjuk's rescue.

★ ★
"When the sun was just returning they used to play a lot of ajagaq . . . by throwing the ajagaq bone up in the air they would appear to trying to get the sun higher."

See page 117.

Toby Otak of Igloolik playing the cup-and-pin game *ajgaq*, traditionally played after the return of the Sun. Photo: John MacDonald.

*"The daughter scorned Atunga's gift, saying,
'What need does and old woman have of beads?'"*

See pages 26–27.

(Top) Brow band. Brass, glass beads, cloth, button. Padlimiut, Eskimo Point, NWT,
1926–1938. Royal Ontario Museum. Reverend Donald B. Marsh Collection.
(Middle) Labrets. Stone with glass beads. Inuvialuit, Mackenzie River area, NWT,
c. 1900. Royal Ontario Museum. Gift of Bishop I. O. Stringer.

★ ★

"Here stars are represented as people wearing parkas . . ."

See page 33.

Woman's parka. Caribou skin and teeth, glass beads, cloth.
Caribou Inuit, Central Arctic, early 20th century.
Royal Ontario Museum. Gift of Robert J. Flaherty.

"Sometimes a ring forms around the sun; it is called qilauta:
the drum of the sun . . ."

See page 158.

(Top) Drum Dancers' Dream. Stonecut print. By Gyta Eeseemailee. Pangnirtung, Baffin
Island, NWT, 1976. Royal Ontario Museum. Gift of Richard C. Martin.
(Bottom) Drum. Wood, depilated skin, sinew. Inuvialuit. Mackenzie River, NWT,
early 20th century. Royal Ontario Museum. Gift of Bishop I. O. Stringer.

So once again the orphan boy visited the old man and, as usual, Uttuqalualuk sang: "*Iliarjugaarjuup katuma arnavit pamiallua ailugu kikkaruk, pamaa!*"—"Orphan, go and get your mother's tailbone and eat the meat from it, pamaa!"

This time, when Uttuqalualuk had finished, the orphan boy summoned all his courage and responded in the manner he had been taught by his grandmother: "*Uttuqalualuup piksuma sakialli angialli qungnikut sallikut kivitipiuk, pamaa!*"— "Uttuqalualuk, your brother-in-law is your secret. On the crack at the further pressure ridge you did sink him, pamaa!"

Having said this, Iliarjugaarjuk, following his grandmother's instructions, fled the igloo. All at once the old man took his knife and started to chase the boy. They ran round and round the igloo, the boy fleeing and the old man following. The grandmother did not immediately notice that Uttuqalualuk was chasing Iliarjugaarjuk, so she was late in coming to the rescue. As she joined the chase, the two in front of her, the boy and the old man, suddenly rose upwards into sky. The grandmother followed and they all turned into stars. The first two are therefore called *Sivulliik* and the late one, that is the one behind, is called *Kingullialuk*. [Paniaq 1990, IE-141]

★ ★ ★

SIKULIARSIUJUITTUQ
TOLD BY GEORGE KAPPIANAQ

The legend of Sikuliarsiujuittuq ("he who never goes on newly formed ice"), explaining the creation of the star Procyon, is not widely known in Igloolik. Other versions of it, including one from Labrador (Rink 1875:449), also omit specific mention of Sikuliarsiujuittuq's transformation into a star. George Kappianaq, however, in an unrecorded preamble to this story, stated that the murdered Sikuliarsiujuittuq actually became a star. In Igloolik, the star Procyon rises, reddish, over the sea ice on midwinter evenings, a fitting emblem for the murdered Sikuliarsiujuittuq. Again, a number of conditions usually necessary for such transformations are included in the narrative: in this case, principally incest and murder.

★ ★

There was once a man named Sikuliarsiujuittuq who was not a very successful hunter and who rarely went out onto the sea ice. Being a huge man he was unable to get an ordinary wife, so he took his own sister for a wife—she being of equal size—as all the other women were too small for him. I suppose their dwelling was large enough to accommodate them both.

When the hunters went out on the ice Sikuliarsiujuittuq never went along with them for he was afraid the ice would not be strong enough to carry his weight, big and heavy as he was. Each time the hunters returned from seal hunts Sikuliarsiujuittuq would check to see if one of them had caught a seal. Finding a hunter with a seal, Sikuliarsiujuittuq would take this hunter's arm, roll up the sleeve of his *qulittaq* and check to see if the hunter's bare wrist was dirty. If, indeed, the wrist was found to be dirty, Sikuliarsiujuittuq would not take the seal from the hunter because only unsuccessful hunters had dirty wrists.[8] As other hunters returned from the ice Sikuliarsiujuittuq would check their wrists in this manner and, when he found one clean and without blotches, he would take the catch away from the hunter. Sikuliarsiujuittuq did this on so many occasions that the camp began to tire of his behaviour and his reputation grew worse.

When the sea ice had reached the thickness of the land-fast ice Sikuliarsiujuittuq started to get encouragement from the other hunters to join them on a seal hunt. And so he was finally persuaded to go out hunting on the ice. The hunters accompanying him decided to camp for the night on the ice.

Sikuliarsiujuittuq had never camped out on the ice before and he asked how one should pass the night when out on his first hunting trip. This he asked just as everyone was settling in for the night. He was told that for people experiencing their first night out on the ice, it was usual practice that they should sleep with their hands tied behind their backs with harpoon thong. In telling this to Sikuliarsiujuittuq the hunters tried to be as convincing as possible. And thus Sikuliarsiujuittuq's hands were tied securely behind his back with harpoon thong. He was also tied around the knees with the remainder of the line. In this position, while trying to get some sleep, Sikuliarsiujuittuq was stabbed by one of his companions. Immediately, Sikuliarsiujuittuq, using his powerful strength, snapped the harpoon thongs in more than one place but the wound was fatal and he died. [Prior to the interview Kappianaq had explained that at this point Sikuliarsiujuittuq rose up to the sky and became a star.]

Next day the hunters started for home, taking with them the severed hand of Sikuliarsiujuittuq so that his wife could see it. Arriving, they took Sikuliarsiujuittuq's severed hand to his wife, saying that it was the paw of a young polar bear but, of course, his wife soon discovered the truth.[9]

As darkness fell and the people of the camp were getting ready to sleep, two men came to spend the night with the murdered man's wife and child. One of the men took his place at the back of the sleeping platform, while the other situated himself next to the woman. The plan was to kill Sikuliarsiujuittuq's wife as well. The men had therefore brought their knives with them, concealed on their persons, so that the woman would not suspect their intentions. (I would imagine that the knives were small in order to hide them from view.) As the men pretended to sleep, Sikuliarsiujuittuq's wife held her suckling child to her breast.

All seemed peaceful. Suddenly the woman kicked the man at the far end of the sleeping platform, at the same time seizing the other man by the throat. Thus the men who had planned to murder Sikuliarsiujuittuq's wife were themselves killed instead, one being kicked to death while the other was choked. [Kappianaq 1990, IE-102]

★ ★ ★

KAUKJAKJUALUK
TOLD BY HERVÉ PANIAQ

In this version of the Orphan Boy legend,[10] the boy's benefactor is never named. Clearly, however, his helper is none other than the Moon-man who, true to form, has come to the aid of the much-abused orphan.

★ ★

Kaukjakjualuk was an ill-treated orphan boy. He was never allowed to sleep inside the igloo, so he made his shelter in the snow porch where he kept warm by sleeping among the dogs. He was never given any food to eat except for *kauk*—walrus hide—which he could only gnaw on with his teeth, being, as well, deprived of a knife. An old woman gave him *amirtakuluk*—fragments of flint—which he would put between his teeth in order to better cut up the *kauk*. But people grew suspicious when they saw he was able to eat faster, so they tried to discover his secret. In vain he attempted to conceal the flints, hiding them everywhere, even in his navel, but to no avail. The flints were soon found and taken away from him.[11]

The ill-treatment continued, Kaukjakjualuk still using the dogs to keep warm, by sleeping among them in the porch.

Late one evening when the Moon was full he heard footsteps nearby, outside the porch. When the sound stopped, he heard someone call out: *"Kaukjakjuuk, anilaurit!"*—"Kaukjakjuuk, come outdoors!"

"Aniniajjangittunga ivvit qipaarjualuuk aningaarit."—"I am not coming out; you, Qipaarjualuuk, go out instead," he replied, telling one of the dogs to go out instead. The dog Qipaarjualuuk went out.

Again, the voice called out: *"Kaukjakjuuk, anilaurit!"*—"Kaukjakjuuk, come outdoors!"

"Aniniajjangittunga ivvit aksakailisaarjualuuk aningaarit."—"I am not coming out; you, Aksaakailisaarjualuuk, go out instead." The dog, Aksaakailisaarjualuuk, went out.

Once more the voice commanded: *"Kaukjakjuuk, ilaak anilaurit!"*—"Kaukjakjuuk, I said come outdoors!"

"Aniniajjangittunga ivvit isigailisaarjualuuk aningaarit."—"I am not coming out; you, Isigailisaarjualuuk, go out instead." The dog Isigailisaarjualuuk went out.

He did not want to go out for fear of the person who was calling him.

Again, the voice insisted: *"Kaukjakjuuk, ilaak anilaurit!"*—"Kaukjakjuuk, I said come out!"

"Aniniajjangittunga ivvit Akisaarjualuuk aningaarit," replied Kaukjakjualuk,—I am not coming out; you, Akisaarjualuuk, go out instead." The dog Akisaarjualuuk went out.

Again came the command: *"Kaukjakjuuk illak anilaurit!"*—"Kaukjakjuuk, I said come outdoors!"

"Aniniajjangittunga ivvit alliniarjualuuk aningaarit."—"I am not coming out; you, Aliniarjualuuk go out instead." The dog Aliniarjualuuk went out.

This kept on until there were no dogs left for Kaukjakjualuk to send out. Once again the voice commanded: *"Kaukjakjuuk, ilaak anilaurit!"*—"Kaukjakjuuk, I said come outdoors!"

As there was now no one but himself to go out, he finally did as he was asked. The man who had been calling Kaukjakjualuk, now took hold of him and led him to a place in the snow where there were no footprints. The man then whipped Kaukjakjualuk until he collapsed and strands of hair fell from the boy's head—in the way hair does when it gets caught in the teeth of a comb.

Again the man whipped Kaukjakjualuk and, as the boy collapsed, caribou hair fell from the discarded socks he was wearing. The whipping continued until there was nothing more that could fall from Kaukjakjualuk. This the man did by pushing Kaukjakjualuk down on the ground.

The man now asked Kaukjakjualuk to split open a rock that was frozen to the ground. The boy succeeded in this task which was then repeated with a bigger rock, while the man continued to whip him. Kaukjakjualuk could not, at first, split open the bigger rock, so the man persisted in his whipping and urged the boy to try harder. Finally, with continued effort, he managed to split this rock.

After more whipping the man asked Kaukjakjualuk to split open a much larger, boulder-sized rock. Again, Kaukjakjualuk failed at first but, after repeated whipping, finally succeeded. The man now relented, saying Kaukjakjualuk had had enough. During his ordeal Kaukjakjualuk had grown in stature and had outgrown his clothing, so the man gave him some clothing that he himself had outgrown. The man also presented Kaukjakjualuk with the whip used to beat him. Finally, he instructed Kaukjakjualuk to hide away from his camp, adding that in the morning he would see three polar bears.

So it happened in the morning that three polar bears came into the camp. The men of the camp tried to hunt the bears but they grew afraid. The people now started to look for Kaukjakjualuk but they could not find him. They were saying: *"Kaukjakjuuk nauk? Uirisautiksatuinaq, pijumisautiksatuinaq."*—"Where is Kaukjakjuuk? He is only good for teasing and distracting the polar bears."

When a child was sent out to look for Kaukjakjualuk, Kaukjakjualuk took hold of the child by the shoulder and crushed him.

Starting back for camp, Kaukjakjualuk now sang a song to himself celebrating his new-found strength. He might not look any different, the song proclaimed, but he was actually in a much stronger position than before.

When Kaukjakjualuk arrived at the camp, he whipped the men and turned them over to the polar bears to be mauled, keeping this up until the men dwindled in numbers. Then he saw the old woman who had tried to help him. She was attempting to hide under a container that was used for carrying dog food when the meat had been cut up. She was extremely afraid, thinking that she might be the next victim. Kaukjakjualuk said to her:

"Qujagi&arpalaurakilli pijjaangitagit."—"Because I have always been grateful to you so I will not harm you."

★ 235 ★

Sealskin Parka. Sealskin, Arctic fox fur. Inuit, Baffin Island, NWT,
early 20th century. Royal Ontario Museum.
Gift of the Anglican Diocese of Toronto Women.

Eventually, Kaukjakjualuk became tired of whipping people and throwing them to the polar bears. So, turning his attention to the bears, he killed them all by throwing them on the ground. [Paniaq 1990, IE-142]

* * *

UINIGUMASUITTUQ
TOLD BY GEORGE KAPPIANAQ

There is no particular celestial significance to the well-known and widely distributed legend of Uinigumasuittuq ("she who never wants a husband"). Of interest here is the account it gives of the creation of European and North American Indian peoples. The events described in this version take place in the vicinity of Igloolik Island, thereby bestowing an immediacy and veracity to the narration that might otherwise be lacking. Placing the action of legends in one's local area is a common device.

* *

They say it happened at Qikiqtaarjuk, which in these days was an island.[12]

There was a family camped [on Igloolik Island] across from Qikiqtaarjuk. Their tent would be frequently visited by a man dressed in a type of parka called a *makkaa* [a parka without a pointed hood]. He also wore an amulet of dog fangs, hanging from his chest. This man, it turned out, was in fact a dog—the only dog owned by the camp. At night he would get into bed with Uinigumasuittuq, the daughter of the camp, and eventually became her husband.

In time, Uinigumasuittuq bore a litter of children, half of which were dog-like, the others being of human form. In all I believe there were ten of them. I have heard that half of the litter became Indians and the other half became white people.

Uinigumasuittuq's father, seeing that his daughter had a dog for a husband, and feeling sorry for the children, took them all across to Qikiqtaarjuk by boat.

From time to time, Uinigumasuittuq would saddle the dog with a backpack and send it across the channel so that her father could return the dog to them laden with meat.

At last the father thought that this was getting to be too much, so one day he filled the dog's backpack with stones, concealing the stones by placing some meat on top of them. At first the dog started to howl but soon the sound was drowned as the dog sank below the water, unable to keep afloat because of the weight of the stones.

With no dog to carry food to Uinigumasuittuq and her children, her father took to bringing them food in his *qajaq*. When he would land on the shore the grandchildren, Uinigumasuittuq's litter, would habitually lick blood from the skin of the *qajaq*. Once after her father had left, Uinigumasuittuq told her children that the next time he comes with food they should eat the *qajaq*'s skin while pretending to be only licking the blood.

So when Uinigumasuittuq's father again landed with food, the grandchildren, happy to see him, went down to the shore. By this time the children must have been quite large. While their grandfather took the meat up to the tent, the children, as usual, started to lick the covering of his *qajaq*. But in fact they were only pretending and, as instructed by their mother, soon ate the *qajaq*'s skin.

Seeing what had become of his *qajaq*, the grandfather lost all hope. He went down to the shore, covered himself with a skin sleeping bag, and lay down on the beach waiting to drown in the rising tide. When his daughter saw that there was now no one to provide for her children she too lost all hope and so she set her children afloat in a boat made from the sole of a boot. A plant stem served as the mast.

From that time on, the grandfather was known as Kannaaluk—"the terrible one down there." His daughter, Uinigumasuittuq, remains with him constantly. [Kappianaq 1990, IE-102]

★ ★ ★

Two Songs
Sung by Emil Imaruittuq

The following songs were sung by Emil Imaruittuq on 30 May 1990. The first song, Akuttujuuk, *refers to the stars Betelgeuse and Bellatrix in the constellation Orion. The second song forms part of the narrative of the* Iliarjugaarjuk *legend and involves the stars Arcturus and Muphrid in the constellation Boötes, and the star Vega in the constellation Lyra.*

★ ★

Akuttujuuk

Akuttujuuk saqqippuk ullur suli tauva,
Aya . . . Aya . . .
Aya alianaittuqarpuq inuunialirtunga,
Aya . . . Aya . . .
Aya qaumatillugu suli sinilaalirivunga.
Aya . . . Aya . . .

Akuttujuuk appear—
Yonder the daylight,
Aya . . . Aya . . .
It is a joyous feeling that
I will go on living,
Aya . . . Aya . . .
Still in the broad daylight
I will sleep,
Aya . . . Aya . . .

★ ★

Iliarjugaarjuk

Iliarjugaarjuup katuma
arnavit pamiallua
ailugu kikkaruk paama

Utuqqalualluup paksuma
sakialli angialli
qungnikkut sallikuun
kivitippiuk paama.

You orphan boy down there,
go and get your mother's tailbone
and eat it, paama.

You old man up there,
did you not secretly sink your brother-in-law
down the second crack, paama.

Akuttujuuk

Iliarjugaarjuk

Transcriptions by Ramon Pelinski

CHAPTER 9
Inuktitut Transcriptions

The following Inuktitut transcriptions are from a selection of the legends given in the previous pages, in free English translation. Leah Otak, of Igloolik, made the transcriptions verbatim from the original audiotape recordings of the elders.

★ ★ ★

ANINGAAT
(THE SUN AND THE MOON)

GEORGE KAPPIANAQ

Taakuaguuq najagiik nunalituanguliqtuk qimaktiqtaujuk, iliarjuullutiklu
ningiuqtiguuq tavvatuarijangak, taimanna tusauma&&arakkik. Aningaaluguuq
tavvuuna tusaumallugu.

Tautunngimmaguuq taanna ania upirnngaksaliqtualuungmagguuq
ilupiruqaq&utiguuq qarmaqaq&utik nanurmiguuq tikiraaqtau&&aqput, tavva
taanna angutikulungat, taassuma niviaqsaaviniup aninga tautunngittuq taanna

ningiungat anaanattianga tautukkaluaq&uni taakuak niviaqsaaqlu, angutikuluk
taanna tautugani angunasuliraluaq&uni tautugunniirniku tikiraaqtaugamiguuq
nanurmik qimmiqannajuk&utiguuq atausirmik qimmiqapanaakkaluarniq&utik
taassuma qimmingattaqai qaujitimmagit taima nanuq tikiraaqtuq
nalunarunniiq&unilu igalaarmuaq&unilu tavvaguuq pisiksiqarmat
ningiungataguuq aaqiksuu&&uniuk taanna nanuq igalaakkut angmarutingmat
takkiungaguuq turaaqti&&uniuk taanna pisiksarutiginiaqtanga aaqikti&&uniuk
atiirmaguguuq taimaarmagu pisiksaq&uni,

"Iqqut pisikpat, iqqut pisikpat"

taannaguuq ningiuraalungat uqaq&uni,

"Iairq, suurluinna nirjut ikpingni&&aqtuq"

taimannaguuq tainna ikpingniqtuq qaujilluniuk, irnngilaumilluniguuq
tisuumivalittingmat taimaililauq&uni taimaaliq&uniuk. Ningiungataguuq
takujaqtuquvaa aputikulunngmugguuq milurliuk takuguniuk milurniaqpaa
takkikaguuq nalajualuk, situumiqqaugami uvuuna tuqtuup kiglingagut kataup
nalaagut takkiunga kingummungaaq situngmat tainna ikisijuq qaujilluniuk,
takkikaguuq nalavuq tavva uqarmmaguuq uqautigivaaguuq aputikulungmut
milurliuk asuilaaguuq aningmigami kappiasukkaluaq&uni aputikulungmut
miluq&uniuk ukpataagut aulajjanngimmaguuq miluraluarmagu atiiguuq
ukpataagut isinngminngniaqpaa aniguni uqautinngminngmaguguuq amma
taima takujaqtu&&apinngmigami, ukpataaguguuq
isinngmiaqtuarjukkaluarmagu suqusinngimat iiguuq tuqungavuruuq taima
anaanattiaraaluaguuq uqaq&uni uluniluguuq tigugamiuk ipiksaq&ugulu
parnajuallak&uni, aak&uniuguuq qimmiruglugluuq taanna qimmituatik
taanna nanurmik qaujikkaijigijatik paningminuguuq qimisaqtaukkaq&uniuk
aaqasiu&&ugulu nanurlu niq&aaqilluniuk taannaguuq anikulua
nannuqaujuugaluaq tamatumingaguuq qimmimik qulissiutivak&uniuk
qimmimik niqiqaqtiliq&uniuk iminngnik paninilu nanurmik niqiqaq&utik
tavvaguuq anini tuqsuk&iutingmagu ningiungatta igluliurmagu taunuuna
taunungaguuq nagligiliramiuk qimmimik niriniaqtanganik uujurulunngmik
pajuqattalirmagu najaata ningiungatta pajuktaukkaqattarmagu

niriliraangamiguuq airmiuttiqssu&&aqpaliqpuq nirijaminik nanuup niqinganik
tavvaguuq pijumajaraangat panini uqautivakpaa irnguttani,

"Aak aniiqaungnai paju&&aqpalirangniai niqimingai
nunguuttisarai&&aqpaliqputit."

Aakkauniraq&uniguuq kaaktu&&aqpakkamiguuq nunguuttisaraiqattaqpuq,
tavvaguuq airmiuttiq&uni uujukulungnik qassinik animinut
taununngaraangami nanuqtuqtippalirmagu uujumik airmiutariallalauq&&ugit.

Taannaguuq aningaa apiri&&aqpaliqpuq,

"Tattit suli qaqsauqalijjavanngilaat?"

angiqpak&uniguuq, aungniqsiqtuqtualuungmagguuq. Apirilirivaaguuq,

"Tattit suli qaqsauqaliqpanngilaat?"

Aakkaguuq qaqsauqaqattaliqturuuq aniniguuq kiulitainnaq&ugu,
Atiiguuq tappaunga tasirmut agjarliuk, ainialiruni inuksukkisurniaqpuq
takanunga qarmamingnut, tassikturlunigit aktuqpallianiaqtanginnik.
Asuilaaguuq tappaunga agjaramiuk inuksukkiqpallianiaq&uni
qaqsauqtaqaqturuuq marrungnik tavvaguuq najani atiquliramiuk tamannaguuq
aqqutigiqqaujatik inuksukkiqsukuluujarniaqpaa qanigiiinik imanna
tassikturlunigit aktuqtarunnarlunigit asuilaaguuq taimannaungmat
atiliramiguuq inuksukkiqtukuluujarlugu takanunga qarmamingnut
tikituinnattiaq&ugu qanigiikuluk&ugit.
Taimaguuq qaqsaunguvalittikatakkami tamaangaguuq saattianganit
qajaqpalla&&aqpuq, taima qaqsaunguvalittikatak&utik tavvagguuq
qaiqunngmaguu ikiqunngmagu tavvunga aquminut tassiktuq&uni takanunga
tusaagami sinaaniinnami upakautigigamiuk. Aquminugguuq
paammaqunngmagu paammak&uni iki&&aqpuq. Sammuutivalittigamiuguuq
aqqauti&&aqpaa taimannaguuq aqaumaksuk&utik ijjanngulisungaliq&uniguuq
nuijutilluniuk, taimanna ijjannguirmagguuq ammailaak
parusigiannguarilluniguuq ammailaak aqqauti&&arivaa,

aqqaumaksuallak&utiguuq ijjannguliqtualuuliq&uniguuq puijjuti&&arivaa
uqautivaaguuq,

"Takurujunngilatiit?"

Iiguuq, qaumarujuliraluaq&utiguuq ijingik, aqqautinngmigamiuguuq
akuniruluguuq ijjanngulittiaq&uni aqqaumajjutingmagu, amma nui&&arivuk,

"Takurujunngilatiit?"

Aakkaguuq tamannaguuq nuna tauturujuliqpaa, tavvaguuq ijingik
aluktuq&unigik uqangaluguuq kijjaq&uniuk imanna kilirnanut
kijjaquujialuk&uniuk, taimailauq&unigik aqqauti&&arivaa
ijjanngujummarialuuliq&uniguuq puingmigamik,

"Suli tautulijjavanngilatiit?"

Aakkaguuq nunaguuq tauvanna tauturujuliqpaa, ammaguuq ijingik
aluktukkanirmagik, aqau&&uniukmu alukturiiramigik,
ijjannguliqtummarialuuluniguuq nui&&aqpuq. Tavvaguuq apirilirivaa,

"Akkua kinngait iviksugangit tautulinngilatiit?"

Aakkaguuq tauturujuliraluaq&unigit isiaqtuguuq tauvakkua ivigsugait,
ammaguuq aqautinngmigamiuk ijjannguliqtummarialuuluni
aqqaumakutaak&utik nuijjutingminngmagu tavva ijjannguliluarami
kappiasurujuliq&uniugami ammaguuq ijingik aluktulaurillunigik
aqqautinngmingmagu tavvaguuq takugiaqulirminngmagu nuigamik,

"Akkua kinngait isiaqtut iviksugangit tautulijjangilatiit?"

Aakkaguuq tautuliqpait, tavvaguuq nunaliarutivaa. Avungaaluk taututtialiqtuq
isiaqtugguuq iviksugangit kinngait tautuliq&unigit. Qiviaqtailiqungmaguguuq
taununga sammusigiarami taununga sagvaruni kisiani takulaaq&uni
qivialaaraluaq&uni, qiviaqtailiqungmaguguuq taununga summulirami

tauvunga tasirmut itijuliasigami qiviaqtailiqulluniuguuq parruqpalattilirmat
suuqaimma taununga qajaqtut tusaqsaungmat unirmiguuq ataagut
takugiaraarju&&aqpuq quliingaguuq amiqajaanngittuq, tavva taimanna
takupillatuarami tautugunniikautigillugu kappiattakkami.

Tamakkuaguuq inuksugakuluit nappaqtiqqaujangit najaata nagligilirmigamigit
tamakkua atuujaq&ugit atilirami kamingmiguuq qulaanit kittaaqsilluni
illuuriaqattaujaq&uni atilirami imiqqᴜtailarnik. Atiramiguuq isirami ningiuqtik
apiriliqpaa,

"Kia qangna nanurautaa?"
"Kia qangna qimmisuutaa?"

Ikkunanngaguuq umianit qaangianit tunniqqusianga,
sagluttiammarirululirnirilluni tavva taanna ningiuq, umianigguuq qaangianit
qimmaqusiani saglullarialungniq&uni tavvunga. Tavva taimannailirami
tautulirami sakkuniksaq&uni sakkuqaliq&uni, qilalugaaluuqattalirmataguuq
taimanna pigiaqattalirami isuqtaniguuq tamakkuninga piararujunngnik
qilalugaqattaqtukuluuliq&uni nauligsivak&uni nunangani tamaani,
ningiuqtiguuq miniliq&ugu, ilaak minimmariktaksarinngikkaluaq&ugu
minimmarikpagu pirlirajaqtuksaungmat.
Taannaguuq kangiujumaqatta&&aliqpuq ningiuq,
piquvangilauruluaq&uniuguuq asuilaaguuq kangiujaqtuq&uni takanunga
saliaqtaulluni kiglaaqtauqattaqtumut takanunnga&&aqpuq ningiuqtik taanna
kangirisigiaq&ugu kangiujumainnalirmat qitingaguguuq qiluaq&ugu.

Tavvaliguuq qilalugaaluungmata saliaqtut isuqtakuluguuq tamanna
tugliqpaulluni tamajja qilalugaaluungmata tugliqpauqataulirmaguuq,

"Majja majja isuqtaatiaq, isuqtaatiaq."

Taanna ningiunga suksaq&uni tamannaguuq isuqtakuluk
nauligiannguaq&uniuk kinguliq&ittiangaguuq tamanna qanigijanga tiggaaluk
nauli&&aqpaa, tavvali ikpingnirami qugluktusinngmat ningiungagguuq
ullaksijukuluungmat alungiguuq taqtatuttainnaq imaup qaangagut

ullalausungaq&uni taima aqqaujau&&aqpuq taima ipijjaanani taunungaguuq
sattiksilluni puijjujau&&aqpuq, nujaniluguuq qipiujaarjuk&ugit tavunga
sivummuł kati&&unigit suuqaimma mittuliramik katinngarujulirmata
tavvunga qipippallliallugit,

"Tappikatuq pinguraajuup qaangani pilangatuq itiqqullu annallu
salummaqpajugikka, ulluq."

Aqqaumaksulauq&utiguuq nuijjujjaungmigami nuijjujjaanuungmigami
sivuniguuq qipiujaq&unigit taimanna tak&iti&&unigit tamajjaguuq
tuugaaliulilauqput taissumanngat ningiungulauqtumit isuqtaattiaq majja
majjaalalauqtumit, tainna tuugaalingnit sivulirijaunniq&uni taimanna
tusaumaujaq&ugu. Nujaniguuq taima qipi&&unigit tuugaarilirmagu taima
qipiqqaquujijjutigijangit taikkua uqausiuvalauqtut.
Tavva ningiuqtik taima aqqaujjaulauqtillugu pisusigia&&arnirivuk
inuksiurialiq&utik taakkua anigaakuk, pisukpakkamiguuq tangmaaqpak&utik
taimanna, niqisivaliq&unilu taimanna pisuksimaliramik inuksitainnaq&utiguuq
tavvunga tangmaaliq&utik igluliliq&uni tavvaguuq qulinani suli
imirungniralirmat aningaat, imiksaisuquliqpaaguuq tavvunga iglumut
ilirasulauruluaq&uniguuq uqquusigami imirulirmat asuilaaguuq
katakmuaq&uni uqaq&uni aningaguuq imiksaisuramiuk tunnganaqtualuguuq
taanna uqaujjanga innarngilaak kusugluniluguuq akkunilu makpiq&unigit
kinguppiq&uni isiq&uni imarmik tunijauniarmat, tavva silaigia&&arnirivuq
kusug&uniluguuq akkunilu makpiq&unigit kinguppiq&uni isisigiaq&uni,
tavvaliguuq qittuangusijualuugami,

"Aningaaq uvvaa,"

tuq&ulaarmat takkingna iglulijuq qaninnami tusarami suuqaimma
igalaarulungallu inalujaugamiqai, igalaanguvalaurmata makua inaluit
ikiaq&ugit igalaaruluagguuq ingulaqtuallak&ugu unaarminut taqqamunga
tugaq&unigit piirmata ilangigguuq tuquruluk&utik killiqattaqtaalugingmagit
qatigarulungit, ittungagguuq uumajuruluk iglirmuasigiakallak&unilu
kukiniluguuq pataqunnguapikillunigit,

"Asuguuq ilaak uqautivakkaluaqpassi, Aningaata pinavaasi purnavaasi."

Uqaqattarniraujarulukkaluaq&uni sagluruluk&uniguuq, tavvaguuq arngisigamiuk takkiunga igluliaminut takkiungaq&utiklukiaq quilluniuguuq tamakkua qittuktaunialungit quivak&unigit taimanna nangmakpaliq&uniuk quivak&unigit tamakkua qittuangunialungit mamittiaq&utik taimanna itiqqumut quqtaarillunigit taasuma Aningaata taimannauniraqtaunguja&&arivuq taimannaguuq pisukpakkamiguuq mami&&uniluguuq inuksi&&arivuk iglurasaullutiguuq nunaliit tikinnamikkuk unnukttukkun uqummiaqattalluguuq makua uquutarmilu tamaani ila taqqaani igluup taqqaani kiglingani aaqqiksuqsimauqtut iliuqqaqsimattiaq&utik uqummiaqattaliuqsimajut tavvaguuq tamaanngat ik&innarmata najaa taanna tigusilluni uqummiqsigiaq&uni,

"Annat taqqakkua, annat taqqakkua."

taimaguuq tusaqsauvuq immaguuq aniiqtuqangilaq tavvaguuq ililluniuk ammaguuq iglulilirmigami imiksaisuqulirivaa taqqamunga iglut ilangannut qanigijamingnut tavvunga kappiasuliq&uniguuq taanna najaa suuqaimma sivuuraliq&uni taimanna suli pijauraalungniarasugilluni tavvaguuq uqautiliqpaa,

"Tuq&ulaguvit saputiniaqtaalugingmigikkit atii aik&ituinnarit" asuilaaguuq kappiasukkaluaq&uniguuq takanungaguuq katangmut ittuarami uqalirivuq,

"Aningaga imirungmat, imiksaisurakku"

tunganarmiiguuq atiiguuq puugutaruuq uvva imalik isirluniguuq imiriaqtulirli tavvaliguuq tunngasuktummarialuugami aninganiguuq aigamiuk isirlutigguuq imiriaqtulirit tavvaluguuq suuqa tamarmik isiliq&utik tunngasaqttammarialuugamigluguuq tunngasuttialiq&utik tujurmmillutiklu tavvani ammalu tavvaniiliq&utik tujurmiqattaliq&utik tavvani taannaguuq aninganga nuliaqtaaq&uni taannaluguuq nayaa uiniktuqtitaulluni ukuaniktugaulluni uitaaq&uni.

Itiqaungittugguuq taakua sunauvva, taimannaguuq ikusingmingnut uningaangittigut najjiliqtittivak&utik taimanna qiturngaqtaaqtittiqattaqtut ikusingmingnut uningittigut tavvunga aktuqtaq&ugu uigijangata taimannaippalirmagu qanuittariaksaŋganiguuq qaujimavaganiuk taannaguuq nuliaqaliqttuq arnatitugguuq tauttuliruluugaluarmat nuliaqtaaqtuugaluaq ŋauk ajurnarmat taimanna ikusingminut unirmigut aktuqtaqtaujumaqattarmat ikusingminut uningagut arnaq taanna nuliariliqtani aktuqtaqpakkaluaq&uniuk tavvaliguuq taanna arnaq singailiq&uni najanga aningangata najanga najjiliq&uni tavvaliguuq irnijualuungmat suuqa iglulijauvalaurmatali irnisuajut taissumani kilinngavaktillugit, iglukululiuqtaullunniguuq naammagijakuluanik tuqsuk&iujjaulluni sakikkugijanginnit tuqsuk&iuliq&uni qaggiqattaqtualuungmataguuq qaggijualuulirmingmataguuq, qaggiliraangataguuq isiqtaugiaq&unilu kinauninga suqquiraniuk qullinga tilaiqtau&&aqpaliqpuq. Qamittaraangamiuk taimanna unataqtau&&aqpaliqpuq pilirianguvak&uni unataqtaulluni kinauningaguuq qaujijunnaraniuk taimannaisimaliramiguuq qaggijualuulirmingmataguuq ukkusikminiguuq kiinani qingani pauqtiq&uniuk imanna paungullarigiaq&uniuk taima taimannaitauniarmigami asuilaaguuq taimaguuq qaggilirmingmata tuqsuk&iugami kinirami iglukululiuqtausimagami tuqsuk&iulluni taimannailirmingmata taima qainiaqtuq nalunarunniirmingmat qaggiliramik anikatajaajunniirmingmata pauqti&&arniqpaa kiinani qingani tavvanngat ukkusingminit taimanna pauqtilauq&ugu utaqqilirniq&uni. Asuilaaguuq tusarniqigiannguaralua akapakarmigami qullia qamitaukautigigilluni taimanna arniriarijigigilluniuk taima taimaulirmigami qaggijunuaqpalittilluni iglamajakpalitti&&aliqpugguuq taanna apumittaluunnirmat kiinanga paumittaqsimalirmat qinganga, tavva kamiktuallakkami anittailigaluaq&uni takujaqtu&&arniqpaa kinaungmangaat qaujijumagami aniaguuq taanna.

Tavvaliguuq suuqa i&uiliq&uniguuq anillattaakulugigamiuk taimalu anaanatik qilalukkamut amujautilauqsimallugu upirngaangaujuksaujuq tavvaliguuq i&uillirami ivianginiluguuq saqqi&&ugu uvuuna nuilamigut naka&&uniuk animinut tunillugu,

"Tamarmik mamaqtugalunga una niriguk"

tavva uqauti&&alirnirivaa, taimanna uqautilauqtilluniuk taanna angutingaaq
pikia&&arniqpuq naniruaq&utik imanna manirulungmik naniruaq&utik
uqsumi&&ugu, anini maliksalirnirivaa taanna ania qamirulungniq&uni, taanna
najaa qamilaungi&&uni maliinnaq&uniuk qaggiruluk taanna kaivi&&ugu
taima quvvaqpallialirniramik majura&&arjuarnirmigamik tappaunga silamut
qilangmunilaak, arnaruuq tainna siqininnguq&uni tainna aninga
taqqiuniraqtaulirami aumainnaugamiguuq inna unnuaqsiutaullᵘini
qaumaanigunnattiangilaq taimannaujarulunginna tusaumajara.

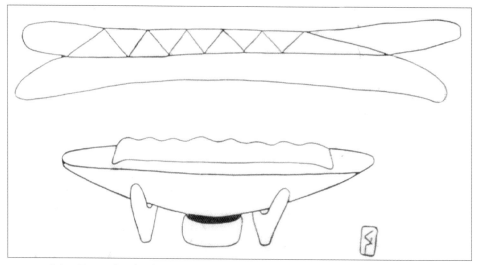

String Figure of Seal-Oil Lamp. Copperplate Engraving. By Pauloosie Sivuak. Itivimiut.
Povungnituk, Quebec, 1961. Royal Ontario Museum.
Presented by the Povungnituk Co-operative Society.

★ ★ ★

ULLAKTUT
(THE RUNNERS—ORION'S BELT)
NIVIATTIAN AQATSIAQ

Aqsaqtuviniit taikkua nanuqsillutik, nanuqsiliramik tisamauguluaq&utik.
Maniraruuq qimaqquujijaalugiliramijjuk ilangattaguuq pualuni kataingmagu
utisilluniuklu ilangitalu qimak&ugu quvvaliq&utiklu nanurluguuq
taikaugaluaq&uni sunauvvaguuq ullurianguliramik, qimagjuaq&ugulu
tamaungalu qangattaanik&utik nanuq taikaulluni. Nanurjuklu, Ullaktullu
tisamaviningat tainna atikkannianii&&uni taima takuksausuunguvuq
pualuminikli utiqsigiaqtuugaluaq kataktaminiguuq qimaktaurjuaqsimalluni
taimannauvuq.

★ ★ ★

ULULIJARNAAT
(A WOMAN FROM EARTH VISITS THE MOON)
ZIPPORAH INNUKSUK

Tainna ningarijaunginnaujaqtualuguuq pailluni uinga
mauliriaqsimaqquuqtillugu tikluktuqtuqarmagguuq taununga
arniriangunasugilluniguuq upanngilauq&uni paigami ammaguuq kingullirmik
tikluktuqtuqarmat upanngilauruluaq&uniuk takujaqtulirniqpaa.
Ani&&aramiguuq pukilaaqtualuguuq (qulittaaqtuq pukiqauqtualungnik
atuqtuq) Taqqiruuq sunauvva, taasuminga aik&iqtuq.
Tavvali aullarutilirniqpaa taassuma nagligiliramiuqai aullarutilirniqpaa
uittailiqulluniuguuq imanna kaliraarunniqpagguuq (tungaqquujijunniiqpat)
uittailiqulluniuk kata&arniarmat tavvali asuilaak uittailimajualuulirniqppuq.
Tavvaliguuq igluanik uipillaarjukkami pualuata iglua katak&uni, tavvali taima
sukasaqpangniqpuq. Taannaguuq sukasaq&uni qimmingit:

"Uau Pualukittuq
Uau Tiriattiaq
Uau Tutiriattiaq."

Taakkuningaguuq qimmiqaq&uni. Tavvaliguuq uqautingmagu
kalirraqaliqpagguuq kisiani uinniaqpuq asuilaaguuq kalirraqalirmat ui&&arami
igalaaraaluiguuq tamakkua, taimali ingirrallutik taimanna taannattauruuq
igalajjiuqtuq anuq&iuq&uni aupaqsittaq&uni taanna ikumanga
anuq&iurnikumut taimaliguuq qiviarami uqaqpuq,
"Qaangianaasiit, qaangianaasiit,

taima uqarniq&uni tavvali tiki&&utiguuq upaktamingnnut
niuvviuriaqtualuungmataguuq nuilakittuutikuluit, taassumaguuq
tiiganillaallunigit taimaguuq aiqqaatigillutik. Tavvaliguuq isirnialiramik
uqautilluniuk isirnialirmat taanna, isisigiaruniguuq maunga taliqpimut
qigsimikttailili tavvaliguuq qiviapillakkami qimiriangataguuq iglua
ikipillak&uni tavvaguuq qunnaaqarmata tappikungaguuq
qinguanuakautigiqulluniuk, qinguanuaruni tuqqialittiarluniguuq
qiviaqulluniuk tavvaliguuq asuilaak tappikunga inginnami
tuqqialittiaq&uniuguuq qiviarami qanuittunniiq&uni. Ilaak
isirniasaaq&utikluguuq uqallautivagiiq&uniuk taimaguuq tissisaarijualungmik
isiqtuqarniarmat Ululijarnaamik atiqaq&uni tainna taimali isirami
tappikungaq&uni tissigusuliruniguuq agganiguuq nanunnguujitillunigit
kinirmi ataanuarlunigit supuannguaqtilaaqpaa taimanna
uqautivagiirniq&uniuk, tavvaliguuq asuilaak tappikunngaq&uni
isiqtuqa&&aqpuruuq ukaliarjukulungmik natiruuq kaiva&&uniuk takanunga
nuqqaq&uni, ammaguuq kinguningagut puugutaaluguuq isi&&armingmat
taimannaguuq suli takanunngaq&uni taimali tainna Ululijarnaat isilirniqpuq
tissisaarillunili tainna inngiqattaqtuvinialuk,
"Paamajaja Paamaja
Tunnirjuakka ihihi'i
Qaujarjuakka ihihi'i."

Tavvaliguuq asuilaak tissigusuliqtualuugami agganiguuq kinirmi
ataanuaq&unigit supuannguaqtimmagit taimaluguuq pikiaq&uni:

"Uqsuqaliktaligjiit, uqsuqaliktaligjiit."
Taakualuguuq anillutik.

Woman Who Went to the Moon. Stonecut/Stencil.
By Tikitu Qinnuayuak. Cape Dorset, 1989.
Reproduced with the permission of the West Baffin Co-operative Ltd.

Taimali kinguningaguuquuqtuq uqaujjauliqpuq siiqqutiguuq qumik&unijjuk,

"siurjuarumatumulliak imailiqtunga,"

sunauvva taimanna irraviiqtauqattarnikuiguuq tissigusuliraangata
iglaqsijaraangata taimannauniraq&uni takannaguuq taunani
qiviaqtailiqqaujanga tainna, angijuqtaujaqaq&aramiguuq
qarlikallaqaqpalaurmata qarlikallaqaq&uniguuq qukturautingik piiqsimallutik
tamannaguuq killianikualuk ilangillu mamisimajut ilangillu
mamittariiqsimanngittut killianikualuit, isumagilluniuguuq qanuittualuikkiaq
makua tavvaliguuq uqasi&&aqpuq,

"Sirlirnaqpangmijuugaluat makua"

ajaraaqattaqtunuguuq nuna kaivaliraangamiuk ajaraanut naak&iraqtaulluni
killianikuuniraq&unigit. (Taimannaikkua tusaqsimalaurattigu
siqiniqaliraangaguuq ajaraatik killuqpalaurmajjuk ajaraaqpagunniiq&utik
taimannaasit pijjutiqaqtitaungujaq&utiqai.)

Tavvali saillisimaliramiguuq taunungaq&utik inna tusaumaquuraluaq&ugu
aiviup kiasiaruluanik pitaqaqtuq ammalu arviup kiasiangaguuq ilakuuqquuqtuq
takannaguuq takanungaqatigijumalluniuk sanirvaktimmaguguuq takannaguuq
inukuluit qitiktualuit takanani amaruujaqtullu takuksauliqput taunani nunami
ilangagguuq takanna aniingujaqtuq paami kinaujariaksanganiguuq
apiqqutigingmagu suuqaimma nalulluni uingaguuq takanna uqautilluniuk
nuliangiqsiqtuq tavvaliguuq uqaq&uni,

"naalaginai"

taunungaguuq tivvua&&aqpuq, sujurliguuq kakkua,

"Ulluriaq ana&&aqpuuq, uluriaq ana&&aqpuuq."

Taimannauniraqtaulluni tavvali qiturngaksaqaliq&uniguuq utiqtitaulirniqppuq
taanna qiturngaqtaanga nalliutilaunginningani uimi anngutanganik

niriqattaqunngi&&uniuk ammalu qullinga uqsaqattaqungi&&uniuk taimali taimannausuujaq&uni qullingalu uqsuiraangat salummattiaq&uniuk ingnaummik uqsakpak&uni taqqaungalu tuqpallaktuqaraangat qiniriaraangami niqigsaminik pivak&uni taimanna atuqsittiaqtuviniuguluaq.

Tavvali uinga ninngarulutainnaqtuksaunnirami niriquulirnirmagu taimali nirigami, tuquniraqtauquu&&alauqpuq.

★ ★ ★

ILIARJUGAARJUK
(THE LITTLE ORPHAN BOY)
HERVÉ PANIAQ

Angutiguuq tainna makkuk&uni sakiaminik inualauqsimanniq&uni anngiarillugulu tavva ittuuliq&uni. Tainnaguuq nutaraq angajuqaaqanngittuq ningiurminii&&uni taikungaguuq Utuqqalualuuniraqtattinnut taikunngatuaraangagguuq tassumaguuq taimannailiuqpak&uniuk:

"Iliarjugaarjuk katuma arnavit pamiallua ailugu kikkaruk, Paama."

Taimannailivak&uniuguuq, tavvaguuq uqaqpanngilauruluaq&uni tavvunga ningiurminut uqarniq&uni taimannailiuqattarninganik taassumaguuq aaqiksijjutigilluniuk imannaililaaquliq&uniuk:

"Utuqqalualuk piksuma sakialli anngialli qungnikkut sallikkut kivitipiuk, Paama." Tavvaguuq iliragimut isiraangagguuq taimailiuqpakkaluaq&uniuk qanuililauqsimanani taimannailiulaaquinnaq&uniuguuq pinasuliqpagu saputilaaqpaaguuq. Taikunngarnirilluni taassumaguuq asuilaak itturuluup taimannailiulirnirivaa:

"Iliarjugaarjuuk katuma arnavit pamiallua ailugu kikkaruk, paama."

Tavvaliguuq taimannailianingmat taannaguuq iliarjukuluk kiulitainnaq&uni:

"Utuqqalualuk piksuma sakialli anngialli qungnikkut sallikut kivitippiuk, paama."

Tavvaliguuq savini tiguallak&ugu, ilaak anigialaaqungmaguguuq taimannailianituarami anigiaq&unilu malikssaqtualuungmat taannaguuq iglu kaivi&&unikkuk maliktualuuluni qimaalluni taanna qaujinasaarami kinguvaq&uni ningiuq maliliraluaq&uni qangattarmmatik kingurngaktikkugguuq qangattarmigami ullurianngurmata,

taakuak sivuliik, piqatingik imailijaullutik. Tainna kinguvalauqttuq kingullialugijaulluni.

★ ★ ★

SIKULIASUIJUITTUQ
(HE WHO NEVER GOES ONTO NEW ICE)
GEORGE KAPPIANAQ

Taissumani tusaumajara tainna aniirajunngi&&unilu sikumuarajunngi&&unilu tainna taimanna tusauma&&arakku arnamiguuq imanna inullattaamik nuliaqarunnannginnami najangminiguuq inna nangminirminik nuliaqtaalauqsimajuq makuaguuq inullataakuluit mikigiluaq&unigit.

Taimali mauliriaraangata angunasugiaraangata ilauvangninngimmat sikumik nangiaqtuq uqinnginnami angigami najanilu taanna nuliarijani angijuuqatigigamiuk, naammagijamingnik igluqaqtuksaunnirivuk. Tavvaliguuq taimanna mauliriat tikittaraangata angunasugiaqtut nattiqtumiguuq tavva imanna nattiqtuqaq&uni tikittuqarmmat tavvaguuq niuvviuriaqpuq aggautaaguuq tavva quilittianga tamanna kangimut tappaunga takunasu&&arjualiqpaa, tavvaguuq aggautaa ippakpat natiqtarijaangilaa tavvaguuq nattirajunnginnami ippangmat agautaa, ammaguuq tavva tikittuqalirmingmat niuvviuriaqpuq imanna unnukut tavvaguuq aggautaa takunasu&&alirivaa siqiiqtiq&ugu qulittanga tamanna ilaak atiginga tavvaguuq iripangmat aggautaa ippaluanngimmat ilaakkuugalaangimmat nattiqtanganiguuq tavva aa&&uniuk taanna nattiqtakulua aggisilluniuk.

Taimannainnaruuq sugalugijauvalirmigamiguuq taimanna tuvaaluulirmingmat taunungaguuq angunasugiaqtunut ilauqujauvakkaluarami ilau&&atainnarmat ilauqujaungmigami siniktaujjaunasu&&alirivuruuq tavva,

★ 254 ★

ilaujariuqtualuungmat sikumut sikuliasujuituulluniluguuq taimanna imminik
uqinngiluarigami siku nangiarimut sikuliaqsiujuittuuniraqtausimalluni
tavvaguuq amma apirittia&&anirivuq qanuq taunani siniktaqataurngaq&utik
angunasugiaqtuni qanuq pivagiaksanginnik sinigasungnialiq&utik
apiri&&alirnirivuq, kikiigusiq&ugiguuq alirmut attungiqsuq&ugit
siniktaqataurngaqtut taimaippakmataguuq uqaujjauttiaq&uni taimanna
suliquujittiaq&uni taimannaungmat, kikiigusiq&uguguuq attungittiaq&ugu
sukatiq&ugu niungiklu quuppitausiq&ugik tamatuma aliup ilanganut taakkuak
aggautingik nimiqtaullutik taimanna kikiigusiq&ugu taimailingaliq&uniguuq
tavva sinigasungnialiq&uni, tavva taimailingasigiarmat
alaummaaqtauraalak&uni kapijau&&arnirami tamannaguuq qilarutialuni aliq
qikturallaakallak&uniuk tuqualuk&uni taanna.

Tavva tuqusalauq&unijjuk qarrutikmajjuk angirrasigamik taanna aggautaa
piiq&ugu iglua nulianganut takuqqujauniaq&uni nannumut atirariniraqtaulluni
tikinnamik agjaqtau&&aqpuq, tavvaliguuq taanna nannumut atirariniraqtaujuq
qaujinniq&uniuk suuqaimma sinigasuliq&utik taanna nutaraqaquuq&uniinna
tainna najanga nuliarijaalua angutiingniguuq tavva marrungnik
tujurmiviugia&&arivuq piqataaguuq kilumut sanniq&uni piqataa tamaunga
kiglinganut sanittianganut inillak&uni taimannaguuq sinigasuliq&utik
sunauvvaguuq taanna arnaq tuqutaujumagaluaq&uni taakkuak savingmingnik
kisukuttirmiutaqaq&utikiaq ikkuak taakkuak savilijaquujingi&&utik
tavvaliguuq taimanna sininngualiq&utik taakkuak angutikuluuk, taanna
qiturnnganilu tavvunga amaamaktitaksarilluniuk tavvaliguuq tappingna
kilumiingaaqtuq tukiq&uniuk tappaunga kilumut taanna piqataa
tuqqujaaksilluniuk taakkuaguuq angutialuuk mianiqsigiaqtuugaluak
tuquttijumaqqaujuk tamarmiguuq tuqusaq&unigik.

KAUKJAKJUALUK

HERVÉ PANIAQ

Kaukjakjualuguuq iliijarijaujukuluungmat iglumiguuq sinilauqsimanngittuq taunani tuqsuungni sinikpak&uni qimminit qaliqumitautuinnaq&uni taimannaippak&uni, ammaluguuq niqimik nirititaulauqsimangittuq kaungmiguuq kigiraujaqtitaulluni nirititaunnajukpak&uni ningiukuluugguuq amiqtakulungmik tuninasukkaangagu kigutimi akunninganuaq&ugu taimanna kigirutiqaruluujaliraangami kigialavaallilirat qinirviulluni tamaunga qalasikkungminut ijikatagasukkaluaq&unigit nanijijauvag&uni aatauvak&uni taimannaguuq iliijaunginnaq&uni qimminut kisiani uqurutiqaq&uni sinikpak&uni.

Tavvaguuq taimannai&&uni tavvaliguuq unnuanguliqtillugu taqqiriktualuulirmat taqqaunga qikirraujuqa&&aqpuq takkiunngaramiguuq,

"Kaukjakjuuk anilaurit,"

"Aniniajjanngittunga, ivvit Qipaarjualuuk aningaarit"

Qimmimuguuq uqaq&uni,

"Kaukjakjuuk anilaurit,"

"Aniniajjanngitunga ivvit Aksakailisaarjualuuk aningaarit",

"Kaukjakjuuk ilaak anilaurit,"

"Aniniajjanngittunga ivvit isigailisaarjualuuk aningaarit",

Aliasuknikumuugaluaq.

"Kaukjakjuuk ilaak anilaurit,"

"Aniniajjanngittunga ivvit akisaarjualuuk aningaarit,"

"Kaukjakjuuk ilaak anilaurit,"

"Aniniajjanngittunga ivvit alliniarjualuuk aningaarit"

Taimannailiulau&uniguuq nungummata,

"Kaukjakjuuk ilaak anilaurit,"

Aniqujaksaqarunniiramiguuq anilluni taassumaguuq tiguallakkamiuk tauvunga
tumitaittuliarutilluniuk tiigaq&uniuguuq urrutikaallakulungmagu
illakualuiguuq katagalaala&&aqput, ammaguuq tiigaq&uniuk
urrutikaallangmingmagu ikirujjaksarnikuvinaaluiguuq katagalaalla&&arivut,
tavvaguuq katagaqattarunniiq&uni taimanna tiigaqpak&uniuk
pinguvak&uniuk asuilaaguuq ujaqqamik makpiqsigiaqulluniuk tamaani
atajurulungmik makpi&&aqpaa, taimailiukkanniallalauq&uniuguuq
tiigaqattakkanniallalauq&uniuk angikkaniqtumik makpiqsigiaqulluniuk
qiqutisimajumik tamaani makpinngimmaguguuq amma
tiigallaakkannialalauq&uniuk taanna suli makpiriaqugilluniuk
makpiqtaalugingmingmaguguuq taimailiukkanniallalauq&uniuguuq
ujarasugjummarirulungmik makpiqsigiaqulirilluniuk
makpirunnanngimmingmaguguuq tiigalaakkannilaurilluniuk
makpiqtaalugingmingmagu tavvaguuq taimaaq&uniuk.

Angiliqtimmagulu annuraaminiguuq mikigilirnikuminik atiti&&uniuk
tiigarunnilu tunillugu, tapaaniguuq timaanni ijiqsimaniaqpuq
ulaannguqpagguuq pingajuqqanik aqqaqtittiniarami asuilaaguuq
ullaannguqtillugu tikiraaqtaaluungmata nanniqinasukkaluaq&utiguuq
iqsigiliq&unijjuk pingajuraullutik tavvaguuq qiniqtaunasuliqpuq taanna
Kaukjakjualuk, nanijaujunnailliqqalluni.
"Kaukjakjuk nauk? uirisautiksatuinnaq, pijumisautiksatuinnaq,"

taimailiukatak&utiguuq. Tappaungaguuq qiniriaqtaunnirmigami nutaqqamit,
taannaguuq tigugamiuk sagvingminut aksaliktuq&uniuk qaaq&uniuk.

★ 257 ★

Takanungaguuq atiujaliqpuq inngiq&uniugaluaq:
pivallirnirminik inngiusiqarluni, pivaliquujjangitturuuq ilaaguuq pivalliqpuq,
taimannaguuq inngiusinganik aasit nalugama.

Takanungaguuq atiq&uni tavvaguuq tamakkua angutialuit
tigujaraangamigigguuq tiigalauq&unigit nannunut igittaraangagit
ugiaqtauvak&utik taimanna nunnguksavalliajangit tigujaraangamigit
tiigalauq&unigit nalukpak&unigit, taannattauruuq ningiukuluk sunauvvaguuq
tainna tunisinasuqattalauqtuq qimiqpirulungmugguuq pusijjutinasuktuq
takulluniuk, kappiasungnikumuuliqtuuq uqautilluniuguuq,

"Qujagi&&aqpalaurakkilli pijjaangitagit"

tavvaguuq taakkua taimannailiuraanikkamigit nanuit tigujaraangamigigguuq
tiigariu&&unigit tuqquallakallakpaliq&unigit taimannauguluaq.

Chapter 10
Selected Legends

People are not fond of thinking.
Only reluctantly do we bother ourselves with
what is hard to understand.
Perhaps that is why we know only so little about
the beginnings of the sky and the earth,
of men and animals.

Perhaps and perhaps not.
For the most difficult of all is to understand how we
ourselves came, and where we go on
the day we no longer live.
Over all beginning and ending there is darkness.

(Apákak, *in* Ostermann 1952)

THE CREATION

FROM: *THE PEOPLE OF THE POLAR NORTH,*
KNUD RASMUSSEN, 1908

TOLD BY ARNARULUK

(Greenland)

This legend tells of the creation of the Earth, its human inhabitants, and dogs. It also explains how the Sun, Moon, and stars came to be. Initially all was darkness and there was no death. But people became too numerous until their numbers were checked by a great flood, the proof of which is seen in sea shells found inland, far from their coastal origin—a common post-glacial phenomenon in many parts of the Arctic. To prevent a recurrence of disastrous overpopulation, light with concomitant death was accepted by the people, and so came the Sun, Moon, and stars "for when people die they go up to Heaven and grow luminous."

★ ★

That time, very long ago, when the earth was made, it dropped down from above—the soil, the hills and the stones—down from the heavens; and that is how the world came into existence. When the world was made people came. They say that they came out of the earth. Babies came out of the earth. They came out among the willow bushes, covered with willow leaves. And they lay there among the dwarf willows with closed eyes and sprawled. They could not even crawl about. They got their food from the earth.

Then there is a story of a man and a woman; but how came it to be? It is a riddle—when did they find each other, when did they grow up? I do not know. But the woman made babies' clothes and wandered about. She found the babies, dressed them, and brought them home.

That is how there came to be so many people.

When there were so many of them they wanted dogs. And a man went out with dogs' harness in his hand, and began to stamp on the ground, calling "Hoc, hoc, hoc!" Then the dogs sprang out of little tiny mounds. And they shook themselves well, for they were covered with sand. That is how men got dogs.

But men increased; they grew more and more numerous. They did not know death, at that time so very long ago, and they grew very old; at length they could not walk; they grew blind and had to lie down.

Nor did they know the Sun; they lived in the dark; the daylight never dawned. It was only inside the houses that there was light; they burnt water in the lamps;[1] at that time water would burn.

But the people who did not know how to die grew too many; they overfilled the earth—and then there came a mighty flood. Many men were drowned, and men grew fewer. The traces of this flood are to be found on the tops of the high hills, where you often find shells.

Then when men had grown fewer, two old women began one day to talk to each other. "Let us be without the daylight, if at the same time we can be without death!" said the one; doubtless she was afraid of death.

"Nay!" said the other, we will have both light and death."

And as the old woman said those words, it was so—light came and with it death.

It is said that when the first man died, they covered up the corpse with stones. But the body came back; it did not properly understand how to die. It stuck its head up from the stone sleeping-place and tried to get up. But an old woman pushed it back.

"We have enough to drag about with us and the sledges are small!"

They were, you must know, just about to start on a seal-catching expedition.

And so the corpse had to return to its stone grave.

As men by this time had light, they could go on long seal-hunting expeditions, and no longer needed to eat the soil. And with death came the Sun, the Moon, and the stars.

For when people die, they go up to Heaven and grow luminous.

The Hare Makes the Earth to be Light

FROM: *The Netsilik Eskimos*
KNUD RASMUSSEN, 1931
TOLD BY NAALUNGIAQ
(Central Arctic, Canada)

In the very first times there was no light on earth. Everything was in darkness, the lands could not be seen, the animals could not be seen. And still, both people and animals lived on earth, but there was no difference between them. They lived promiscuously: a person could become an animal, and an animal could become a human being. There were wolves, bears, and foxes, but as soon as they turned into humans they were all the same. They may have had different habits, but all spoke the same tongue, lived in the same kind of house, and spoke and hunted in the same way.

That is the way they lived here on earth in the very earliest times, times that no one can understand now. That was the time when magic words were made. A word spoken by chance would suddenly become powerful, and what people wanted to happen could happen, and nobody could explain how it was.

From those times, when everybody lived promiscuously, when sometimes they were people and other times animals, and there was no difference, a talk between a fox and a hare has been remembered:

"Taaq, taaq, taaq!" "Darkness, darkness, darkness!"said the fox. It liked the dark when it was going out to steal from the caches of the humans.

"Ulluq, ulluq, uuluq!" "Day, day, day," said the hare. It wanted the light of day so that it could find a place to feed.

And suddenly it became as the hare wished it to be; its words were the most powerful. Day came and replaced night, and when night had gone day came again. And light and dark took turns with each other.

THE FLIGHT TO THE MOON

FROM: *THE CENTRAL ESKIMO*
FRANZ BOAS, 1888
(Eastern Arctic, Canada)

A mighty *angakoq* [shaman], who had a bear for his *tornaq* [helping spirit], resolved to pay a visit to the moon. He sat down in the rear of his hut, turning his back toward the lamps, which had been extinguished. He had his hands tied up and a thong fastened around his knees and neck. Then he summoned his *tornaq*, which carried him rapidly through the air and brought him to the moon. He observed that the moon was a house, nicely covered with white deerskins, which the man in the moon used to dry near it. On each side of the entrance was the upper portion of the body of an enormous walrus, which threatened to tear in pieces the bold intruder. Though it was dangerous to pass by the fierce animals, the *angakoq*, by help of his *tornaq*, succeeded in entering the house.

In the passage he saw the only dog of the man of the moon, which is called Tirie'tiang and is dappled white and red. On entering the main room he perceived, to the left, a small additional building, in which a beautiful woman, the sun, sat before her lamp. As soon as she saw the *angakoq* entering she blew her fire, behind the blaze of which she hid herself. The man in the moon came to meet him [the *angakoq*] kindly, stepping from the seat on the ledge and bidding the stranger welcome. Behind the lamps great heaps of venison and seal meat were piled up, but the man of the moon did not yet offer him anything. He said: "My wife, Ululiernang, will soon enter and we will perform a dance. Mind that you do not laugh, else she will slit open your belly with her knife, take out your intestines, and give them to my ermine which lives in yon little house outside."

Before long a woman entered carrying an oblong vessel in which her *ulo* lay. She put it on the floor and stooped forward, turning the vessel like a whirligig. Then she commenced dancing, and when she turned her back toward the *angakoq* it was made manifest that she was hollow. She had no back, backbone, or entrails, but only lungs and heart.

The man joined her dance and their attitudes and grimaces looked so funny that the *angakoq* could scarcely keep from laughing. But just at the right moment he called to mind the warnings of the man in the moon and rushed out of the house. The man cried after him, "Uqsureliktaleqdjuin." ("Provide yourself with your large white bear *tornaq*"). Thus he escaped unhurt.

Upon another visit he succeeded in mastering his inclination to laugh and was hospitably received by the man after the performance was finished. He showed him all around the house and let him look into a small additional building near the entrance. There he saw large herds of deer apparently roaming over vast plains, and the man of the moon allowed him to choose one animal, which fell immediately through a hole upon the earth. In another building he saw a profusion of seals swimming in an ocean and was allowed to pick out one of these also. At last the man in the moon sent him away, when his *tornaq* carried him back to his hut as quickly as he had left it.

During his visit to the moon his body had lain motionless and soulless, but now it revived. The thongs with which his hands had been fastened had fallen down, though they had been tied in firm knots. The *angakoq* felt almost exhausted, and when the lamps were relighted he related to the eagerly listening men his adventures during his flight to the moon.

★ ★ ★

THE ORPHAN BOY AND THE MOON-MAN
From: *The Labrador Eskimo*
ERNEST HAWKES, 1916
(Labrador, Canada)

Near Okkak there is a rock, curiously marked with what the Eskimo say are the blood and brains of the people in the following story.

A long time ago there lived in a village near Okkak a poor orphan boy. He had no relatives and the people he lived with treated him very badly. They made him sleep in the entrance tunnel with the dogs and flung him only bones to pick. They would not give him a knife, but the little daughter of the house gave him one secretly, and carried him bits of food when she could do so. Her kindness pleased him very much, and made him long to escape and improve his hard condition in life.

One night he was lying on the ground, outside the passage-way, trying to think of a plan for escape, and gazing at the moon. The more he gazed at it, the more he thought he discerned the outlines of the face of a man in it. Finally he was sure it was a man, and cried out to him to come down and help him escape from his hard life.

The man in the moon heard him, and came down. He took the little orphan boy down to the beach and beat him with a big whip. Every time he struck him he grew bigger and stronger. When he had finished, the little orphan boy was so strong, he could throw about big boulders like so many pebbles. Then the Moon-man went back up into the sky. The boy practised lifting and throwing big rocks all night; then he went home.

When the people with whom he lived saw how big and strong he had grown, and remembered how they had abused him, they were very much afraid. But the minute he saw them, he went mad with anger. He seized them by the legs and dashed their brains out on the rocks. The boy killed everyone but the little girl who had been kind to him. He took her for his wife. He took all the possessions of his former housemates, and became the head man of the village.

★ ★ ★

THE MAN IN THE MOON AND THE ENTRAIL-SNATCHER

FROM: *THE POLAR ESKIMOS*
ERIK HOLTVED, 1951
TOLD BY AMAUNALIK
(Northwest Greenland)

It is related of a man and his wife that they began to beat each other. At last, while they were beating each other, he stabbed his wife in the foot-soles with a knife. Now she would no longer stay in the house, but fled from her home as a mountain walker, crawling along in the moonshine. When she had got up into the country, she sat down there in the bright moonshine, and there she now remained.

At last she began to say: "Moon, come down to me!"

And then she again remained sitting for some time. To be sure, it now began to darken. The Moon was darkened, it began to grow quite dark. At last she could begin to hear a tremendous rumbling, something that rumbled tremendously. It was the Moon coming down to her, the great man in the Moon. He began to open his great sledge-skins, beautiful, large bear-skins. Only the lower one he left where it was. Then he said to the poor beaten woman: "Please, now only sit down there."

She sat down on his sledge, and when she had sat down, he covered her with the other skins. Then they drove off. The Moon carried her away with him. They drove and drove.

After some time, the sledge ceased making a noise; it could be heard no longer to have firm ground under it. When she realized that, she discharged her spittle. When she had done so, it did not last long before they could again be heard to make a noise. But now the Moon said to her: "For the time being thou must let be spitting!"

Then again they drove for a little while, and it did not take long, before they could again be felt not to have firm ground under them, because the sledge now made no noise. Thus they now kept on driving along.

At last they seemed to have stopped, and the Moon began to open the many sledge-skins, and when he had removed them all, she indeed opened her eyes wide. On the large meat platform she could see the animals moving; they were alive, both bears and other great animals. When she now came up beside him, he, the Moon, invited his (new) wife to enter, saying: "Please enter, but take care not to look into the side-house, for my little sister is apt to singe all that is strange to her!" Thus the Moon said to her.

She now went in, and she was on the point of glancing towards the side-house, but alas one side of the border of her hood was singed. Then she sat down on the sleeping platform and for the time being remained sitting there. At the front wall of the house she caught sight of some poor human beings; their faces were one broad grin—they had no entrails. Thus she now sat there.

At last, after some time, the Moon entered, and he now said: "Look at those poor fellows there without entrails, they are those my cousin has deprived of their entrails!"

He had given one of them something to chew, but as usual it fell down through him, where the entrails had been removed. Whenever they swallowed something, they had chewed a little, it fell right through them. The Moon now said to her: "Look here! My poor cousin, the entrail-snatcher, he will surely come in to take away thy entrails, but now listen how to act. Thou must begin to blow and at the same time to thrust thy hands in under the front flap of thy fur coat, holding them so that they resemble a bear; then he must take himself off. Do thus, whenever thou art on the point of smiling." Thus he told her to act.

Finally, at one time, he could really be heard to enter to them, he, the poor cousin of the Moon, the entrail-snatcher. He entered, carrying a dish and a large knife, in order to try to snatch the entrails of the human being. And look! At the window his wife stood and kept on saying: "She smiles!"

The entrail-snatcher began to dance a drum dance, with ridiculous movements, and they only looked at him, while he sang:

"My little dogs, I get them food,
My little dogs, I get them food,
ha-ahing, ha-ahing, ha-ahing."

While he acted thus, his poor wife all along stood at the window saying: "She smiles, she smiles, she smiles!"

She was tremendously busy telling her husband that she smiled. At last she could hardly let be smiling when looking at him, but she placed her hands under the front part of her fur coat and blew violently, as the Moon had told her to do. And indeed he took himself off, the entrail-snatcher, over there, saying: "One with blubber (i.e., a bear) is heard!"

Then he disappeared, and the Moon took his dish and flung it violently into the window platform. There it now lay, while the entrail-snatcher took himself off.

When he had taken himself off, it did not last long before he attempted to send for it.

"His dish, it is said, can he have it?"

"He may fetch it himself," said the Moon. "Let him fetch it himself!"

"His dish, it is said!"

Thus they continued for a long time. But when the Moon only kept on saying that he himself should fetch it, then the other one said at last: "The entrail-snatcher is going to overturn the great mountain, it is said!"

But the Moon only answered: "All right, let him overturn it!"

And indeed the other one answered: "All right, it is said, let them only look on!"

The great Moon went outside, and there the entrail-snatcher sat, facing the mountain and beginning to move his feet. The large mountain indeed began to move a little.

"Give it him, give it him!" the Moon said at last. "Give it him, give it him."

Finally he gave it him, and then the entrail-snatcher took himself off for home.

When he had now returned home, and evening fell, the Moon and the woman went to bed, but they had difficulty in sleeping. All along she could hear something groaning. Then the Moon took it and threw it away from the platform—it was the thigh-bone of a seal. His little wife—she was very jealous, indeed. He only threw her away. Thus she now lived there, and the Moon at last began to go out hunting and always stayed away long.

One day when cleaning the house, she caught sight of the shoulder-blade of a reindeer behind the lamp. She removed it, and what did she see? A large hole, deep, deep down. Thus they now lived there.

Sometimes, it is told, when the Moon was out hunting and stayed away long, the Sun used to come and peep in. It wore men's kamiks, and its hams were bleeding violently. One day it said to her: "I have wounds on the hind parts of my thighs, because thy children make string figures, while the Sun shines, at the time of the year when it rises higher in the sky!"

At last, one day, it is told, the Moon opened the reindeer shoulder-blade over there at the wall behind the lamp and said to the woman: "Peep down there!" It was dark. "They are down there, thy relatives!"

And then he closed it again. And thus they now lived there all along. One day the Moon began to whittle a walrus tusk; he whittled violently at it, and at last he let his whittling fall down through the hole and closed it again. After some time he opened it again a little, and he again said to her: "Peep down there!"

She again began to peep down, and now she saw her family, her two children, who were out in the open. Her husband stood at the entrance of the store-house with his hands in his sleeves, looking at his two children playing. When she saw him stand thus, looking with his hands in his sleeves (because it was cold), she pitied them. Then the Moon again closed the hole and said to her: "If there is anything special thou desirest to eat (during thy pregnancy), then I will bring it thee!"

And she ever remained there.

Then at long last she really became pregnant. She really became with a child, the Moon having her as his wife. Then one day they went on a visit to the entrail-snatcher: "Let us go to pay a visit to my cousin!"

The poor dogs of the entrail-snatcher were crawling on the floor and in under the sleeping platform: they were quite hairless. She looked at them: "How horrible they are!"

When they had been there for a little while, they left them again and went out. Thus she now lived there, while the Moon ever went out hunting.

At last she had become pregnant indeed, and the man in the Moon made up his mind to take her away. When she began to be desirous of eating special things, because she was with child, he brought her down to her relatives; and when he had taken her home, he said to her: "I will always provide thee with food."

The Moon took her home on his sledge. Now at last she was again at home with her relatives. When he had brought her down from up there, she immediately went to see her little children, and from then onwards she remained at home with her husband. Indeed, she sometimes heard something falling down, and being now very near her time, she used to go out in order to take the things which were meant for her to eat. Also her lamp was always amply provided with blubber, coming down from the drying frame. Of what her husband caught she never ate. Then, at last, she gave birth to a large boy. Her husband said that she should eat from what he had caught, but she kept on eating from what the Moon dropped to her, never wanting to eat from what her husband had caught. However, her large boy now began to grow older.

At last an old woman once gained a march upon her and took that which had fallen down outside the house, and then the Moon ceased to drop things. Neither was her lamp any more provided with blubber. Thus she was at last obliged to eat from what her husband had caught. Her large boy now grew fast, and having once begun to go out hunting, he soon became a very able hunter. All kinds of animals he caught which were sent to him by the generous man in the Moon. Whenever he drove on a sledge towards the icebergs, a large bear used to emerge from them. Her large son often caught bear, when he grew older, and thus he ever went on.

★ ★ ★

KANAK

FROM: *TALES AND TRADITIONS OF THE ESKIMO*
HENRIK RINK, 1875
(Greenland)

Kanak, on fleeing from mankind, felt himself lifted up from the ground, and following the way of the dead. At length he lost his senses, and on awakening again found himself in front of the house where the spirit (or owner) of the moon resided. This man of the moon assisted him to get inside, which was a perilous undertaking, the entrance being very large, and guarded by a terrible dog. The Moon-man having then breathed upon Kanak in order to ease the pain that racked his limbs, and having restored him to health, spoke thus: "By the way thou camest no man ever returned; this is the way thou must take," upon which he opened a door, and pointed out to him a hole in the floor, from which he could overlook the surface of the earth, with all the dwelling-places of man. He regaled him with eating, which was served and brought in by a woman whose back was like that of a skeleton.

Kanak was getting afraid on perceiving that, on which the Moon-man said, "Why, that's nothing; but lo! soon the old woman will appear who takes out the entrails of everyone she can tempt to laugh. If thou canst not withhold thy smiles, thou only needst to rub thy leg underneath the knee with the nail of thy little finger."

Soon after the old hag entered, dancing and whirling about, licking her own back, and putting on the most ridiculous gestures; but when Kanak rubbed his leg with the nail of his little finger, she gave a sudden start, at which the Moon-man seized her, and threw her down in the entrance. She went off, but afterwards a voice was heard, "She has left her knife and her platter, and if she does not get both, she says she will overthrow the pillars of heaven."

The Moon-man having thrown the knife and platter down the entrance, again opened the hatch in the floor, and blowing through a great pipe, he showed Kanak how he made it snow upon the earth. Lastly, he said to him, "Now it is time to leave me, but do not be the least afraid, lest thou never shalt come alive."

He then pushed him down through the opening, on which Kanak swooned; and on recovering, he heard the voice of his grandmother, whose spirit had followed and taken care of him; and at length he reached the earth's surface, arose and went to his home, after which he grew a celebrated *angakok*.

A Barren Wife

From: *Tales and Traditions of the Eskimo*
Henrik Rink, 1875
(Greenland)

A barren wife, who was treated badly by her husband, went off one winter night and met with the Moon-man, who came driving in his sledge, and took her along with him to his home. Many days after in spring, she again appeared and went to live with her husband. Ere long she perceived that she was with child, and gave birth to a son, who when he grew up was taken away by the Moon-man.

★ ★ ★

Manguarak

From: *Tales and Traditions of the Eskimo*
Henrik Rink, 1875
(Greenland)

Manguarak, unheeding the warnings of his father caught a white whale which, having a black spot on one side, was known to belong to the animals of chase set apart for the spirit of the moon. On a fine winter night the moon-man was heard to call him outside and challenge him to fight. When he came down upon the ice, the moon-man said, "Well, we will presently begin, but first let us name all the animals of chase we have caught during our lifetime."

They then, each in his turn, named the different sorts of birds, seals, and whales they had chased; and beginning with the fishes, Manguarak went on to tell how he once assisted at a halibut-fishing, when they happened to haul up a *kêrak (Anarrichas lupus)*. On hearing this, the moon-man exclaimed, "What art thou saying, man? Now just wait, and listen to me."

He then went on to tell how, when a child, and still living among mankind, he had once seen some people haul up a fish of that same kind, at which he was so terrified that he had never since tried to catch that fish.

"And now," he continued, "that I know thou hast caught an animal which I never ventured to pursue, I will do thee no harm. I begin, in fact, rather to like thee; so come along with me and see my place."

Manguarak accordingly went up to ask his father's permission, which having gained, he returned to the ice, where he found the moon-man waiting with a sledge drawn only by a single dog. When he had taken his place on the sledge, away they drove at a great pace, and gradually rising from the ground, they seemed to fly though the air. At midnight they came to a high land, upon which they still travelled on. They went through a valley covered with snow, and had to pass by a dark-looking cliff, inside of which lived the old hag who was wont to cut out the entrails of people who could not forbear laughing. As to the rest of the adventures of Manguarak, they are much the same as those encountered by Kanak.

★ ★ ★

THE SUNRISE

FROM: *TALES AND TRADITIONS OF THE ESKIMO*
HENRIK RINK, 1875
(Greenland)

A man from the east coast of Greenland, from love for his home, never left it even during the summer-time; and among his principal enjoyments was that of gazing at the sun rising out of the ocean. But when his son grew up he became desirous of seeing other countries, and, above all, accompanying his countrymen to the west coast. At length he persuaded his father to go with him. No sooner, however, had he passed Cape Farewell, and saw the sun about to rise behind the land, than he insisted upon returning immediately. Having again reached their home island, he went out from his tent early next morning, and when his people had in vain waited for his return, they went out and found him dead. His delight at again seeing the sunrise had overpowered and killed him.

★ ★ ★

The Sun and the Moon

FROM: *The Eskimo About Bering Strait*
EDWARD NELSON, 1899
(St. Michael, Alaska)

In a coast village once lived a man and his wife who had two children, a girl and a boy. When these children grew large enough, so that the boy could turn over the gravel stone, he became in love with his sister. Being constantly importuned by the boy his sister finally, to avoid him, floated away into the sky and became the moon. The boy has pursued her ever since, becoming the sun, and sometimes overtakes and embraces her, thus causing an eclipse of the moon.

★ ★ ★

The Sun and the Moon

FROM: *Narrative of an Expedition to the Shores of the Arctic Sea*
JOHN RAE, 1850
(Repluse Bay, Canada)

Their theory regarding the sun and the moon is rather peculiar. It is said that many years ago, not long after the creation of the world, there was a mighty conjuror (Esquimaux of course), who gained so much power that at last he raised himself up into the heavens, taking with him his sister (a beautiful girl) and a fire. To the latter he added great quantities of fuel, which thus formed the sun. For some time he and his sister lived in great harmony, but at last they disagreed, and he, in addition to maltreating the lady in many ways, at last scorched one side of her face. She had suffered patiently all sorts of indignities, but the spoiling of her beauty was not to be borne; she therefore ran away from him and formed the moon, and continues so until this day. Her brother is still in chase of her, but although he sometimes gets near, he will never overtake her. When it is new moon, the burnt side of her face is towards us; when full moon, the reverse is the case. [This story was provided "through interpreters" to Rae by "a boy named Arkshuk (Aurora Borealis)" in the vicinity of Repulse Bay.]

THE SUN AND THE MOON

FROM: *THE ESKIMO ABOUT BERING STRAIT*
EDWARD NELSON, 1899
(Lower Yukon, Alaska)

In a certain village on the great river once lived four brothers and a sister. The sister had for a companion a small boy of whom she was very fond. This boy was lazy and could never be made to work. The other brothers were great hunters and in the fall hunted at sea, for they lived near the shore. As soon as the Bladder feast was over they went to the mountains and hunted reindeer.

The boy never went with them, but stayed at home with his sister, and they amused each other. One night the sister awoke and found the boy lying in bed close to her, at which she became very angry and made him go to sleep in the kashim with the men. The next evening when she carried food to her brothers in the kashim she gave none to the boy; instead she went home, and after mixing some berries and deer fat, cut off one of her breasts, placed it in the dish, and carried it to the boy. Putting the dish before him she said, "You wanted me last night, so I have given you my breast. If you desire me, eat it."

The boy refused the dish, so she took it up and went outside. As she went out she saw a ladder leading up to the sky, with a line hanging down by the side of it. Taking hold of the line, she ascended the ladder, going up into the sky. As she was going up her younger brother came out and saw her and at once ran back into the kashim, telling his brothers. They began at once to scold the boy and ran out to see for themselves.

The boy caught up his sealskin breeches and, being in such a hurry, thrust one leg into them and then drew a deerskin sock upon the other foot as he ran outside. There he saw the girl far away up in the sky and began at once to go up the ladder toward her, but she floated away, he following in turn.

The girl then became the sun and the boy the moon, and ever since that time he pursues but never overtakes her. At night the sun sinks in the west and the moon is seen coming up in the east to go circling after, but always too late. The moon, being without food, wanes slowly away from starvation until it is quite lost from sight; then the sun reaches out and feeds it from the dish in which the girl had placed her breast. After the moon is fed and gradually brought to the full, it is then permitted to starve again, so producing the waxing and waning every month.

THE SUN AND THE MOON

FROM: *THE AMMASSALIK ESKIMO*
GUSTAV HOLM, 1914
TOLD BY SANIMUINAK
(East Greenland)

The Moon dwelt in a house in this country, where his sister the Sun also dwelt.

When the lamps were put out in the evening, the Moon went and lay with his sister. As she wished to find out who it was lay with her night after night, she smeared her hands one evening with lamp-soot. When the lamps had been put out, and he lay with her as usual, she rubbed her hands over his shoulders. Next morning when the lamps were lit, his sister said that there was someone who had soot on them, but when she found out that it was her brother, she took her knife, sharpened it, cut off one of her breasts and tossed it to her brother, saying: "As you seem to be so fond of me, eat me then!" She now took a small stick, stuck some moss on one end of it, dipped it in train-oil, and set fire to it. Then she ran out, and as she ran, she rose up in the air. When the Moon came out and saw that she was up in the air, he ran in and stuck some lamp-moss on his sermiaut,[2] set fire to it, and ran out with it in pursuit of his sister. But when he came up in the air, the lamp-moss went out, leaving only some glowing embers.

When the Moon's lighted stick is about to go out, he blows on it, so that sparks fly out in all directions, and it is these that turn into stars.[3] The Moon does not shine so brightly, because he has only a glow, and sometimes he must go down to earth to hunt seals; but the Sun shines brightly and gives forth warmth, for the lamp-moss was still burning, when she came up into the air.

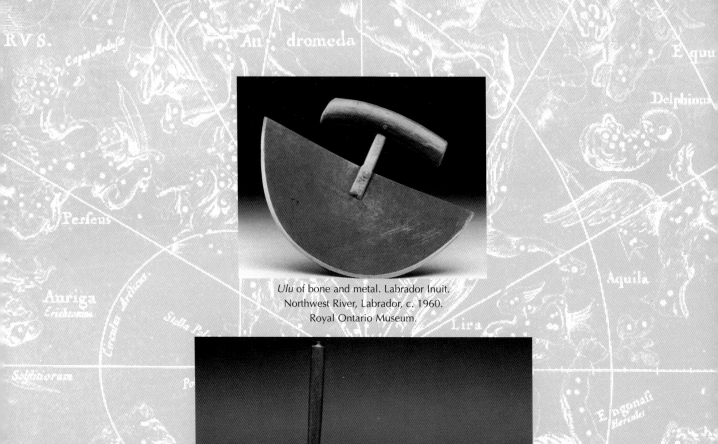

Ulu of bone and metal. Labrador Inuit.
Northwest River, Labrador, c. 1960.
Royal Ontario Museum.

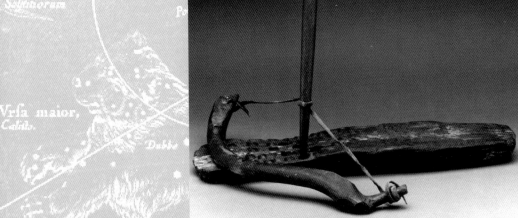

Bow Drill and Fire Stick. Wood, depilated sealskin, antler. Inuvialuit.
Mackenzie River, early 20th century. Royal Ontario Museum.

The Origin of the Sun and the Moon

FROM: *The Nunamiut Eskimos, Hunters of Caribou*
NICHOLAS J. GUBSER, 1965
(Alaska)

A brother and sister were living alone in one house. The brother told his sister that she ought to marry and bring a hunter into the household to help out. The sister refused, saying they did not need help. She asked her brother to seek a wife, but he too refused, saying that he had enough clothing.

In those days, there was no sun or moon.

One night the brother sneaked over to his sister's bed and forced her to submit to him. The sister, wanting to find out who was violating her, marked the man's face with ashes. The sister awoke early and went to the *karigi* and saw the ashes on her brother's cheek. He was sitting alone looking very sad but his sister did not say a word. She left the *karigi* and walked home. As soon as she entered the house, she picked up an *ulu* and cut off her breasts. She then mixed her own urine and blood together with cut-up breasts and made *akutaq* (Eskimo ice cream). She carried the dish to the *karigi* and gave it to her brother, saying, "Here, eat." She then told everyone what had happened the night before and announced that she was going to leave forever.

She went home, picked up an Eskimo stone lamp, and started to walk in a circle counterclockwise. Slowly she rose up into the air. The people shouted at her to come back, but she would not listen.

The brother was riven with sorrow. He picked up his tool bag and also started to walk in a circle counterclockwise. Soon he too rose into the air. As the sister continued rising into the sky, her lamp became warmer and warmer, giving out heat and light to the country. As the brother rose he became bright, but he never became hot.

From that time on the moon, the brother, pursued the sun, his sister. But he never caught up with her, he was always behind. The heat from the sun comes from the Eskimo stone lamp, and the dark spots on the moon look like a man carrying a tool bag.

THE GREAT BEAR

FROM: *THE PEOPLE OF THE POLAR NORTH*
KNUD RASMUSSEN, 1908
TOLD BY AISIVAK
(Northwest Greenland)

A woman who had had a miscarriage had run away from her family. As she ran she came to a house. In the passage lay the skins of bears. She went in.

The inhabitants turned out to be bears in human shape.

But she stayed with them. One big bear caught seals for them. He pulled on his skin, went out, and remained away some time, but always brought something home. One day the woman who had run away took a fancy to see her relations and wanted to go home, and then the bear spoke to her.

"Do not talk about us when you get back to men, " he said to her. He was afraid that his two young ones might be killed by men.

So the woman went home, and a great desire to tell came over her; and one day, as she sat caressing her husband, she whispered in his ear, "I have seen bears!"

Many sledges drove out, and when the bear saw them coming towards his house he had great compassion on his young ones and bit them to death. He did not wish them to fall into the power of men.

Then he rushed out to look for the woman who had deceived him, broke into the house where she was, and bit her to death. When he came out again the dogs closed up in a circle round him and rushed upon him. The bear defended himself, and suddenly they all became luminous and rose up into the sky as stars. And those are what they call Qilugtûssat; they who are like a flock of barking dogs after a bear.

Since then all men have been cautious about bears, for they hear what men say.

★ ★

"They became useful landmarks long after their original purpose had been served or forgotten."

See page 190.

★ ★
". . . the molting of bumblebees, the appearance of a reddish tinge
on the feathers of snow-buntings, and, in particular,
the uncoiling of the tasselled seed styles
of the malikkaan . . .*"*
See page 130.

Malikkaan—the mountain avens—in seed, one of several indicators
of the transition between summer and fall.
Photo: John MacDonald.

"The power of the Sun could also be manifest through amulets made from red lichen . . ."

See page 130.

Worshipping the Rising Sun. **By Agnes Goose Nanogak. Holman, 1972.**
Reproduced with the permission of the artist.

The sea near Igloolik, NWT, during the brief open-water season, early August to mid October.
Photo: John MacDonald.

Qilugtussat

From: *The Polar Eskimos*
Told by Amaunalik
Erik Holtved, 1951
(Northwest Greenland)

A married couple, it is told, began to fight, and when the man beat her, the wife at last went away as a mountain-walker. For a long time she wandered along. Suddenly she caught sight of a large house-entrance. She stood right in front of a large house-passage where a large bear-skin was suspended, and the bear now began to get scent of her. She heard someone calling from within the house: "Only enter, it will not hurt thee!"

She passed the bear-skin, but she could see the nostrils sniffing greatly. Then she entered the house. It was a bear in a human shape, which lived there together with its little children, and it was its skin she had seen in the house-passage. Now she had entered their house.

At last the great bear said to her: "Now keep my two children company, then I will fetch food for thee!"

Then it went out, and remained away for some time. When it came back, it had a large seal in its mouth. It took it into the house and began to flense and divide it up, and when it had finished it, it gave it to them to eat, large chunks with much blubber on them. The human being was not accustomed to eat blubber, so she cut off the blubber. When the children saw it, they said to their mother: "Aunt, put blubber on it!"

But the mother said to her children: "Now only eat it as it is, we must do as the human beings do!"

The bear used its gall as a lamp. The woman now remained with them for some time, staying with the bears.

At last she again began to want to go away, and the bear said to her: "Now let be talking (of us). I should be sorry for the sake of my children, as they are not yet quite grown up!"

She agreed: "I will say nothing whatsoever!"

Then she went out and wandered homewards. She was in a great hurry getting off, and then she came home to her family.

Here she lay down to sleep for a little while, but in lying down she said to her husband, "Let me louse thee!"—pretending that she felt a great inclination to do so. She began to louse him and bent right down to his ear: "I have come across bears some distance from here; I have met them myself."

Heigh-ho, her husband indeed became very busy.

"Bears, she says, which she has met some distance from here."

He was in a great hurry to make himself ready to set off. But now the poor woman said: "Wherever shall I hide?"

"Under the platform, in the side-house."

Here she now crept in and hid, as he had said, and then he set off.

When they now had left, it is told, a large bear began to approach. It came right up to the house and entered it. Here it asked a man: "Where is the poor thing?"

The man only pointed towards her, towards the space under the platform without saying anything. The bear hauled her out and carried her outside. It bit well into her fur-hood and dragged her along by her hair. When it had taken her out, it tore off her head and only threw the body on the refuse-heap. The head it kicked in front of it and thus carried it away.

While it thus played at ball with her poor head, the dogs began to pursue it. They pursued it with all their might, and as they would not abandon the pursuit, the bear at last began to rise upwards, all the time playing at ball with the poor head of the woman. But the dogs pursued it up into the air. All of them ascended to heaven and were transformed into Qilugtussat, the constellation of "the Pleiades."

Detail from *Esquimaux in the Bear Lands*. Ink on paper. By Enooesweetok. Sikosuilarmiut. Baffin Island, NWT, 1915. Royal Ontario Museum. Gift of Mrs. Robert J. Flaherty.

VENUS

FROM: *THE PEOPLE OF THE POLAR NORTH*
KNUD RASMUSSEN, 1908
TOLD BY MAISANGUAQ
(Northwest Greenland)

There was once an old man who stood out on the ice and waited for seals to come to the breathing-holes to breathe. But close to him, on the shore, a large troop of children were playing in the cleft of the field; and time after time they frightened the seals away from him, just as he was about to harpoon them. At last the old man became furious with them for disturbing his seal-catching and shouted, "Close, cleft, over those who frighten my catch away!"

And immediately the cleft closed in over the playing children. One of them, who was carrying a little child, got the tail of her fur-coat cut to bits.

Then they all began to scream inside the cleft of the rock, because they could not get out. And no one could take food to them down there, but they poured a little water down to them through a tiny opening in the fissure. And they licked it up from the side of the rock.

At last they all died of hunger.

The rock which is spoken of in this story is near Igdluluarssuit, up towards Neqe.

People then attacked the old man who had made the rock close over the children by his magic. He started off at a run and all the others ran after him.

All at once he became luminous and shot up to the sky, and now he sits up there as a great star. We see it in the west when the light begins to return after the long Dark; but very low down—it never comes up very high. We call it Nâlagssartoq: he who stands and listens. Perhaps because the old man stood out on the ice and listened for the seals to come up to breathe.

Nâlagssartoq

FROM: *THE POLAR ESKIMOS*
ERIK HOLTVED, 1951
TOLD BY AMAUNALIK
(Northwest Greenland)

The great Nâlagssartoq, it is told, used to catch seals at breathing-holes at a short distance from the shore. There he always stood waiting at the breathing-hole. At one time at last a number of children began to play at the huge crack in the mountain at Agpalersoq, while Nâlagssartoq stood waiting at the breathing-hole below. While playing they shouted and made a terrible noise, so that Nâlagssartoq stood at last said to them: "You make my seal keep down, you make my seal keep down!"

But they still would not keep silent, the children up there. One of them carried a small child in her amaut. They were quite absorbed in playing at the large crack in the mountain. As they still continued in the same manner, Nâlagssartoq called to them a few times more: "You make my seal keep down, you make my seal keep down!"

Then at last he exclaimed: "Let them be locked in, those up there, let the crack close above them!"—because they all along frightened off the seal, which he was lying in wait for. In this manner he locked them in.

As the crack closed above them, there was one who just managed to get out; but she who carried a child in her amaut did not get out. He now ran up to Agpalersoq saying: "Nâlagssartoq has locked my comrades into the large mountain crack, he has caused them terrible harm!"

When the people heard it, they immediately set off towards him, but first they went to see, how it was with the children which had been locked in. Armed with lances they then approached Nâlagssartoq in order to kill him. There he stood and could see them approach, and when there was only a short distance between him and them, he suddenly rose up into the air.

When he had now risen right up into the air and was transformed into the constellation Nâlagssartoq ("Venus") they had to give up getting hold of him, and they therefore returned home in order to see how the children fared. They were woefully locked into the crack, and they could hear the little child crying incessantly. For some time they tried to get down to set them free, but this turned out to be impossible. The little one down there with the child in the amaut could be heard to say: "Mother up there—the kamik soles, in order to finish them she had taken off the kamik sole." Thus she could be heard to sing down there.

They were just able to get into touch with them through a little aperture in the huge mountain crack. But although they managed to get bits of meat and water down into the crack, the children nevertheless died with hunger, while she for a long time could still be heard to sing: "Mother up there—the kamik soles, in order to finish them she has taken off the kamik sole."

For some time they kept on providing for them, as well as they could, by sending something down through the little aperture. But at last they buried them by putting large stones over them, and since then nothing has been heard of them.

* * *

THE PEOPLE WHO BECAME AGRUKS

FROM: *THE ESKIMO STORYTELLER—*
FOLKTALES FROM NOATAK, ALASKA
EDWIN S. HALL, JR., 1975
TOLD BY PAUL MONROE
(Noatak, Alaska)

This short story nicely incorporates the widespread Inuit regard for the agruk (Aagjuuk) stars as harbingers of the returning Sun and the joy experienced at this event. However the celestial placement of grandmother (the smaller star—presumably Tarazed) below the grandson (the larger star—presumably Altair) is reversed in astronomical reality, unless one of the lesser stars below Altair is indicated, which is unlikely.

* *

Some people lived down at the coast, including a grandmother and her grandson. The grandson always took his grandmother's potty out, every evening and every morning. One time in the evening he didn't come back for a long time, so the grandmother went out to look for him. Towards morning when the agruks [the two beams of light cast by the sun when it first reappears above the horizon in late December] came out, the grandmother looked for her grandson.

It was getting bright and she looked towards the sun and saw her grandson doing an Eskimo dance. He was real lively because he was so happy about the reappearance of the agruks. The grandmother thought, "What should I do? Should I try to scare or surprise him?" She went over behind the boy, who was real happy, and scared him from the back. The grandson didn't know what to do. He started running and then flying towards the agruks. The grandmother didn't know what to do, so she followed him, flying too. The grandson landed in the sky and became a star. The grandmother stopped below him and became the smaller star. When the agruks come up the grandmother and grandson always move towards them and become agruks. When the agruks go down they go back to being stars.

★ ★ ★

Two Stars—Agssuk

FROM: The Polar Eskimos
Erik Holtved, 1951
Told by Arnaitsoq
(Northwest Greenland)

A small orphan boy, who only had his grandmother, used to go visiting an old woman. Whenever he came on a visit to her, the old woman used to say to him: "Go and gnaw the rear coat-flap of thy mother!"

Whenever he came visiting, she said thus to him, when they were on the point of returning, because she had got coat-flaps of sealskin. At last the boy said to his grandmother: "The old woman always says to me: 'Go and gnaw the coat-flap of thy mother.'"

The grandmother said to him: "Then thou must say to her: 'Thy daughter-in-law, hast thou killed her, by locking her into a crack far up towards land?' Say thus when thou comest visiting her!"

When next time the boy went to visit the old woman, she again said to him: "Go home and gnaw the rear coat-flap of thy mother!"

But then, when they were on the point of returning home, he at last said to her: "Thy daughter-in-law, hast thou killed her, by locking her into a crack far up towards land?"

The old woman became furious. When the child had left, she took her stick and followed it. She began to pursue it, ever running around the house. At last they rose up into the air and were transformed into stars. They can be seen up there, the one being large, the other one quite small.

AAGJUUK AND SIVULLIIT

FROM: *INTELLECTUAL CULTURE OF THE COPPER ESKIMOS*
KNUD RASMUSSEN, 1932
TOLD BY TATILGAK
(Western Arctic, Canada)

The following are Irinaliutit, *"magic words"—a morning supplication,* makilirut, *offered on rising, when the day dawns, by those who are going hunting. Rasmussen adds: "Said by the man who is going sealing, and when saying it he must be the only one with his clothes on."*

★ ★

By which way, I wonder the mornings—
You dear morning, get up!
See I am up!
By which way, I wonder,
the constellation *Aagjuuk* rises up in the sky?
By this way—perhaps—by the morning
It rises up!

Morning, you dear morning, get up!
See I am up!
By which way, I wonder,
the constellation *Sivulliit*
Has risen to the sky?
By this way—perhaps—by the morning.
It rises up!

THE CONSTELLATION UDLEQDJUN

FROM: *THE CENTRAL ESKIMO*
FRANZ BOAS, 1888
(Eastern Arctic, Canada)

Three men went bear hunting with a sledge and took a young boy with them. When they approached the edge of the floe they saw a bear and went in pursuit. Though the dogs ran fast they could not get nearer and all of a sudden they observed that the bear was lifted up and their sledge followed. At this moment the boy lost one of his mittens and in the attempt to pick it up fell from the sledge. There he saw the men ascending higher and higher, finally being transformed into stars. The bear became the star Nanuqdjung (Betelgeuse); the pursuers, Udleqdjun (Orion's belt); and the sledge, Kamutiqdjung (Orion's sword). The men continued the pursuit up to this day; the boy, however, returned to the village and told how the men were lost.

★ ★ ★

THE CONSTELLATION TUATSIAT (THE HUNTERS)

FROM: *THE MACKENZIE ESKIMOS*
H. OSTERMANN, ED., 1942
TOLD BY ANGUSINAAQ
(Western Arctic, Canada)

Bear hunters, hunting with dogs, came across a bear but they could not overtake it. They let loose a dog [hoping the dog would engage the bear]. They could see the dog and the bear ahead of them but were unable to catch up. The hunters continued their pursuit and then along with the bear and the dog they were raised up to the sky. Still the hunters did not reach the bear. Up in the sky it is said they received the name of the "hunters"—they are the stars that lie close to one another.

THUNDER AND LIGHTNING

FROM: *THE NETSILIK ESKIMOS*
KNUD RASMUSSEN, 1931
TOLD BY MANELAQ
(Eastern Arctic, Canada)

Once in bygone days people ferried their women and children and all their possessions over the great river at Netsilik, using kayaks that were tied together. But there were two children, a brother and sister, who had no family, two poor, lonely orphans. Nobody cared to trouble about them, and the result was that they were left behind, because nobody felt inclined to ferry them over the rushing river.

The boy and his sister stood long, gazing after those that were departing, without knowing what they should do. They had nothing, and did not know what to do to get food and clothing without the help of others. Then it occurred to them to go back to their old camp to see if they could not pick up something that had been forgotten that might be useful to them. The sister found a firestone, the boy a piece of dried caribou skin; it was a piece of kamik skin with the hair taken off, and it was very stiff. They took them unthinkingly and they had no idea what to do. Then the brother said suddenly: "Sister, we will be human beings no longer; but what shall we be?"

"Caribou," suggested his sister.

"No, for then we would be gored to death," answered her brother.

"Sister, what shall we be?"

"Seals," his sister suggested.

"No, for then we would be torn to death."

And in that manner they named all the animals, but there was not one they wanted to be. At last the sister proposed thunder and lightning.

"Yes," said her brother, and so they became thunder and lightning. They turned themselves into spirits of the air and rushed across the sky, the sister striking sparks with her firestone, the brother striking his piece of dried skin like a drum, so that the heavens roared . . . and in that way they rose up to the sky.

Later they revenged themselves upon those who had left then to die of hunger. This was the way of their revenge: they thundered and lightened just over their camp. When some travellers came through the camp later on, all the people lay dead in their tents; the dogs, too, lay dead outside; but otherwise they were not changed at all and had no wounds—there was only a redness in their eyes. That was from terror. But when the travellers touched them they crumbled away to ashes.

In that way people discovered that the thunder spirits were very dangerous. Since then, when thunder is heard striking his skin drum and the sparks from the firestone of the lightning spirits are seen, people shoot an arrow in the direction whence they came. Ordinary people cannot see the spirits themselves, only the shamans can do that; they pursue them and stab them with knives.

Not far from the Netsilik Lake there is a house built of stone, and over it is a roof of large, flat stones; the doorway is narrow, and the house itself is no bigger than that only two people can be in it. People say it is the house of the thunder spirits.

★ ★ ★

Origin of the Winds and Rain

FROM: *The Labrador Eskimo*
Ernest Hawkes, 1916
(Labrador, Canada)

There is a giant spirit who lives in the north. When he blows his breath, violent snowstorms occur. Other spirits live in the east and west. They breathe soft winds and summer weather. Female spirits dwell to the south. They live up in the sky and keep the rain in big bags. When they run across the sky the water escapes. The thunder is the noise of their running across the sky.

★ ★ ★

The Great Flood

FROM: *The Central Eskimo*
Franz Boas, 1888
(Eastern Arctic, Canada)

A long time ago the ocean suddenly began to rise, until it covered the whole land. The water even rose to the top of the mountains and the ice drifted over them. When the flood had subsided the ice stranded and ever since forms an ice cap on the top of the mountains. Many shellfish, fish, seal, and whales were left high and dry and their shells and bones may be seen to this day.

Introduction

1. Amundsen (1908, II:48) had a similar impression: "Natural phenomena, such as the aurora borealis, shooting-stars, thunder and lightning, rainbows, etc., they regarded with complete indifference." Lieutenant Zagoskin, reasoning that his "ignorance of the native language" might have been responsible, found the "astronomical ideas [of the Kang-yulit, Norton Sound, Alaska] so confused that I could learn nothing definite about them" (Michael 1967:231).

2. Birket-Smith had every intention of doing justice to the astronomy of Egedesminde: "While I was travelling in the Egedesminde District, it was too light at night for the stars to show. When in September I travelled north I left a star map with my interpreter and asked him to get some information, which he very willingly undertook" (Birket-Smith 1924:436). Unfortunately, the results of this assignment as presented in *Ethnography of the Egedesminde District* are incomplete and confusing.

3. Peary seems to be mistaken in assigning male and female personifications respectively to the Sun and Moon. Recorded Northwest Greenland mythology holds the opposite to be true.

4. With reference to Greenland, Robert Petersen writes: "My impression of . . . traditional knowledge . . . is that there is . . . common knowledge, and besides, knowledge which one kept for himself/herself. The latter probably transferred down within the families" (Robert Petersen, pers. comm., 1994).

5. The term "Amitturmiut" refers to Inuit living in the Northern Foxe Basin area, including particularly, the present communities of Igloolik and Hall Beach.

Chapter 1

1. Stefánsson (1922:115) also stressed that "pitch darkness such as we have in the tropics of 'temperate' lands is unknown in the Arctic, for even on a cloudy midwinter night there is enough light from the stars behind the clouds reflected by the snow on the ground so you can see a man in dark clothes ten to fifty feet away."

2. There are, however, enough clear nights to give the remarkable visual acuity of Inuit its full range: the faint star Alcor, and its brighter companion, Mizar, form a

"naked-eye double" in Ursa Major, which is designated the "caribou tail" by some Igloolik elders. And Graham Rowley recalls Pat Baird, geographer of the British-Canadian Arctic Expedition of 1937–1941, mentioning that Inuit are able to see one more star in the Pleiades cluster than Europeans normally do (Graham Rowley, pers. comm., 1991).

3. Italics mine.

4. Across the Bering Strait, Evenk mythology accounts for star transformations in much the same way (Anisimov 1959:162).

5. The Inuit constellations *Ursuutaattiaq* (entry 16) and, to a lesser extent, *Tuklurjuit* (entry 14) are exceptions.

6. See also Rink (1875:457–58) who notes that the legend of the *Igdlokok* is sometimes adapted to account for the manifestation of either the *Siagtut* (Orion's belt) or the *Kilugtûssat* (the Pleiades).

7. Deneb, the brightest star in the constellation Cygnus, combines with Vega and Altair to form a distinctive triangular feature commonly known in more southerly latitudes as "the summer triangle."

8. Mythology is, of course, much more than this. For an excellent overview of the major approaches to mythological analysis in an astronomical context see Chapter 1 of Thomas D. Worthen's *Myth of Replacement* (1991). R. J. Stewart (1989) rejects the notion of myth as explanation. But whatever deeper purpose myth may serve it is clear that Inuit, at least at a conscious level, used it to account for many aspects of natural phenomena.

9. When the tracks spiral outwards from a central point the animal is said to have survived the fall. However, should the tracks spiral inwards it is a sign that the animal perished.

10. The *Amiqlaq*, with its thick winter claws, is known for the speed with which it burrows in snow. Amulets made from its claws would be given to Inuit boys to enable them to become proficient igloo builders (Emil Imaruittuq, pers. comm., 1993).

11. Rasmussen's emphasis.

12. A version of this tale, without the reference to angelica, is found in Rink (1875:464).

Chapter 2

1. See Nungak and Arima (1969:60) for a photograph of a carving representing people at the edge of the world.
2. Versions of this tale recorded by Rasmussen (1929:285–86) and Nungak and Arima (1969:58–61) make no mention of beads. Significantly, in a footnote to an Alaskan rendering of this tale, Erik Holtved mentions yet another version of it, published by Rasmussen in *Festens Gave*, in which the hero, Misana, collects stones which later turn out to be "*sungaujarpait*, the precious great beads which are said only to be found at the end of the world" (Ostermann 1952:218).
3. Johnny Annanack added that the story has a moral: those that are active and move about remain young while those who stay put age quickly.
4. In Unaleq's version of the myth, the magic song is given as follows: "A human being here/A penis here/May its opening be wide/And roomy/Opening, opening, opening!" (Rasmussen 1929:252).
5. In a well-known Greenlandic version of this myth, the hair of the "Sea Goddess" (Uinigumasuittuq's equivalent) becomes dirty and tangled when Inuit break taboos. All the creatures of the sea become trapped in her matted hair. She is then visited by a shaman who, in an act of propitiation, combs out the tangles in her hair, thus releasing the animals and saving the people from starvation.
6. Bogoras (1928:197) has noted similarities in star designations and related mythology between the Chukchi and the Lapps. Both peoples see the constellation Orion as "a powerful hunter," and Cassiopeia "the reindeer which he pursues."
7. Nelson (1899:458) refers to this star as *i-gha-lum ki-mukh-ti*, "the Moon-dog." Elsewhere (p. 449) he equates this name with the star Sirius.
8. When George Kappianaq talks about shamanistic flight he does so with striking certainty; he has absolutely no doubt that the celestial realms are accessible to shamans. This unshakable conviction recalls an experience of Stefánsson's when he was describing for one of his Inuit companions the physical features of the Moon: "But had any white man ever been to the moon," Stefánsson was asked. "When I replied that no one ever had, they said that while they did not have any telescopes as long as ships' masts, yet they did have men, and truthful men, too, that had been to the moon, walked about there and seen everything, and they had come back and told them about it" (Stefánsson 1912:404).
9. A myth given by Freuchen (1961:174) tells how *Sila* was personified. Some women find a giant baby boy lying helpless on the ground. He is mistreated by the women and rises up to the sky and is transformed into the spirit of *Sila*. Note the consistency in circumstance—social transgression—between the transformation of *Sila* and that of the various humans and animals personified as stars.

Chapter 3

1. Gubser attributes a similar belief to the Nunamiut of Alaska: "Toward spring the stars are said to rotate faster in the sky than in the winter" (Gubser 1965:195).
2. *Aku*—back flap of woman's parka.
3. Elders' attempts to identify all but the most obvious constellations using printed star maps were, for the most part, unsatisfactory—a problem, perhaps, of the maps' scale and perspective. More useful were "real time" computer-generated maps, displayed in colour, on a computer monitor.
4. Richardson's Inuktitut vocabulary lists *Agsuk* as "a star surrounded by a halo" (Richardson 1852:483).
5. Holtved is cited as the source of this information. Interestingly, the stars Procyon and Gomeisa in Canis Minor have a configuration and magnitude roughly matching Altair and Tarazed respectively. However, Canis Major does not share with Aquila that unique relationship to the Sun's winter position which is the hallmark of *Aagjuuk*. Nor is Canis Minor ever seen in a "northerly direction" at the latitude of Thule.
6. Maguire's inclusion of the star Vega in the grouping is puzzling because, at the latitude of Point Barrow, Vega is circumpolar and therefore neither rises nor sets.
7. John Etalook of North Alaska made *Aagjuuk*'s (his *aagruuk*'s) association with dawn and winter particularly clear: "The real morning's two stars they call them *aagruuk*. . . . They are next to each other, one on top of the other. . . . Where there is no daylight the *aagruuk*'s will come out . . . through the dawn" (Etalook 1983).
8. Rasmussen (1932:116).
9. Taamusi Qumaq in his *Encyclopedia* writes: "*Aajjuuk*—two stars that are one above the other. The only time

these stars will come out is at pre-dawn as the new day starts. The only period these stars will come out is at the moon of *Aajjuliuti* or what is properly called in English the month of March" (Qumaq 1988:54, trans. Louis Tapardjuk). Taamusi Qumaq's designation of *Aajjuliuti* as March is at odds with the testimony of Moses Qumak and Johnny Annanack and with the astronomical facts as well.

10. Throughout the Eastern Arctic this character is more commonly known as *Ululijarnaat* (see page 223).

11. Also spelled Aluk by Jenness.

12. In areas on or below the Arctic Circle, where no returning Sun ended the playing of string games, the appearance of *Aagjuuk* in the dawn sky could have served the same purpose.

13. Labrets, the circular lower-lip ornaments of some Western Arctic Eskimo groups, certainly evoke an astral image if we recall that early Inuit graphic representations of stars were usually circular. See, for instance, the illustration on page 102 of Birgitte Sonne's *Agayut: Eskimo Masks from the 5th Thule Expedition* (1988).

14. Venus as a seasonal marker is discussed in Chapter 3.

15. A Christmas card issued by the Greenland Post Office in 1989 features an Inuit family pointing to the *Aagjuuk* stars.

16. *Aagjuuk's* unique relationship with the Sun seems to have been even more pronounced in earlier times. Thomas Worthen, author of *Myth of Replacement* (1991), calculated the effects of precession on Altair, *Aagjuuk's* principal star. He concludes: "The farther back in time I went, the better the correspondence between the star's and the sun's azimuth from rise to culmination with 100 BC being about the optimum date" (pers. comm., 7 January 1992).

17. From "The Breath of Arctic Men," by Duncan Pryde. In *Reflections: The Anthropological Muse*, Iain Prattis (ed.), 1985, pp. 241–42.

18. A version of this song, transcribed in Inuktitut with an accompanying English translation and standard musical notation, is found on page 239.

19. Rasmussen does not actually identify *Kajorjuk* as Aldebaran but the context makes it clear that this is the star in question.

20. In Igloolik, the term *pajuktuijuq* implies to bring or send a gift, usually food, to another household.

21. In Jacobson's *Yup'ik Eskimo Dictionary* (1984:193) the term *kaviaret* ("little foxes") is given for "Ursa Minor or the Pleiades." However, on page 255 he translates the term *nayipar(aq)* as "little dipper," suggesting, perhaps, an alternate name for Ursa Minor.

22. Peck attaches this name to the "three greatest stars forming a triangle at the Persius [Perseus]." I have, however, tentatively included this reference under Cassiopeia for the following reasons: the constellation Perseus is adjacent to Cassiopeia; the stars in Perseus forming the triangle are rather faint, hardly begging recognition; elsewhere the same name is attributed to some of the stars in Cassiopeia; and I am aware of no other Inuit references to any of the stars in Perseus.

23. A detailed account of this epic migration has been published by Fr. Guy Mary-Rousselière: *Qitdlarssuaq: The Story of a Polar Migration*, Wuertz Publishing, Winnipeg, 1991.

24. In Igloolik, some use the term *Qanngiamariik* to refer to the Great Nebula in Orion. See entry 17.

25. A drawing, illustrating the stars set within the outline of a human torso, accompanies Simpson's description.

26. Schultz-Lorentzen's *Greenlandic Dictionary* defines *qutuk* as "collar-bone" (Schultz-Lorentzen 1927:108).

27. Spearman, on the basis of Arctic John Etalook's description of these stars (Etalook 1983), reasonably assumes them to be the Pleiades.

28. Rochfort Maguire copies this information from Simpson's Journal. In Simpson's own "Essay on the Eskimos of Northwest Alaska" the term, spelled *Pa-chukh-lu-rin*, is attributed to Aldebaran (entry 5), the Hyades stars (entry 8), and "some smaller ones around" (Bockstoce 1988:546).

29. Birket-Smith (1929:157) translates this term as "branches on antlers."

30. Rasmussen (1931:211n), clearly in reference to the Pleiades, gives the Netsilik term as *Agiagtait*.

31. By "Greenland" he means West Greenland.

32. An exception is the name given to the Pleiades in the Egedesminde District. Here, according to Birket-Smith, the cluster is called *Tartututut*, "those who eat reins [kidneys], which has evidently some bearing upon the old idea that white stars live on reins and red ones on liver" (Birket-Smith 1924:436).

33. The brightest stars in Ursa Major, those comprising the

"Big Dipper," are sometimes referred to as the "seven stars." In this case, however, Cranz is clearly referring to the Pleiades.

34. Jacobson's *Yup'ik Eskimo Dictionary* gives the Yup'ik term *kaviaret* as "Ursa Minor or the Pleiades, *lit. little foxes*" (Jacobson 1984:193).

35. William Onalik of Hopedale, Labrador, mentioned, specifically, that the "breast-bone" is that of *nattiq*, the "ringed seal" [*Phoca hispida*] (William Onalik, pers. comm., 1994).

36. Rosie Iqallijuq (IE-421, 1990) recalls a little song her grandfather would sing to the Pleiades on a clear night:

Sakiattiak namut pivisiik?	Sakiattiak, which way are you going?
Qaujaraarjungut,	Towards the light of day,
Ullujaraarjungut.	Towards the morning light.
Qummuttiaq,	Straight upwards,
Amuttiaq.	Straight downwards.
Takugiarit!	Look and see!

Note the similarities between this song and the one Rasmussen gives for the *Aagjuuk* stars (page 47).

37. Duncan Pryde (pers. comm., 1995) suggests Jenness's term should be rendered as *siqupsiqqat*—the one he (Pryde) recorded for the Pleiades at Point Barrow. Meaning "fragmented," this is certainly an appropriate designation. However, Jenness's linking of the term with "sleeping" (presumably from the root *siqu*—"to go to sleep") might well be confounded with the fact that the Pleiades was a marker for bedtime in some parts of Alaska.

38. Among the Paadlirmiut, Birket-Smith (1929:157) "once heard Arcturus called [*ulluriakjuaq*] 'the big star' but possibly this is no proper name."

39. In this context, Birgitte Sonne is considering a Nunivak Eskimo drawing collected by Rasmussen during the 5th Thule Expedition. The drawing shows "a round disk, a waxing moon and a star" (Sonne 1988:101). The proximity of the star ("the Moon's dog") to the Moon may be significant: Nelson mentions that "Sirius is the Moondog which makes high winds when it is near the moon" (Nelson 1899:449).

40. The plural form, *Sivulliit*, rather than the dual form *Sivulliik*, is sometimes used when referring to this constellation in spite of the fact that only two objects are designated.

41. An Alaskan tale, also involving Arcturus and Muphrid, is different in detail but of similar theme, concluding with the pursuit of a young boy by an old man (Ostermann 1942:78–80).

42. With the exception of Sirius, which, though spectacular, is limited to short, midwinter, late-night appearances, Arcturus is the brightest star in the sky at the latitude of Igloolik.

43. Chukchi of Northeast Siberia held similar views about the relationship between Arcturus and Vega: "[They] are called in Chukchi 'the heads' (Arcturus is the 'Front head', and Vega is the 'Rear head'). While travelling at night across the open tundra, the Chukchis determine their direction by the position of the two 'heads' in relation to each other and to the North Star" (Anisimov 1959:212).

44. For the Point Barrow area, according to John Simpson, "Venus is called *Su-ga-run* large & round (?) and Mars the same" (Bockstoce 1988:351).

45. Ray's vocabulary is also included in Murdoch (1892).

46. According to Schultz-Lorentzen (1927), *Nalerqat* derives from the term *naleraq* (meaning "mark of direction") and is the name given to "Charles's Wain" (Ursa Major).

47. For Greenland's Egedesminde District Birket-Smith mentions that the designation *Asalûsat* is not applied to Ursa Major but to "four stars which form a cross." He suggests that these might be in the constellation Cepheus (Birket-Smith 1924:436). More convincingly, they could be the stars of the so-called Northern Cross—Deneb, Gienah, Albireo, and δ Cygnus in the constellation Cygnus.

48. For the North Alaskan Eskimo, Spencer (1959:258) states that "the Dipper was called an animal with a horn, possibly a narwhal." But most other accounts from this area clearly indicate a caribou.

49. The plural designation could also refer to the plurality of stars said to depict the caribou. Some informants, for instance, referred to the constellation as *Tukturjuit* but claimed it represented a single caribou.

50. In 1963 the Greenland Post Office issued a series of stamps depicting the "dipper" portion of Ursa Major, the North Star, and the aurora borealis. The "Christmas seal" of 1974 depicts the Dipper and the Pole Star (Rolf Gilberg 1989:28, 45).

51. Pasha Abraham (of Kuujjuaq, Northern Quebec) also gave *Qallutik* as an alternative "Inuktitut" name for *Tukturjuit*. She explained that she first heard this name applied to the

"Dipper" by James M. Clarke, Anglican missionary at Fort Chimo (c. 1950–1975) who used to say sometimes that "he could see the *Qallutik*." Clarke, it seems, was simply translating his own term for the constellation into Inuktitut (Pasha Abraham, pers. comm., 1992).

52. In Niviattian Aqatsiaq's version of the *Ullaktut* legend there are four "runners." The fourth turns back to retrieve a dropped mitt, and so falls behind his companions. He is transformed into one of the two lower stars in Orion, either Rigel or Saiph (Rigel, being considerably brighter, may be the more likely candidate) and designated *Kingulliq* in Inuktitut.

53. *Qaqqunnilik* means having a scar, possibly caused by an animal bite.

54. For Labrador, Hawkes (1916:29) gives *ka'mut'iqdjuaq* as the name for Orion. No particular stars in the constellation are identified.

55. *Agiattat* as a designation for the Pleiades is more typical of the Repulse Bay and Pelly Bay areas than of Igloolik proper.

56. Jenness's glossing of *Tubaryuit* as "early risers" seems to be based on the mistaken assumption that the term derives from the root *tupa(k)*, meaning "(to) wake up." In fact the term relates to *tuvak*, "land-fast sea-ice" and, by extension, *tuvattaat*, "those who hunt at the breathing holes on the land-fast sea-ice" (Duncan Pryde, pers. comm., 1996).

57. Kroeber, on the basis of information from Robert Peary, states that *Pitoohen* means "the three stones supporting a lamp"—a clear reference to the three brightest stars of Cassiopeia, rather than to the entire constellation (see entry 7, *Pituaq*).

58. An Inuktitut vocabulary compiled by A. B. Reader at Pond Inlet in 1912–1913 and appended to Alfred Tremblay's *Cruise of the Minnie Maud* lists the "Milky Way" as *Ah-wig-noon*, clearly a corruption of *Aviguti* (Tremblay 1921:548).

59. In the higher Arctic regions, the 263-day interval between Venus's "morning star" and "evening star" phases cannot be observed due to the daylight regime above the Arctic Circle. Venus also has a cycle of eight years between appearances in the same spot of the sky, a rather lengthy cycle for semi-nomadic Inuit to note. (Data on Venus cycles from Anthony Aveni's *Empires of Time*, 1990.)

60. Taken from computer-generated data using the U.S. Naval Observatory's *Floppy Almanac*, 1988 and 1990 editions.

61. Note that *Kajuqtuq* (*Kayaktuq, Kayuqtuq*) appears to be the name given to the star Sirius in the Coppermine area. See Chapter 3, entry 12.

62. In addition, planets, unlike stars, do not appear to twinkle—making it even more probable that the reference here is to Sirius.

63. An Iglulingmiut version of this legend, in which the seal hunter is changed into frost, was recorded by Rasmussen (1930b:12).

Chapter 4

1. *Qaggiq*—a large igloo usually built for celebrations; also the celebration itself.

2. *Qilliq*—a semi-circular lamp made from soapstone.

3. "I think all of me is tasty so eat this too."

4. See, for instance, Edward Nelson (1899:481); John Rae (1850:79); and F. W. Peacock (1988:29–30).

5. John Ross makes a curious claim for the "Nattilingmiut" of the Boothia Peninsula: "[That] which gave us pleasure [the Sun's return] had no such effect on the Esquimaux, to whom the night of this region is their day . . . since it is of far more value to them in hunting the cunning and cautious seals. [They] always returned home when the day broke; complaining of the light as their enemy" (Ross 1835:268).

6. Inuit living below the Arctic Circle did not share their more northerly relatives' concern about the Sun's movements. Of the Nunivak (Alaska) Eskimo Margaret Lantis writes: "These people paid relatively little attention to the coming and going of the sun. Since here on latitude 60°N every day in the year has some sunlight, weather permitting, there is not the contrast between summer and winter solstices that occurs on latitude 70°N" (Lantis 1946:171).

7. Schneider (1985:401) gives *taujaq* as a designation for the "December moon" in Baker Lake, NWT. Among the Nunamiut of Alaska, this month was called *Uvluilaq*, "which means the month where there is no daylight" (Etalook 1983).

8. Polar night is defined as "the period of winter lasting more than 24 hours, where there is no twilight" (Burn 1996). The phenomenon occurs in the Arctic only north

of latitude 73°33'N.

9. By contrast, Inuit of the Mackenzie Delta, having access to greater resources, including wood for fuel, used the sunless period to hold their great winter festivities. Inuit from all around the Delta would gather at Kitigariuit to play games and feast. Interesting firsthand descriptions of this period are given by Nuligak in *I, Nuligak* (ed., Maurice Metayer, 1966, pp. 16–20) and Thomas Umaok in *Echoes into Tomorrow* (Marsh 1991:117).

10. Noah Piugaattuk repeatedly stressed that survival during *Tauvikjuaq* was particularly difficult in the days when Inuit relied completely on their own technology for hunting. The introduction of firearms greatly increased the chances of securing a sufficient supply of game during this period.

11. Of *irinaliutit* Rasmussen says: "These simple, heathen prayers, whispered out into the air from some spot in the snow where no foot has left its mark, were for the Eskimo sacred words, which in some mysterious way brought aid." A lengthy account of *irinaliutit* is given by Rasmussen in *Intellectual Culture of the Iglulik Eskimos* (1929:157–68).

12. Some of these illnesses were likely introduced by Parry's expedition.

13. For a recent overview of factors linked to this condition, see Lyle Dick's "Pibloktoq (Arctic Hysteria): a Construction of European-Inuit Relations?" *Arctic Anthropology* vol. 32, no. 2 (1995).

14. Ross reports a similar occurrence on the Boothia Peninsula in approximately the same latitude as Igloolik: "We saw the upper limb of the sun to-day. . . . This was the result of refraction, since its astronomical disappearance had occurred six days ago" (Ross 1835:227).

15. *Dutton's Navigation and Piloting* notes that in polar regions refraction varies "with temperature and barometric pressure, but there are other factors which are imperfectly known. Refractions of several degrees have occasionally been observed, resulting in the sun appearing several days before it was expected in the spring, or continuing to appear for days after it should have disappeared below the horizon" (Maloney 1983:848).

16. Elsewhere, Cranz has the following to say about the Greenlanders' "Sun-feast": "As the Greenlanders are wont to treat one another about the solstice, in order to

express their joy at the return of the sun, ours [meaning the Christian converts] were allowed on the 22d of December after the Sunday's preaching, to have a fellowship in four houses, at which however all the usual merriment and riot of the heathen was dropped. This is what we may call the Greenlanders' new-year. . . . At these festivities of our baptized . . . more is spoke of the wounds of Jesus, than of the sun" (Cranz 1767, I:231).

17. Technically, the Sun would have appeared above the horizon four or five days prior to the 19th but continuous overcast skies prevented it from being seen. Parhelia are rainbow-coloured bars which under some atmospheric conditions appear on each side of the Sun. They are commonly known as "mock suns" or "sun dogs." See page 157).

18. Captain Rochfort Maguire, who spent two winters at Point Barrow in the 1850s, similarly makes no mention of the Inuit's reaction to the return of the Sun. However, Maguire's own "expression of satisfaction" took the form of "a gun [being] fired and the Ensign hoisted in Commemoration of the event" (Bockstoce 1988:329).

19. The ritual extinguishment and relighting of fires as an act of renewal is reported from many Indo-European societies. Called "needfire" ceremonies, they usually took place around the summer solstice (Worthen 1991:33).

20. Parry gives the following description of fire-making: "For the purpose of obtaining fire the Esquimaux use two lumps of common iron pyrites, from which sparks are struck into a little leathern case, containing moss well dried and rubbed between the hands. If this tinder does not readily catch, a small quantity of the white floss of the seed of the ground willow is laid above the moss. As soon as a spark has caught, it is gently blown till the fire has spread an inch around, when the pointed end of a piece of oiled wick being applied, it soon bursts into a flame, the whole process having occupied perhaps two or three minutes" (Parry 1824:504). In later times, flint and steel (usually an old file) were used to make fire (Emil Imaruittuq, pers. comm., 1990). A detailed description of fire-making in the Coronation Gulf area is given by Jenness (1946:55–57).

21. The idea that weather is affected by the interrelationship of celestial bodies is widespread. For the Bering Strait Eskimos high winds are caused when Sirius is close to

the Moon (Nelson 1899:449). The Melanesians have many "fighting stars" which cause storms when the Moon in either a waxing or a waning phase (Thomas 1987:273).

22. Piugaattuk specifies that the smiling should be done with the left side of the face. This may have made it more difficult for most of the younger children to accomplish, ensuring the adults a great deal of amusement (see Niviattian Aqatsiaq's comments). The "half smile" seems to be a motif incorporated in a number of Inuit masks, particularly those from the Bering Sea area. An example is found in Nelson (1899, facing p. 414, pl. C11, fig. 3).

23. In Klutschak's case the Sun, of course, could have been obscured by mountains or valleys, but this hardly creates conditions comparable to the "polar night" he is attempting to depict.

24. Bernard Saladin d'Anglure (1990:108) holds the opposite view. However, the overwhelming impression conveyed by Iglulingmiut elders questioned on the matter seems to indicate that *Pualutaniktuq* (occurring in the first week of March) was the more significant marker of winter's end. His claim that Inuit had an original way of determining the equinox with their arms appears to be based on erroneous translation: a confusion between the word *talittuq* (implying that the Sun has set or is obscured by the horizon) and the word *taliit*, meaning "arms."

25. Prior to the establishment of the Hudson's Bay Company Post at Igloolik (1939), the time around the vernal equinox marked the start of trading journeys by dog-team to the post at Pond Inlet. Not much attention was paid to the autumnal equinox except at the time food-storing for the coming winter began and "caches were secured so that the foxes would not get into them" (Piugaattuk 1990, IE-147).

26. A *qaggiq* was a community feast or celebration usually involving games and drum-dancing. It was often held in a large igloo specifically constructed for this purpose. Such an igloo was also known as a *qaggiq*. Joe Tassiuk of Igloolik, who referred to the mitt measurement as *Pualutaqalirpuq*, remembers little in the way of festivities taking place at the time "because food was too scarce" (Joe Tassiuk, pers. comm., 1990).

27. Note that Niviattian Aqatsiaq's method of determining

Pualutaniktuq differs slightly from Piugaattuk's. In practical terms, however, the difference is insignificant, amounting to a mere half-degree of arc, the Sun's apparent diameter.

28. Other peoples also sought to enmesh the Sun: "In a pass of the Peruvian Andes stand two ruined towers on opposite hills. Iron hooks are clamped into their walls for the purpose of stretching a net from one tower to the other. The net is intended to catch the sun" (Frazer 1922:79).

29. Mutilation of the personified Sun's back is a widely recurrent theme in Inuit mythology.

30. "Asiit" are the *Aagjuuk* stars (see entry 1). By this measure spring in Angmagsalik would begin on or about 17 April.

31. Curiously, Rasmussen (1932:271), writing about the Inuit of the Coronation Gulf area, states that string figures "may only be made in the light time, i.e., the time of the year when the sun can be seen." This is at variance with Jenness who claims that "from Kotzebue sound, in Alaska, to Kent peninsula at the eastern end of Coronation gulf, there was a taboo against playing the game except in the winter, when the sun no longer rose above the horizon" (Jenness 1924:181b).

32. About the Nunivak Eskimos, who did not lose the Sun during winter, Margaret Lantis writes: "Cats' cradles were supposed to be made only inside, in winter, and during the day, not in the evening. Only the females played with string figures. If boys or men made them, their harpoon line would become tangled when they were out hunting" (Lantis 1946:217). The cautioning of boys about the danger inherent in string figures was widespread but in other areas moderation rather than prohibition was prescribed.

33. Boas notes that *Ajagaq* was played to encourage the Sun's rising after it had returned to the horizon. A children's song intended to accompany the *Ajagaq* game is found in Thalbitzer. Although its connection with the returning Sun is not mentioned, the first few lines are certainly consistent with this notion: *"ajarte!"* ("Let him [them] push upwards!"), *"qut.aia.rarte!"* ("Let him [them] rise in the air!"), etc. (Thalbitzer 1914, II:205).

34. *Mauliq*—seal-hunting at breathing holes.

35. Merbs also notes that in some areas the gender of the deceased had a bearing on burial orientation. In this

connection, Donald Marsh writes: "They inclined an upright pole towards the west, away from the head, to signify that a man or boy was here. A pole slanted towards the north denoted a woman or girl" (Marsh 1987:145).

36. Lyon (1824:371), too, refers to this practice which was not, however, universally followed. Parry (1824:551) records an instance where a child was buried "with its head to the north-east," meaning that the feet would be pointing southwest, indicating, by Hooper's report, a person "in the decline of life." Burial practices among the Umingmakturmiut (Bathurst Inlet area) required that the body "be placed so that the face turns towards the rising sun" (Rasmussen 1932:45). In Point Hope, Alaska, "[The] feet of the dead were also aligned toward the sunrise" (Lowenstein 1992:17).

37. Also among the Umingmakturmiut (Rasmussen 1932:46).

38. Ceremonial circular movement to the right, or "sun-wise" is an ancient and widespread ritual. Thomas Worthen (1991:19–37) gives a fascinating and thorough analysis of the practice, which he terms "the ritual of Right Running."

39. The differences between Inuit summer and winter life were summed up by Mauss (1979:76) as follows: "In the dense concentrations of the winter, a genuine community of ideas and material interests is formed. Its strong moral, mental and religious unity contrasts sharply with the isolation, social fragmentation and dearth of moral and religious life that occurs when everyone has scattered during the summer."

40. The term *malikkaan* (plural *malikkaat*) is said to derive from the root *malik-*, meaning "to follow," a reference perhaps to the "heliotrophic" ability of the dryas flower to follow or focus on the Sun and, by extension, to follow or accompany the Sun on her seasonal rounds.

41. The Inuit of Perry River, NWT, apparently referred to sunspots as *unnguq* ("warts") but this may have been a jocular reference (Duncan Pryde, pers. comm., 1994).

42. While most accounts of extra-terrestrial shamanistic flights indicate the Moon as the destination, a few mention the Sun. Gustav Holm, for instance, in his Angmagsalik material, records that the *angakuk* relate going up to heaven or "to remote quarters of the earth or up to the sun or the moon" (Holm, *in* Thalbitzer 1914, part 1:97).

43. The phenomenon rests on the fact that the Moon's path around the sun is not on the same plane as the Earth's. In higher latitudes, the resulting effect makes the Moon appear higher or lower in the sky in any given year over an 18.6-year cycle. Weyer (1956:17) gives a detailed explanation. Cranz noted the phenomenon in Greenland: "In the shortest days sometimes the moon never goes down" (Cranz 1767, I:48). The circumpolar-moon has been mentioned by others, including MacMillan (1927:106) and Nansen (1893:278). Elisha Kent Kane (1856:140) waxes poetic on the subject: "She [the Moon] is a glorious object: sweeping around the heavens, at the lowest part of her curve, she is still 14° above the horizon. For eight days she has been making her circuit with nearly unvarying brightness." Further discussion of this phenomenon is found in Saladin d'Anglure (1990).

44. The supposed link between the full Moon and cold weather was noted by John Ross during a winter spent on the Boothia Peninsula in 1830: "It is worthy of remark, be it explained as it may . . . that all the coldest days occurred near the time of full moon, and a little after" (Ross 1835:300). For the Nunamiut of Northern Alaska, however, Gubser notes that "when the moon is full, the night is considered to be a little warmer" (Gubser 1965:193).

45. The ceremonial thirst-quenching of newly killed sea mammals was practiced by many Inuit coastal groups.

46. The Alaskan Nunamiut expected an eclipse of the Moon whenever the Moon was seen to "catch up with a star and envelop it" (Gubser 1965:193–94).

47. It is clear that the instrument being used was a sextant, which through the use of mirrors, brings a reflected image of the Sun down to the horizon.

48. This is a well-known phenomenon frequently associated with total eclipses.

49. According to Parry (1824:176).

50. Note that in Igloolik the term for eclipse, *pulamajuq*, is also used to describe a person covered with a blanket. To get under the bed covers during an eclipse suggests a mimicking of the eclipse.

51. This is one of the few accounts where the Sun and the Moon are characterized respectively as brother and sister. Another occurs in Rae (1850:79). The otherwise universal

personifications of the Sun as female and the Moon as male throughout the Inuit world may suggest that these apparent reversals of the "norm" are erroneous.

Chapter 5

1. In Igloolik the term *ingnirujait* is also used for phosphorescence in sea water.
2. Schneider (1985), for West Hudson Bay, lists *ignirugaq* as "shooting star."
3. An Igloolik elder, Inuki Kunnuk (1990, IE-116) mentioned that when shamans take their spirit flights *(ikiaqqijut)* their movement through the atmosphere is sometimes traced by a phosphorescent trail, *ingnirujait*.
4. Kroeber records that, among the Polar Eskimo, there is no "myth about the aurora borealis" (Kroeber 1899:319). Davis (1992:164–67) summarizes various aurora legends across the Inuit area.
5. *Amaruujaq*—the "wolf game"; a childrens' game of "tag."
6. Traditionally when walrus were killed they would be harpooned in such a manner that they virtually bled to death. This was done to prevent the liver becoming congested with blood. (Emil Imaruittuq, pers. comm., 1990). For Niviattian Aqatsiaq it is thus entirely consistent that walrus heads should share a spirit world reserved for the souls of those who had died from blood loss.
7. Fortescue et al. (1994:178) gives *kiuʀuya* as the North Alaskan Inuit term for aurora. The word may derive from the root *"kiu-"* (answer), a reference "to the alleged response of the aurora to calling" (or whistling).
8. Johnny Annanack, of Kangiqsualujjuaq, Northern Quebec, also likened auroral sound "to people walking on hard snow or a sled moving over hard snow" (pers. comm., 1992).
9. However, some investigators have been willing to consider the possibility of auroral sound, attributing the cause to such mechanisms as "very-low-frequency electro-magnetic waves" or "coronal discharge." These mechanisms and their possible links to auroral sound are explained in *The Aurora Watcher's Handbook* (Davis 1992).
10. But at a later date in his Arctic life Hooper says,"I fancied that I heard this aurora, but the noise was indubitably produced by the cracking of ice on the lake" (Nourse 1879:84).
11. Haloes of 46° are less common. A particularly rare 26°

halo segment, apparently elliptical, was observed by Parry at Winter Harbour (Melville Island, NWT) in 1820 (Parry 1821:164). The phenomenon is now known as "Parry's Arc" (Parry 1963:64).
12. Parry (1824:493–94), referring to the "hair stick" as *togleega*, gives the following description: "[The women] separate their locks into two equal parts, one of which hangs on each side of their heads and in front of their shoulders. To stiffen and bind these they use a narrow strip of deer-skin, attached at one end to a round piece of bone, fourteen inches long, tapered to a point and covered with leather. This looks like a little whip, the handle of which is placed up and down the hair, and the strap wound round it in a number of spiral turns. . . . The strap . . . when bound round the hair, [shows] alternate turns of white and dark fur, which give it a very neat and ornamental appearance."
13. A related word, *ajakutaq*, refers specifically to the wooden supports used in snowhouses in the early spring to prevent the walls from caving in (M. Arnatsiaq, pers. comm., 1994).

Chapter 6

1. From Duncan Pryde's "The Breath of Arctic Men." In *Reflections: The Anthropological Muse*, Iain Prattis (ed.), 1985, pp. 241–42. The Fox Star *(Kayuqtuq)* is probably a reference to the star Sirius.
2. Amundsen (1908, II:110), commenting on the ability of Inuit at Gjoa Haven to navigate in fog, remarks, "For these people to have been able to row a straight course with such extraordinary precision, without a glimmer of daylight, seems to show that they must be possessed of a sixth sense." Stefánsson (1912:146–49), however, rejects this, saying, "There are few misconceptions about [the Inuit] more prevalent than the one that they have a sort of 'sixth sense,' which may be called the sense of direction or locality and which prevents them from being lost under any circumstances." Interestingly, Inuit seem to have been impressed by European navigational skills: "They [the Europeans] knew how to find their way and exactly determine their position by the sun" (Rasmussen 1931:128).
3. An essay on Inuit navigation, *Eskimo Wayfinding and Spatial Orientation*, by George Simeon (1983) explores, among other things, the conceptual differences between

indigenous land-based navigation and ocean voyaging.

4. The intent of names such as Mittimatalik (Pond Inlet) and Qillaqarvik, which refer to the burial places of Inuit individuals, seems more topographical than commemorative. In the Igloolik area there are only a few Inuit place names directly commemorating persons. One is a small lake north of Murray Maxwell Bay called Iviksukuni, after a kayaker who drowned there. Another is Umiligaarjuk, a spot on the coast of Melville Peninsula just south of Hall Beach where Reynold Bray was lost during the British-Canadian Arctic Expedition of 1937–1941. Umiligaarjuk, "the little bearded one" was Bray's Inuktitut name.

5. Names such as Nunavut (in the Northwest Territories) and Nunavik (in Northern Quebec) were invented for geo-political needs following the settlement of land claims. Interestingly, discussing the choice of Nunavik, one elder from Kangirsualujjauq pointed out that the name referred specifically to the largely uninhabited part of the land well inland from the sea. He thought the term *Iluiliq,* corresponding approximately to the littoral islands, would have been more appropriate.

6. J. Sonnenfeldt (pers. comm., 1994) points out that the mountainous terrain through which the Nunamiut travel does not lend itself well to star-based orientation.

7. According to Duncan Pryde (1995), Inuit travelling by dog-team in the Coronation Gulf area used stars low on the horizon to maintain their heading. This, apparently, also gave the lead dog a visible target to head towards, thus necessitating fewer course corrections on the part of the driver.

8. Pryde adds that the "lead-dog picks up the star too and doesn't wander off course as much as it usually does when travelling by drifts alone."

9. Usuittuq, *in* Norman Hallendy, letter to the author, 20 February, 1991.

10. Literally, "the one that never moves."

11. James Follett's views on the significance of Polaris for European navigators are interesting, if overstated: "It was a star whose reliable presence had triggered the explosive spread of civilization, exploration and trade in the northern hemisphere, while culture in the southern hemisphere, with no equivalent accurate star, had stagnated. It was Polaris—the Pole Star" (Follett 1982:130).

12. See Chapter 3, entry 6.

13. Makuttunnaaq—"the little young person"—Graham Rowley's Inuktitut name.

14. Snowdrifts are also known by the names of the winds that form them, hence: *uangniut*—northwest drift; *niggiut*—southeast drift; *kanangniut*—northeast drift; *akinnarniut*—southwest drift (Aivilik dialect *pingangniut*—southwest drift.)

15. Some of the indigenous people of Siberia were apparently as adept as Inuit at "reading" snowdrifts: "When caught in a blizzard, the Evenk did not lose his self-possession. Guided by experience founded on many centuries of everyday observations, he found the correct direction by groping with his hand along the wind-blown ridges of the snow" (Anisimov 1959:221).

16. Bernard Saladin d'Anglure (1990:99) suggests the contrary.

17. This orientation is also emphasized when igloo-building where it is customary to place the first snowblock facing either northwest or southeast, thereby making the most efficient use of the drift's formation along this axis (Maurice Arnatsiaq, Emil Imaruittuq, pers. comm., 1993).

18. The primacy of the northwest/southeast axis in Iglulingmiut orientation confers an interesting advantage in their occasional, but increasing, use of the magnetic compass, particularly at sea. Local magnetic variation around Igloolik is approximately 43°W, meaning that the compass needle, at rest, indicates almost northwest. From the Inuit point of view this direction is "true," requiring no correction to a north/south axis in that it coincides nicely with the area's other natural indicators of direction—*Uangnaq*, the northwest wind, and its resultant snowdrifts.

19. In a short section on snowdrift navigation in *Arctic Manual*, Vilhjalmur Stefánsson repeats this point: "Your memory of recent storms will aid in these interpretations [of snowdrifts] and will help to give you your bearings" (1944:347–48).

20. The term *ipakjugait* is also used for the grain in wood, particularly weathered wood, and for creases in cloth.

21. Note that here the Avilik Inuit are in fact using snowdrifts rather than wind direction as the ultimate determinant of their correct course.

22. Inuit names for wind directions vary from region to region. They are "absolute" in the sense that they usually relate to local coastal orientation rather than to some

universal marker such as "true" north. This system, Michael Fortescue argues, "may be a more reliable guide to Eskimos discussing journeys over complex Arctic terrain than compass orientation can provide" (Fortescue 1988:3).

23. Emil Imaruittuq, pers. comm., 24 September 1993. The bearings of the winds (in degrees) were determined by a theodolite set up outside the Igloolik Research Centre, Igloolik, and aligned (astronomically) to "true" north. Note that when using English, knowledgeable Iglulingmiut usually translate *uangnaq* and *nigiq* as northwest and southeast respectively. Among many of the younger generation the "nominalization" process is taken even further; *uangnaq* becoming "north" and *nigiq*, "south," a liberty that earns the disapproval of some of the older hunters.

24. The frond of the kelp points downstream, thereby indicating the direction of the current's flow.

25. The "water-sky" is defined by Parry (1824:xx) as a "dark appearance" in the sky, indicating "clear water" in that direction, and forming a striking contrast with the "blink" over land or ice. Parry also noted Igloolik's water-sky: "Open water still observed at a distance of two or three miles in the offing, with columns of frost-smoke over it and a bluish 'water-sky' about that part of the horizon (1824:378). Stefánsson (1912:298) describes a similar effect: "When clouds of a uniform color hang low there is reflected in them a map of the earth below them. . . . This sky map is of the greatest use to sledge travelers always. . . . Where the landmarks themselves are below the horizon their position is accurately indicated by their reflection in the clouds."

26. Also known as *inuksuk* (plural *inuksuit*).

Chapter 7

1. The Inuktitut suffix *-vik* can signify either "place"—*iqalugasugvik* ("the fishing place") or "time"—*quviasuvvik* ("the time of happiness," Christmas). The combination of place and activity is a basic element of Inuit time perception.

2. In Igloolik, this term specifically relates to the action of going outdoors early in the morning to observe the weather.

3. Inuit "social time" was marked in terms of the physical growth and social achievement of an individual rather than in years. There were, for instance, at least seven terms used to describe the development of a boy from birth to adulthood. In addition to the obvious developmental stages such as crawling and walking, other markers referred to a boy's increasing ability to participate in hunting activities: *ilaujalittukuluutillgu* (old enough to accompany adults on hunting trips); *mianissijunnasijukuluutillgu* (old enough to tend the dogs); *sugiaqqanasigunnarsitillugu* (old enough to hunt on his own) (Imaruittuq 1990, IE-161).

4. The problem arises from the impossibility of dividing (without remainder) the lunar month (approximately 29.5 days) into the Sun's yearly cycle (approximately 365.2 days). Anthony Aveni in *Empires of Time* (1990) provides a thorough explanation of the problem and how it was addressed by various cultures throughout history.

5. The information presented in the calendar was supplied during a combined interview with Michel Kupaaq, Mark Ijjangiaq, and George Kappianaq (1991, IE-187).

6. In parts of Arctic Quebec the Inuktitut word for Sunday is *allituqaq* referring to "those who respect a taboo" (Dorais 1983:5). In Igloolik the word is *sanataili* ("prevent work").

7. These would have been Scripture Union cards "widely used by Inuit as a calendar" (Rowley 1996:71).

8. When pencils were not available a needle would be used instead: "Every morning when they woke up they would make a small puncture mark [on the calendar]" (Kupaaq 1996, IE-370).

Chapter 8

1. The meaning here is that she was walking on the heels of her skin boots *(kammiks),* i.e., the heels had slipped down in the way that socks might in ill-fitting boots.

2. Franz Boas (1888:599) gives the phrase as *Uqsureliktaleqdjuin*—"provide yourself with your large white bear *tornaq* (spirit)."

3. *Singuuriq* is the star Sirius, the brightest in the sky. Due to the effects of refraction its appearance in Arctic regions is usually spectacular.

4. Literally, "a star is shitting!"

5. Most Iglulingmiut accounts of the *Ullaktut* legend omit mention of the "fourth man." In this version he becomes *Kingulliq* ("the one behind"), the star Rigel, in Orion.

Iglulingmiut also apply the name *Kingulliq* to the star Vega, here referring to one of the personalities in the *Iliarjugaarjuk* legend.

6. *Sila*—in this sense "the universe." Here the narrator means that the hunters were moving in the same (apparent) direction as the stars.

7. *Nanurjuk,* the star Aldebaran.

8. Clean wrists, by contrast, are the mark of good hunters, all dirt having been washed away by blood in the process of butchering their catches.

9. Inuit frequently point to the similarities between polar bear and human anatomy. This view supports their belief that the polar bear is the most intelligent of all animals.

10. The name Kaukjakjualuk probably comes from the word *kauk,* "walrus skin,"—a reference to the diet on which the orphan boy was forced to subsist. Although it was edible, Inuit considered *kauk* a starvation food, under normal circumstances fit only for their dogs.

11. In some versions of this legend the orphan boy hides the flints under his foreskin.

12. Qikiqtaarjuk now forms the northeast peninsula of Igloolik Island. Conventional geology agrees with Inuit tradition that, in the distant past, Qikiqtaarjuk was, indeed, insular. Due to the post-glacial phenomenon known as "isostatic rebound," land in the Igloolik area is rising at a rate of around 1 m each century.

Chapter 10

1. There is a tradition in Igloolik that in legendary times new snow could be used as fuel for lamps.

2. *Sermiaut*—an instrument of bone or wood for scraping ice from a kayak.

3. Holm explains in a footnote: "Another version (Hanserak) says that the moon burnt himself on the Sun, so that a number of small pieces flew off from him, and these became stars."

★ BIBLIOGRAPHY ★

Note: Citations that carry "IE" numbers can be found in the list of Igloolik elders' interviews following the bibliography.

AKATSIAQ, VICTOR

1989   "Reading Weather." *Isumasi* (Inuit Cultural Institute, Arviat) 1(2):26–28.

ALAYCO, SALOMONIE

1985   Interview by Simon Aliqu. Transcript held at Inuttigut Pirrusiit Documentation Centre on Nunavik History, Avataq Cultural Institute, Montreal.

ALLEN, RICHARD H.

1963   *Star Names: Their Lore and Meaning.* New York: Dover Publications. (First published as *Star-Names and Their Meanings* in 1899 by G. E. Stechert.)

AMUNDSEN, ROALD

1908   *The North West Passage.* 2 vols. New York: E. P. Dutton and Company.

ANISIMOV, A. F.

1959   *Cosmological Concepts of the Peoples of the North.* Reprinted *in* Henry N. Michael, ed., *Studies in Siberian Shamanism,* 1963 (reprint; Toronto: University of Toronto Press, 1972).

AVENI, ANTHONY

1990   *Empires of Time.* London: I. B. Tauris.

BERGSLAND, KNUT, ED.

1987   *Nunamiut Stories.* Barrow, Alaska: The North Slope Borough Commission on Inupiat History, Language and Culture.

BESSELS, EMILE

1884   "The Northernmost Inhabitants of the Earth: An Ethnographic Sketch." *The American Naturalist* 18(9):861–882.

BIRKET-SMITH, KAJ

1924   *Ethnography of the Egedesminde District.* Copenhagen: Bianco Lunos Bogtrykkeri.

1929   *The Caribou Eskimos—Material and Social Life and Their Cultural Position.* Vol. 5 of *Report of the Fifth Thule Expedition 1921–24.* Copenhagen: Gyldendalske Boghandel.

1953   *The Chugach Eskimos.* Copenhagen: Nationalmuseets Skrifter, Etnografisk Raekke 6.

BOAS, FRANZ

1888   "The Central Eskimo." *6th Annual Report of the Bureau of American Ethnology for the Years 1884–1885,* pp. 399–669. Washington: Bureau of American Ethnology. Reprint. Toronto: Coles Publishing Company, 1974.

1907   "The Eskimo of Baffin Land and Hudson Bay." *Bulletin of the American Museum of Natural History* 15:4–570.

BOCKSTOCE, JOHN, ED.

1988   *The Journal of Rochfort Maguire 1852–1854.* 2 vols. London: Hakluyt Society.

BOGORAS, WALDEMAR

1928   "Ethnographic Problems of the Eurasian Arctic." In W. L. G. Joerg, ed., *Problems of Polar Research.* New York: American Geographical Society, Special Publication No. 7, pp. 506–538.

BOMPAS, WILLIAM CARPENTER—see YERBURY, J. C.

BORUP, GEORGE

1911   *A Tenderfoot with Peary.* New York: Frederick A. Stokes.

BUGGE, A., K. KYNGE, A. FUGLSANG-DAMGOORD, and F. NIELSEN

1994   *Dansk-Grønlandsk Ordbog.* Nuuk, Greenland: Atuakkiorfik.

BURCH, DAVID

1986   *Emergency Navigation.* Camden, Maine: International Marine Publishing.

BURCH, ERNEST S., JR.

1988   *The Eskimos.* Oklahoma: University of Oklahoma Press.

Burn, Chris

1996   *The Polar Night.* Scientific Rpt. no. 4. Inuvik: Aurora Research Institute.

CAMPBELL, JOSEPH
1991 *Primitive Mythology*. New York: Arkana.
CARPENTER, EDMUND
1973 *Eskimo Realities*. New York: Holt, Rinehart and Winston.
CASWELL, HELEN
1968 *Shadows from the Singing House*. Rutland, Vermont: Charles E. Tuttle.
CHARTRAND, MARK R., III
1982 *Sky Guide: A Field Guide to the Heavens*. New York: Golden Press.
CLARK, DAVID H., and RICHARD F. STEPHENSON
1978 "An Interpretation of the Pre-Telescopic Sunspot Records from the Orient." *Quarterly Journal of the Royal Astronomical Society* 19:387–410.
COLLINSON, RICHARD
1889 *Journal of H.M.S. Enterprise, on the Expedition in Search of Sir John Franklin's Ships by Behring Strait, 1850–1855*. Edited by T. B. Collinson. London: Sampson, Low, Marston, and Rivington.
COLOMBO, JOHN ROBERT, ED.
1981 *Poems of the Inuit*. Ottawa: Oberon Press.
COOK, FREDERICK A.
1951 *Return from the Pole*. New York: Pellegrini and Cudahy.
CRANZ, DAVID
1767 *The History of Greenland* . . . . 2 vols. London: Printed by the Brethren's Society for the Furtherance of the Gospel Among the Heathen and sold by J. Dodsley.

DAVIS, NEIL
1992 *The Aurora Watcher's Handbook*. Fairbanks, Alaska: University of Alaska Press.
DORAIS, LOUIS-JACQUES
1983 *An Analytical Lexicon of Modern Inuktitut in Quebec-Labrador*. Quebec City: Les Presses de l'université Laval.
ERDMANN, FRIEDRICH, ED.
1864 *Eskimoisches Wörtebuch gesammelt von den Missionaren in Labrador*. Budissin, Germany: E. M. Monse.

ETALOOK, ARCTIC JOHN
1983 "Nunamiut Survival Tapes." Nos. 12 and 13: "Ethnoastronomy." Translated by Muriel Hobson. Transcripts of interviews on Nunamiut Ethno-astronomy, Grant Spearman, coordinating researcher, North Slope Borough Inupiaq History, Language and Culture Commission, Barrow, Alaska.

FIENUP-RIORDAN, ANN
1988 "Eye of the Dance: Spiritual Life of the Bering Sea Eskimo." *In* W. Fitzhugh and A. Crowell, eds., *Crossroads of the Continents: Cultures of Siberia and Alaska*, pp. 256–270. Washington, D.C.: Smithsonian Institution Press.
FITZHUGH, WILLIAM W., and ARON CROWELL, EDS.
1988 *Crossroads of the Continents: Cultures of Siberia and Alaska*. Washington, D.C.: Smithsonian Institution Press.
FLEISCHER, JØRGEN
1990 *Qeqertarsuaq*. Nuuk, Greenland: Atuakkiorfik.
FLEMING, ARCHIBALD L.
1928 *Dwellers in the Arctic Night*. London: The Bible Churchmen's Missionary Society.
1965 *Archibald the Arctic*. Reprint. Toronto: Saunders, 1970.
FOLLETT, JAMES
1982 Churchill's Gold. New York:
FORTESCUE, MICHAEL
1988 *Eskimo Orientation Systems*. Meddelelser om Grønland, Man and Society 11. Copenhagen.
FORTESCUE, MICHAEL, STEVEN JACOBSON, and LAWRENCE KAPLAN
1994 *Comparative Eskimo Dictionary*. Alaskan Native Language Centre, Research Paper no. 9. Fairbanks, Alaska: University of Alaska.
FOULKS, EDWARD FRANCIS
1972 *The Arctic Hysterias of the North Alaskan Eskimo*. Ann Arbor: University Microfilms.
FREUCHEN, PETER
1961 *Peter Freuchen's Book of the Eskimos*. Edited by Dagmar Freuchen. New York: World Publishing Company.

FREUCHEN, PETER, and FINN SALOMONSEN
1958   *The Arctic Year.* New York: Putnam.
FRAZER, J. G.
1922   *The Golden Bough.* London: Macmillan.
GAD, FINN
1973   *The History of Greenland II: 1700 to 1782.* Montreal: McGill-Queen's University Press.
GAGNÉ, RAYMOND
1968   "Spatial Concepts in the Eskimo Language." *In* Victor F. Valentine and Frank G. Vallee, *Eskimo of the Canadian Arctic,* pp. 30–38. Toronto: McClelland and Stewart.
GEORGIA
1982   *Georgia: An Arctic Diary.* Edmonton: Hurtig.
GIDDINGS, J. L.
1961   *Kobuk River People.* Fairbanks, Alaska: University of Alaska.
GILBERG, R., ED.
1989   *Greenland Seen Through 50 Years of Stamps, 1938–1988.* Copenhagen: Kalaallit Allakkeriviat (The Greenland Post Office).
GRAAH, W. A.
1837   *Narrative of an Expedition to the East Coast of Greenland, etc.* London: John W. Parker.
GREENAWAY, KEITH J.
1951   *Arctic Navigation.* Ottawa: Arctic Research Defence Board.
GUBSER, NICHOLAS J.
1965   *The Nunamiut Eskimos: Hunters of Caribou.* New Haven, Conn.: Yale University Press.
GUSSOW, Z.
1960   "Pibloktok Hysteria Among the Polar Eskimos." *Psychoanalytic Study of Society* 1:218–236.

HALL, CHARLES F.
1865   *Life with the Esquimaux.* London: Sampson Low, Son, and Marston.
HALL, EDWIN S., JR.
1975   *The Eskimo Storyteller: Folktales from Noatak, Alaska.* Knoxville: University of Tennessee Press.
HAWKES, ERNEST W.
1916   *The Labrador Eskimo.* Ottawa: Geological Survey of Canada, Memoir 91, Anthropological Series 14.
HOLM, GUSTAV, 1888, 1911, 1914—see THALBITZER, WILLIAM, 1914–1941.
HOLTVED, ERIK
1951   *The Polar Eskimos* (Language and Folklore Part II: Myths and Tales). Meddelclser om Grønland, Bd. 152, Nr. 2. Copenhagen.
HOOPER, W. H.
1823   Manuscript Journal 1821–1823 (original manuscript at the Royal Geographical Society, London, England).
HRDLICKA, ALES
1944   *The Anthropology of Kodiak Island.* Philadelphia: The Wistar Institute of Anatomy and Biology.

IYAITUK, MARKUSIE
1985   Interview. Transcript held at Inuttigut Pirrusiit Documentation Centre on Nunavik History, Avataq Cultural Institute, Montreal.
INUKSAAQ, SIMON
1990   Interview by Louis Tapardjuk. Transcript held at Inuttigut Pirrusiit Documentation Centre on Nunavik History, Avataq Cultural Institute, Montreal.

JACOBSON, STEVEN A.
1984   *Yup'ik Eskimo Dictionary.* Fairbanks, Alaska: Alaskan Native Language Center, University of Alaska.
JENNESS, DIAMOND
1922   *The Life of the Copper Eskimos.* Vol. 12, Pt. A of *Report of the Canadian Arctic Expedition 1913–1918.* Ottawa: King's Printer.
1924   *Eskimo String Figures.* Vol. 13, Pt. B of *Report of the Canadian Arctic Expedition 1913–1918.* Ottawa: King's Printer.
1946   *Material Culture of the Copper Eskimos.* Vol. 16 of *Report of the Canadian Arctic Expedition 1913–1918.* Ottawa: King's Printer.
JENNESS, STUART, ED.
1991   *Arctic Odyssey: The Diary of Diamond Jenness 1913–1916.* Ottawa: Canadian Museum of Civilization.

KANE, ELISHA KENT

1856   *Arctic Explorations in the Years 1853, '54, '55.* 2 vols. Philadelphia: Childs and Peterson.

KLUTSCHAK, HEINRICH

1987   *Overland to Starvation Cove.* Translated and edited by William Barr. Toronto: University of Toronto Press. (Original journal of Heinrich Klutschak published in 1881.)

KOESTLER, ARTHUR

1959   *The Sleepwalkers.* Hutchinson. Reprint. London: Penguin Books, 1986.

KROEBER, A. L.

1899   "The Eskimo of Smith Sound." *Bulletin of the American Museum of Natural History* 12(21):265–327. Reprint. New York: G. P. Putnam's Sons, 1900.

LANTIS, MARGARET

1946   "The Social Culture of the Nunivak Eskimo." *Transactions of the American Philosophical Society,* n.s. 35(3):153–323.

LE MOUËL, J.-F.

1978   *"Ceux des mouettes"—Les Eskimo naujâmiut, Groenland-Ouest.* Mémoire 16. Paris: Institut d'Ethnologie, Museé de l'Homme.

LEDEN, CHRISTIAN

1990   *Across the Keewatin Icefields.* Translated from the German by Leslie Neatby; edited by Shirlee Anne Smith. Winnipeg: Watson and Dwyer. (Original journal of Christian Leden published in 1927.)

LOPEZ, BARRY HOLSTUN

1986   *Arctic Dreams.* Toronto: Collier Macmillan.

LOWE, RONALD

1984   *Uummarmiut Uqalungiha Mumikhitchirutingit—Basic Uummarmiut Eskimo Dictionary.* Inuvik: Committee for Original Peoples Entitlement (C.O.P.E.).

LOWENSTEIN, TOM

1992   *The Things That Were Said of Them.* Vancouver: Douglas and McIntyre.

LYON, GEORGE F.

1824   *The Private Journal of Captain G. F. Lyon . . . .* London: John Murray.

McCRICKARD, JANET

1990   *Eclipse of the Sun.* Glastonbury: Gothic Image Publications.

MacLEAN, EDNA AHGEAK

1980   *Abridged Iñupiaq and English Dictionary.* Fairbanks, Alaska: University of Alaska.

MacMILLAN, DONALD BAXTER

1927   *Etah and Beyond.* New York: Houghton Mifflin Company.

MALAURIE, JEAN

1982   *The Last Kings of Thule.* New York: E. P. Dutton.

MALONEY, ELBERT S.

1983   *Dutton's Navigation and Piloting.* Annapolis, Maryland: Naval Institute Press.

MARSH, DONALD

1987   *Echoes for a Frozen Land.* Edited by Winifred Marsh. Edmonton: Hurtig.

1991   *Echoes into Tomorrow.* Edited by Winifred Marsh. Three Hills, Alberta: Prairie Graphics and Printing.

MARY-ROUSSELIÈRE, GUY

1969   *Les Jeux de ficelle des Arviligjuarmiut.* Bulletin 233. Ottawa: National Museums of Canada.

MATHIASSEN, THERKEL

1928   *Material Culture of the Iglulik Eskimos.* Vol. 6, no. 1 of *Report of the Fifth Thule Expedition 1921–24.* Copenhagen: Gyldendalske Boghandel. Reprint. New York: AMS Press, 1976.

MAUSS, MARCEL

1979   *Seasonal Variations of the Eskimo.* Translated by James J. Fox. London: Routledge and Kegan Paul.

MERBS, CHARLES F.

1969   "The Significance of Age, Sex, and Time of Burial in the Interpretation of Thule Eskimo Burial Patterns." (Paper presented at the 34th Annual Meeting of the Society for American Archaeology, Milwaukee, Wisconsin, 1969.)

MICHAEL, HENRY N., ED.

1963   *Studies in Siberian Shamanism.* Reprint. Toronto: University of Toronto Press, 1972.

1967   *Lieutenant Zagoskin's Travels in Russian America 1842–1844.* Arctic Institute of North America.

Anthropology of the North: Translations from Russian Sources, no. 7. Toronto: University of Toronto Press.

MOSSMAN, J. E.
1989 "A Comprehensive Search for Sunspots Without the Aid of a Telescope, 1981–1982." *Quarterly Journal of the Royal Astronomical Society* 30:59–64.

MURDOCH, JOHN
1892 "Ethnological Results of the Point Barrow Expedition." *9th Annual Report of the Bureau of American Ethnology for the Years 1887–1888*, pp. 19–441. Washington, D.C.: Smithsonian Institution.

MÜLLER-WILLE, LUDGER
1987 *Gazetteer of Inuit Place Names in Nunavik (Quebec, Canada)*. Inukjuak: Avataq Cultural Institute.

NANSEN, FRIDTJOF
1893 *Eskimo Life*. Translated from the Norwegian by William Archer. London: Longmans, Green, and Company.

NELSON, EDWARD WILLIAM
1899 "The Eskimo About Bering Strait." *18th Annual Report of the Bureau of American Ethnology 1896–1897*, pp. 3–518. Reprint. Washington: Smithsonian Institution Press, 1984.

NELSON, RICHARD K.
1969 *Hunters of the Northern Ice*. Chicago: University of Chicago Press.

NOURSE, J. E., ED.
1879 *Narrative of the Second Arctic Expedition Made by C. F. Hall, 1864–1869*. Washington: U.S. Government Printing Office.

NULIGAK
1966 *I, Nuligak*. Edited and translated by Maurice Métayer. Toronto: Peter Martin Associates.

NUNGAK, Z., and E. ARIMA
1969 *Unikkaatuat sanaugarngnik atyingualiit Puvirngniturngmit: Eskimo Stories from Povungnituk, Quebec*. Anthropological Series 90. Bulletin 235. Ottawa: National Museums of Canada.

OMAN, LELA KIANA
1975 *Eskimo Legends*. Anchorage: Alaska Methodist University Press.

OSTERMANN, H., ED.
1938 *Knud Rasmussen's Posthumous Notes on the Life and Doings of the East Greenlanders in Olden Times*. Meddelelser om Grønland, Bd. 109, Nr. 1. Copenhagen. Reprint. New York: AMS Press, 1976.
1939 *Knud Rasmussen's Posthumous Notes on East Greenland Legends and Myths*. Meddelelser om Grønland, Bd. 109, Nr. 3. Copenhagen.
1942 *The Mackenzie Eskimos*. Vol. 10, no. 2 of *Report of the Fifth Thule Expedition 1921–24*. Copenhagen: Gyldendalske Boghandel.
1952 *The Alaskan Eskimos*. Vol. 10, no. 3 of *Report of the Fifth Thule Expedition 1921–24*. Copenhagen: Gyldendalske Boghandel.

OSWALT, W. H.
1967 *Alaskan Eskimos*. San Francisco: Chandler.

PARRY, ANN
1963 *Parry of the Arctic*. London: Chatto and Windus.

PARRY, WILLIAM E.
1821 *Journal of a Voyage for the Discovery of a North-West Passage from the Atlantic to the Pacific: Performed in the Years 1819–1820*. London: John Murray.
1824 *Journal of a Second Voyage for the Discovery of a North-West Passage from the Atlantic to the Pacific: Performed in the Years 1821–22–23, in His Majesty's Ships Fury and Hecla*. London: John Murray.
1835 *Three Voyages for the Discovery of a North-West Passage, etc.*, 4 vols. London: John Murray.

PEACOCK, F. W.
1974 *Eskimo-English Dictionary*. St. John's, Newfoundland: Memorial University of Newfoundland.
1981 *The Labrador Inuit Lore and Legend*. St. John's, Newfoundland:
1988 *Nuna Nunamiullo—The Land and the People*. St. John's, Newfoundland: Jesperson Press.
n.d. *English-Eskimo Dictionary*. St. John's, Newfoundland: Memorial University of Newfoundland.

PEARY, ROBERT E.

1898   Northward over the "Great Ice": A Narrative of Life and Work Along the Shores and Upon the Interior Ice-cap of Northern Greenland in the Years 1886 and 1891–97. 2 vols. London: Methuen and Co.

PECK, EDMUND J.

1925   Eskimo-English Dictionary. Hamilton, Ontario: Church of the Ascension Thank-Offering Mission Fund.

PICCO, ED

1993   "Hall Beach (Sanirrajak)." In W. Richard Hamilton, ed., The Baffin Handbook, pp. 248–253. Iqaluit: Nortext.

PRATTIS, J. IAIN, ED.

1985   Reflections: The Anthropological Muse. Washington, D.C.: American Anthropological Association.

PRYDE, DUNCAN

1995   Letter to the author (30-page commentary), 20 July 1995. (To be deposited in Northwest Territories Archives.)

QUMAK, MOSES

1985   Interview by Simon Aliqu. Transcript held at Inuttigut Pirrusiit Documentation Centre on Nunavik History, Avataq Cultural Institute, Montreal.

QUMAQ, TAAMUSI

1988   Sivulitta Piusituqangit. Quebec City: Association Inuksiutiit Katimajiit Inc.

1991   Inuit Uquasillaringit: A Dictionary of Definitions in Nunavik (Arctic Quebec) Inuktitut. Quebec City: Association Inuksiutiit; and Inukjuak and Montreal: Avataq Cultural Institute.

QUTTIUTUQU, PAUL AND MARTHA

1990   Interview by Louis Tapardjuk. Copy of audio tape and transcript held at the archives of the Inullariit Society, Igloolik, NWT.

RAE, JOHN

1850   Narrative of an Expedition to the Shores of the Arctic Sea in the Years 1846 and 1847. London: T. and W. Boone.

RASMUSSEN, KNUD

1908   The People of the Polar North: A Record. Edited by G. Herring. London: Kegan Paul, Trench, Trübner.

1921   Greenland by the Polar Sea: The Story of the Thule Expedition from Melville Bay to Cape Morris Jesup. Translated by Asta and Rowland Kenney. London: William Heinemann.

1927   Across Arctic America. New York: G. P. Putnam's Sons.

1929   Intellectual Culture of the Iglulik Eskimos. Vol. 7, no. 1 of Report of the Fifth Thule Expedition 1921–24. Copenhagen: Gyldendalske Boghandel.

1930a   Observations on the Intellectual Culture of the Caribou Eskimos. Vol. 7, no. 2 of Report of the Fifth Thule Expedition 1921–24. Copenhagen: Gyldendalske Boghandel.

1930b   Iglulik and Caribou Eskimo Texts. Vol. 7, no. 3 of Report of the Fifth Thule Expedition 1921–24. Copenhagen: Gyldendalske Boghandel.

1931   The Netsilik Eskimos: Social Life and Spiritual Culture. Vol. 8, nos. 1–2 of Report of the Fifth Thule Expedition 1921-24. Copenhagen: Gyldendalske Boghandel.

1932   Intellectual Culture of the Copper Eskimos. Vol. 9 of Report of the Fifth Thule Expedition 1921–1924. Copenhagen: Gyldendalske Boghandel.

RAY, DOROTHY JEAN

1967   Eskimo Masks: Art and Ceremony. Photographs by Alfred A. Blaker. Seattle: University of Washington Press.

RAY, P. H.

1885   Report of the International Polar Expedition to Point Barrow, Alaska, in Response to the Resolution of the House of Representatives of December 11, 1884. Washington, D.C.: U.S. Government Printing Office.

REVILLON FRÈRES

1923   Igloo Life. New York: Self-published.

RICHARDSON, JOHN

1852   Arctic Searching Expedition: A Journal of a Boat-voyage through Rupert's Land and the Arctic Sea. New York: Harper and Brothers.

RINK, HENRIK

1875   Tales and Traditions of the Eskimo: With a Sketch of Their

Habits, Religion, Language and Other Peculiarities. Edited by Robert Brown. Edinburgh and London: W. Blackwood and Sons. Reprint. Montreal: McGill-Queen's University Press, 1974.

ROBBE, PIERRE, and LOUIS-JACQUES DORAIS
1986   *Tunumiit Oraasiat.* Collection Nordicana no. 49, Centre d'études nordiques, Université Laval.

ROSS, JOHN
1835   *Narrative of a Second Voyage in Search of a North-west Passage, etc., 1829–1833.* London: A. W. Webster.

ROWLEY, GRAHAM
1996   *Cold Comfort: My Love Affair with the Arctic.* Montreal: McGill-Queen's University Press.

RUGGLES, CLIVE L. N., and NICHOLAS J. SAUNDERS
1993   *Astronomies and Cultures.* Niwot: University Press of Colorado.

SALADIN D'ANGLURE, BERNARD
1990   "Frère-lune (Taqqiq), soeur-soleil (Siqiniq) et l'intelligence du Monde (Sila)." *Etudes/Inuit/Studies* 14(1–2):75–139.

SCHNEIDER, LUCIEN
1985   *Ulirnaisigutiit—An Inuktitut-English Dictionary of Northern Quebec, Labrador and Eastern Arctic Dialects.* Quebec City: Les Presses de l'université Laval.

SCHULTZ-LORENTZEN, CHRISTIAN W.
1927   *Dictionary of the West Greenland Eskimo Language.* Copenhagen: Meddelelser om Grønland 69.

SIMEON, GEORGE
1983   *Eskimo Wayfinding and Spatial Orientation.* Unpublished manuscript, April 1983. National Museums of Canada ref. Contract No. 1630-8-988.

SIMPSON, J.
1875   "Observations on the Western Eskimo and the Country They Inhabit, from Notes Taken During Two Years at Point Barrow." In *Arctic Geography and Ethnology: A Selection of Papers, pp. 233–275.* London: Royal Geographical Society.

SMITH, R. G.—see Weyer, Edward M., 1932.

SNYDER, L. L.
1957   *Arctic Birds of Canada.* Toronto: University of Toronto Press.

SONNE, BIRGITTE
1988   *Agayut: Eskimo Masks from the 5th Thule Expedition.* Copenhagen: Gyldendal.

SPALDING, ALEX
1960   *A Grammar of the East and West Coasts of Hudson's Bay.* Ottawa: Queen's Printer.

1972   "Doctor Faust and the Woman in the Sea." *Artscanada* 28(6):102–103.

1979   *Eight Inuit Myths.* Ottawa: National Museums of Canada (National Museum of Man, Mercury Series, Canadian Ethnology Service Paper No. 59).

1993   *Inuktitut: A Grammar of North Baffin Dialects (Volume 2, Parts Two and Three).* Winnipeg: Wuerz.

SPEARMAN, GRANT
1988   *Nunamiut Ethnoastronomy.* Unpublished manuscript. Simon Paneak Memorial Museum, Anaktuvuk Pass, Alaska.

SPENCER, ROBERT F.
1959   *The North Alaskan Eskimo: A Study in Ecology and Society.* Bureau of American Ethnology, Bulletin 171. Washington, D.C.: Smithsonian Institution.

STEENSBY, HANS P.
1910   *Contributions to the Ethnology and Anthropogeography of the Polar Eskimos.* Copenhagen: Meddelelser om Grønland 43(7).

STEFÁNSSON, VILHJÁLMUR
1912   *My Life with the Eskimo.* New York: Harper and Brothers. Reprint. New York: Macmillan, 1921.

1922   *Hunters of the Great North.* New York: Harcourt, Brace and Company.

1944   *Arctic Manual.* New York: Macmillan.

STEWART, R. J.
1989   *The Elements of Creation Myth.* Longmead, Dorset: Element Books.

THALBITZER, WILLIAM
1914–1941 *The Ammassalik Eskimo: Contributions to the Ethnology of the East Greenland Natives.* Meddelelser om Grønland 39–40. Copenhagen.

THERRIEN, MICHÈLE
1987   *Le Corps Inuit (Québec arctique).* Paris: SELAF.

THOMAS, STEPHEN D.
1987   *The Last Navigator.* New York: Ballantine Books.
TREMBLAY, A.
1921   *Cruise of the Minnie Maud—Arctic Seas and Hudson 1910–11 and 1912–13.* Translated and edited by A. B. Reader. Quebec: Arctic Exchange and Publishing.
TURNER, LUCIEN M.
1894   "Ethnology of the Ungava District, Hudson Bay Territory." Edited by John Murdoch. *11th Annual Report of the Bureau of American Ethnology for the Years 1889–1890*, pp. 159–350. Washington. Reprinted and retitled as *Indians and Eskimos in the Quebec-Labrador Peninsula.* Quebec: Presses Coméditex, 1979.

U.S. NAVAL OBSERVATORY
1988   *Floppy Almanac 1988.* Diskette.
1990   *Floppy Almanac 1990.* Diskette.

VAN DER POST, LAURENS
1975   *Jung and the Story of Our Time.* New York: Pantheon Books.
VENIAMINOV, IVAN
1840   Zapiski ob ostravakh Unalashkinskago otdiela. St. Petersburg: Russian-American Company. English edition: *Notes on the Islands of the Unalaska District*, edited by Richard A. Pierce. Kingston: The Limestone Press, 1984.

WEYER, EDWARD M., JR.
1956   *Daylight and Darkness in High Latitudes.* United States Navy, Op-O3A3. Washington, D.C.: USN.
1932   *The Eskimos: Their Environment and Folkways.* New Haven, Connecticut: Yale University Press. Reprint. Hamden, Connecticut: Archon Books, 1962.
WHITNEY, HARRY
1910   *Hunting with the Eskimos.* New York: The Century Company. Reprint. Toronto: Coles Canadiana Collection, 1974.
WORTHEN, THOMAS D.
1991   *The Myth of Replacement: Stars, Gods, and Order in the Universe.* Tucson: The University of Arizona Press.

YERBURY, J. C.
1984   "Bishop William Carpenter Bompas' Notes." *FRAM: The Journal of Polar Studies* 1(2):507–521.

★ Bibliography of Igloolik Elders' Interviews ★

The following list of interviews with Inuit elders of the Northwest Territories during the years 1986–1997, are part of a major on-going oral-history project organized by the Igloolik elders in cooperation with the Igloolik Research Centre. Most of the elders interviewed are from Igloolik; the exceptions are Paatsi Qaggutaq from Pelly Bay, Isapee Qanguq from Pond Inlet, and Philip Qipanniq from Repulse Bay. The original interviews on audio-tape cassettes, together with their derived transcripts and translations, are held in the archives of the Inullariit Society, Igloolik Research Centre, Igloolik, NWT. Copies of these materials have been deposited at the Northwest Territories Archives, Prince of Wales Northern Heritage Centre, Yellowknife, NWT.

AMAAQ, ELI:
IE-073—December 1989
IE-074—December 1989

AMARUALIK, HUBERT:
IE-212—January 1992
IE-252—January 1993
IE-314—October 1994

AQATSIAQ, SUZANNE NIVIATTIAN:
IE-079—January 1990
IE-149—June 1990

ARNATSIAQ, CATHERINE AALULUUK:
IE-077—January 1990

ARNATTIAQ, PETER TATIGAT:
IE-186—February 1991

IJJANGIAQ, MARK:
IE-081—January 1990
IE-138—March 1990
IE-184—February 1991
IE-187—February 1991
IE-203—October 1991

IKUMMAQ, THEO:
IE-263—December 1992

IMARUITTUQ, EMIL:
IE-101—February 1990
IE-161—November 1990

INNUKSUK, AIPILIK:
IE-035—January 1988
IE-039—November 1988
IE-068—December 1989
IE-164—December 1990
IE-165—December 1990
IE-324—February 1995

INNUKSUK, ZIPPORAH:
IE-088—February 1990

IQALLIJUQ, ROSIE:
IE-421—November 1997

IQQAQSAQ, CAIN:
IE-257—February 1993

KAPPIANAQ, GEORGE AGIAQ:
IE-071—December 1986
IE-096—February 1990
IE-102—February 1990
IE-155—October 1990
IE-174—January 1991
IE-187—February 1991
IE-253—January 1993
IE-265—February 1993
IE-267—1990
IE-273—March 1993
IE-329—January 1995

KUNNUK, INUKI:
IE-116—February 1990

KUNUK, PAULI:
IE-087—January 1990
IE-171—January 1991

KUPAAQ, MICHEL:
IE-153—September 1990
IE-166—December 1990
IE-182—February 1991
IE-187—February 1991
IE-370—June 1996

NASOOK, MARTHA:
IE-151—July 1990
IE-159—November 1990

PANIAQ, HERVÉ:
IE-126—March 1990
IE-141—March 1990
IE-142—March 1990

PANIKPAKUTTUK, ZACHRIAS:
IE-201—September 1991
IE-219—March 1992

PIUGAATTUK, NOAH:
IE-040—December 1988
IE-044—January 1989
IE-052—March 1989
IE-054—February 1986
IE-057—April 1986
IE-070—April 1986

IE-147—June 1990
IE-148—June 1990
IE-153—September 1990
IE-170—January 1991
IE-177—January 1991
IE-181—February 1991
IE-246—June 1992

QAGGUTAQ, PAATSI:
IE-169—January 1991

QANGUQ, ISAPEE:
IE-266—April 1990

QIPANNIQ, PHILIP:
IE-197—September 1991

QUASSA, FRANÇOIS:
IE-156—October 1990

TASIUQ, JOE:
IE-137—March 1990
IE-267—1990

ULAYURULUK, ABRAHAM:
IE-211—January 1992
IE-256—January 1993

UYARASUK, RACHEL:
IE-076—January 1990

⋆ Inuit Stars, Planets, and Constellations ⋆

⋆ European Stars, Planets, and Constellations ⋆

Cover Images
(Front) Nunavut. By Kenojuak Ashevak. Cape Dorset, NWT.
(Back) Inuksugat photograph by John MacDonald.
(Background) Northern Hemisphere. (detail). Engraving on paper.
By Joan Blaeu, Amsterdam, 1648.